LabVIEW™
for LEGO® MINDSTORMS® NXT

Michael L. Gasperi

NATIONAL TECHNOLOGY AND SCIENCE PRESS

Library of Congress Cataloging-in-Publication Data on File

ISBN: 978-1-934891-03-2

Publisher: Tom Robbins
Marketing Manager: Brad Armstrong
Technology Manager: Mark Walters
NTS Press General Manager: Erik Luther
Compositor: International Typesetting and Composition

This book is dedicated to Audrey, Max, Sara, and Molly.

About Us

National Technology & Science Press or **NTS Press** is sponsored by engineers for engineering, science and mathematics students dedicated to the publication of scholarly material of lasting value. Our products are for educators who desire a high degree of integration among classroom text, hardware and software to permit hands-on, visual learning. Our success will be judged by the influence our publications have in inspiring you and others to pursue careers in engineering, science, and mathematics.

We believe the learning process is most rewarding if you build up an intuitive understanding of concepts by pausing to tinker, explore and reflect. Thus, our publishing philosophy follows the belief that learning takes place when you are actively involved and we attempt to encourage this process in several ways. We build our textbooks with a plethora of worked-out examples, with reinforcing and advanced problems, and with interactive computer visuals. We address the computational aspects of problem solving by integrating computer-based learning tools into these presentations to enhance the discussion and analysis of engineering and science applications. In several cases our educational materials are developed with hardware experimentation platforms in mind, such as Universal Serial Bus (USB) devices for acquiring, generating and analyzing information. Owning your own portable laboratory equipment permits you to perform experimentation and take measurements anywhere and at anytime, thereby reinforcing your understanding of theoretical concepts. Having a little fun is okay too.

Clearly, rising textbook costs have an enormous effect on the way you view educational material. And there is little doubt that the Internet has been the most influential agent of change in education in recent time. The prevalence of search engine technology combined with a variety of open-source, open-content, and Wiki sites designed to deliver content has created a proliferation of freely available information and has circulated it more widely. Authored, edited, printed material is being overtaken by community libraries of digitized content from which new content is constructed, remixed, reordered and reassembled, often absent of continuity, flow, and accountability. This free content seems to address concerns about rising textbook prices, but it still has a cost. By contrast we try carefully to design products that come together in one piece with the author's judgment, passion, and imagination intact. These books are available with a reasonable price, and may be counted on as "reputable islands of knowledge in the vast ocean of unscrutinized information."

Contents

Preface   xv
Foreword   xix

1 Hello, World   1

Launching LabVIEW 1
Starting a New Program 1
The Block Diagram 3
The Functions Palette 5
The While Loop 6
Three Tools 9
Creating Constants 10
Display Text 11
Saving Files 13
NXT Terminal 14
Reflections 16

2 Let There Be Light   17

Opening Files 17
Deleting 17
The Light Sensor 19
Converting Numbers to Strings 21
Manually Connecting Wires 22
Debugging 23
Controls 24
Indicators 25
Charts 28
Reflections 30

3 **A Moving Experience** **31**

Elmer 31
Sync Unlimited 32
Move Until Touched 34
Sequence Flow 35
Come to the Light 36
Comparisons 36
Adding Labels 37
The Tools Palette 38
Fixing Broken Wires 40
Loops within Loops 41
Reflections 42

4 **Deciding to Decide** **43**

NXT Buttons 43
The Case Structure 43
Generating Sound 45
Stop Sound 46
Play Tone 46
The Select Block 48
Changing Representations 49
Numeric Cases 50
Boolean to (0...1) 51
Multiply and Add 51
Adding Cases 52
Compile and Download 54
Printing 54
Reflections 57

5 **Taken It Easy File Functions** **59**

Data Logging 59
Delete File 61
Easy Write File 61

Easy File Close   62
Wait   62
Loop Interation   62
Sending Files to the PC   64
Dealing with Data Files   64
Music Box   65
Easy File Read   66
Arrays   67
Preparing the Music File   68
Sending Files to the NXT   69
Record/Play   70
Play Sound File   71
Reflections   73

6 Drawing Conclusions   75

Simple Sketch   75
The Rotation Sensor   75
Display Point   76
Clusters   77
Creating SubVIs   78
Using the New SubVI   84
Quotient and Remainder   86
Coercion Dots   87
Reflections   88

7 Uncharted Territory   89

Simple Chart   89
Improved Chart   89
Selective Screen Clearing   91
Display Picture   92
Better Chart   93
Shift Registers   94
Best Chart   94
Display Line   95
Chart SubVI   96

Restore Default   98
Display Circle   99
Bouncy Ball   99
Reflections   100

8   It's Not Easy Files   101

Open for Read   101
Open for Write   101
Read File   102
Write File   103
Close File   103
Make Icon   103
Display Format   105
Build Array   106
Making Square.ric   106
Rename File   108
Get File Handle   108
Dissecting a Text File   109
Array Indicator   109
ASCII   111
Binary Files   113
Reflections   116

9   Time Flies   117

Keep Alive   117
Tick Count   118
Hour Clock   118
Concatenate String   120
Wait   121
Event Time Logging   122
Local Variables   123
Reaction Timer   124
Random Number   125

Timer 126
Wait for Completion 126
Stop 126
Reflections 127

10 General Motors 129

Motor Unlimited 129
Stop Motor 130
TriBot 130
Line Following 131
Bang-Bang Control 132
Proportional Control 133
Motor Distance 134
Sound Control Robot 135
Sound Sensor 136
Logic 137
Motor Time 137
Motor 138
Sync Distance 139
Ultrasonic Distance Sensor 140
Measure Pi 141
Reset Motors 142
Sync Time 143
Reflections 144

11 Something Old, Something New 145

Legacy Motor 145
Legacy Lamp 146
Legacy Temperature 147
Legacy Light 147
Legacy Touch 148
Legacy Rotation 148
Calibrate 149
Reflections 154

12 Something Blue 155

NXT to NXT 155
Write Message 156
Read Message 157
Master/Slave Programs 157
NXT to PC 158
Reflections 160

13 Deeper Debugging 161

Controls Palette 161
Numeric Controls 161
Changing Scale Range 163
Boolean 164
Block Diagram 166
Reflections 168

14 Making a Connection 169

NXT Direct Commands 169
Connections Palette 169
Scan for NXT 172
Get NXT Info 172
Find NXT 173
Create NXT Object 173
Get Battery Level 173
Get Device Info 174
Get Firmware Version 174
List Files 175
Destroy NXT Object 175
Front Panel 175
Bluetooth Connection Blocks 177
Is Paired 177
Rename NXT 179
Reflections 180

15   Up, Down, and All Around   181

Controlled Data Logging 181
Download File 183
Start Program 183
Get Current Program Name 184
Upload File 184
Read Text File 185
Stop, Delete, and Defrag 185
Reflections 186

16   Making Sense   187

Charting Program 187
Read NXT Sensors 189
Other Inputs 189
Read Sensor 190
Set Input Mode 191
Get Input Values 192
Counting Modes 192
Clear Input Value 193
Low-Speed Communications 193
LS Write 194
LS Get Status 195
LS Read 195
NXT Rotation Sensor 195
Reset Motor 197
Get Output Values 198
Cage Monitor 198
Keep Alive 200
Analysis 200
Exporting Graphs 203
Reflections 204

17 Sound Out 205

Motors 205
Motor Unlimited 205
Stop Motor 206
Radio Buttons 207
Set Output State 208
Forward One Second 210
Flat Sequence Structure 210
Bundled by Name 211
Sounds 212
Play Tone 212
Stop Sound 213
Play Sound File 213
Reflections 214

18 Read, Write, and Bluetooth 215

IOMap 215
Read IOMap 216
Write IOMap 217
Write IOMap 217
Bluetooth 218
Message Write 218
Message Remote 218
Message Read 220
Send Button 221
Reflections 222

19 NXT Block Internals 223

NXT Block Internals 223
Draw Rectangle 225
Read Power 235
Period Count Sensor 237
Reflections 241

20 Web Publishing   243

Mini Fig's World   243
Fwink   243
Automatic Error Handling   247
Web Publishing Tool   248
Port Forwarding   251
Reflections   253

21 Final Reflections   255

More MINDSTORMS   255
More LabVIEW   257

Appendix A   NXT Block Reference   259

Appendix B   Direct Commands Reference   307

Appendix C   Creating Custom NXT-G Blocks   337

Appendix D   Using Vernier Sensors with the NXT   359

Index   369

Preface

> *Begin at the beginning and go on till you come to the end: then stop*
> *—The King to the White Rabbit*

It's safe to say that if you are reading this, you probably own a LEGO MINDSTORMS NXT and you're looking for a more powerful way to program it. You're comfortable with the NXT-G language and the development environment that came with the set, and interested in exploring more advanced programming techniques. LabVIEW is the natural extension of NXT-G, because NXT-G is really just a streamlined version of it. Much of what you have already learned programming in NXT-G will be useful for programming in LabVIEW.

What Can You Do Now with LabVIEW

LabVIEW offers much functionality that extends the capabilities provided in NXT-G, some of these extensions are based on the language itself, and others come from the development environment. As programs grow to become larger and more complex, they become difficult to manage and don't easily fit on one screen. LabVIEW blocks, and the ability to create sub-vis, allow you to create code that is graphically denser and that utilizes the language to build more hierarchal structure that hides insignificant details.

When editing and running a program, it can be tricky to figure out why a running program is not working like you expect. One method for debugging is to sprinkle your program with display blocks to show the current state of the program on the NXT display. LabVIEW adds great debugging features that allow you to tap into everything that is going on inside the program while it is running. This debugging capability is so powerful that you will find that you only run some programs in debug mode.

LabVIEW programs, like NXT-G also run on the LEGO brick, but can also be designed to run on a PC. The PC has a substantially faster processor, more memory, larger display, and access to networks, allowing the NXT to become a natural extension of your computer, behaving like another peripheral to your computer like a mouse or printer.

LabVIEW provides many methods for accessing variables, and includes the array data type for capturing data over time. LabVIEW also contains additional math functions like remainder and bit logic, and additional files types for reading and writing data to file. It offers some programmable control of the NXT operating system, and can also be used to create custom blocks that can be inserted back into NXT-G enhancing and customizing its capabilities.

MINDSTORMS

LEGO introduced the original MINDSTORMS product in the fall of 1998. It was so successful that it went largely unchanged for eight years. This is unheard of in the rapidity changing world of consumer electronics. It parallels LEGO's long running success with its trademark brick construction product that hasn't significantly changed for over fifty years. Due to educational curriculum momentum, the original product will still be available and supported for many more years to come, but in 2006 LEGO introduced a second generation of MINDSTORMS called the NXT. The NXT is an improvement in absolutely every respect to the original product. Most importantly, the NXT is programmed using a visually enhanced version of the popular graphical language called LabVIEW.

Prior to MINDSTORMS, robot building required skills in electronics, carpentry, machining, plumbing, hydraulics, programming, control, and much more. Often the term Mechatronics is used to describe the blend of disciplines required. The MINDSTORMS products are successful because they are based on a common set of building blocks, no pun intended, which allows designs to be easily constructed and, perhaps most importantly, shared. Thousands of people can build exactly the same model because they all have exactly the same parts.

LabVIEW

LabVIEW stands for Laboratory Virtual Instrumentation Engineering Workbench. Its origin dates back to 1986, and was initially designed for instrument control in laboratories. There must be hundreds of computer languages in use today. Most of them are designed for very specific applications, but a few like C and Java are more general purpose. Also, most of them are text based and one dimensional. You write a program in much the same way as you write a story. LabVIEW and NXT-G are graphical general purpose languages and your program is more of a diagram than a story. Most people learn graphical languages faster, and program more efficiently with them, because these languages don't have the rigorous syntax that complicates learning.

This Book

This book is intended to take someone with little programming and absolutely no LabVIEW experience to the point where they can write sophisticated programs for the NXT. For the most part, it only covers LabVIEW in the context of MINDSTORMS and not in general. That would require a much larger book, and frankly there are already many good general LabVIEW books. It would be helpful if you were comfortable with NXT-G before starting this book if only because it shares some of the same programming techniques. However, I don't dwell on NXT-G and you will do just fine even if you've only casually played with it.

Chapters 1 to 13 and Appendix A represent Part 1 which explains LabVIEW for programs that run on the NXT itself like NXT-G does. Chapters 14 to 19 and Appendix B cover Part 2 which explains LabVIEW programs that run on the PC and use the NXT as a peripheral. In Chapter 19 we return to NXT Blocks and look at how they are made. Appendix C is Part 3 which explains how to write new blocks for the NXT-G environment, and finally Chapter 21 reflects on the whole book and offers resources for further study.

Foreword

It was a little more than 20 years ago when we first formed ideas of what is now known as LabVIEW. We had a vision to create something that would do for engineers and scientists what the spreadsheet did for financial analysts. We never dreamt that one day LabVIEW would be used by children to build robots.

Over the years, LabVIEW has evolved, but the core graphical paradigm has remained the same; this graphical way of designing and describing systems helps many people build complex applications, including the hundreds of thousands of people programming LEGO® MINDSTORMS® NXT.

Our collaboration with LEGO Education began in 1998 when ROBOLAB, the software powered by LabVIEW and developed by the Tufts University Center for Engineering Educational Outreach, was launched for the original LEGO MINDSTORMS robotics software. ROBOLAB grew out of the visionary leadership of Dr. Chris Rogers, who saw that a graphical approach helped younger students learn programming skills. In 2006, LEGO MINDSTORMS NXT, the current generation of LEGO robotics, was co-developed by NI and LEGO to provide students with the latest hardware and software technology for building advanced, autonomous robotics. By combining the intuitive and interactive interface of LabVIEW graphical development software with the physical experience of building models out of LEGO bricks, we can bridge the physical and virtual worlds to provide the ultimate hands-on learning experience.

Today, students of all ages have access to a robotics platform that combines graphical programming with a LEGO building system. Students as young as 7 years can learn basic programming using LEGO Education WeDo™, a robotics platform for primary school education. Innovative programs initiatives such as the *FIRST*[1](For Inspiration and Recognition of Science and Technology) Robotics Competitions utilize LEGO MINDSTORMS NXT and LabVIEW to inspire a love of learning and interest in engineering. Students participating in *FIRST* begin with *FIRST* LEGO League in elementary school where they solve real-world problems with LEGO MINDSTORMS NXT robots programmed with NXT-G. As student learning progresses, they can advance to more complex competitions such as the *FIRST* Tech Challenge, and finally the *FIRST* Robotics Competition, where they are confronted with a complex engineering challenge that must be accomplished in a short, six-week build period. Starting in 2009, the 150,000+ students in all of these competitions can use LabVIEW graphical programming, thus learning skills they can use in college and in their careers. Today, LabVIEW is truly used from kindergarten to rocket science!

---

[1]http://usfirst.org/

The ecosystem surrounding the LEGO MINDSTORMS NXT continues to expand. For example, new sensors and sensor adapters are being developed by companies like HiTechnic and Vernier. This ecosystem is building on the LEGO block's ability to inspire creative thinking and problem-solving, and creating endless opportunities for tinkering, exploring, and interacting with the world.

Now, thanks to Mike Gasperi and NTS Press we have a valuable new resource. Until now, there hasn't been any real documentation, guides, or how to's on the NXT Toolkit for LabVIEW, so I'm delighted this book is now available. The author has done a very nice job of knittingtogether LabVIEW programming concepts into an effective and readable presentation. I especially like the way Mike applies each function to an exercise. Anyone with a little programming experience working from this book should in no time be writing a higher level of programs and building more complex, highly-developed designs using LabVIEW.

If you are an instructor, use this book as a resource. If you are a professional, I encourage you to share your engineering talent by volunteering with one of the organizations I mention above. If you are a student learning from this book, I hope this sparks your interest in engineering, science, and math.

RAY ALMGREN
Vice President of Academic Relations
National Instruments

Hello, World

1

The only way to learn a new programming language is by writing programs in it.—The C
Programming Language by Kernighan and Ritchie

Computer programs consist of three basic parts: input, process, and output. The first program most people write when they learn a new language prints the words "Hello, World." That demonstrates that they can at least output something. The challenge here is that you are learning both a new language and its development environment at the same time. In the beginning I'll keep things simple and show you everything step-by-step. After awhile, I'll assume you've got the hang of it, and I'll leave out some of the gory details. Let's start with a quick introduction to the LabVIEW environment and the obligatory "Hello, World" program.

Launching LabVIEW

First, you need to launch LabVIEW by either double-clicking on the icon shown in Figure 1.1 or launching it through the Windows START menu. I'm using the Student Edition of LabVIEW 8.5, but other versions look very similar. For the most part, only the menu arrangements differ from version to version. The Student Edition has a distinctive watermark in the lower-right corner of the window it appears in.

The splash screen (see Figure 1.2) will appear, with some status information changing in the lower-right corner. LabVIEW is pretty big, and it will take a while to fully load, and this is especially true for the first time it loads. Be patient and wait for the Getting Started window to come up.

Starting a New Program

When LabVIEW has fully loaded, the Getting Started screen will appear, as shown in Figure 1.3. There are some important things to notice on this screen. In the Resources area you'll find some general LabVIEW tutorials and documentation.

National
Instruments
LabVIEW 8.5

Figure 1.1
LabVIEW Icon

I highly encourage you to explore these and get a feel for the LabVIEW environment. However, the part of LabVIEW that we'll be using in this book is only a small piece of the whole LabVIEW world. The Open area has a list of recent files that you have been working on. You will reopen your programs from there.

For now, click on Blank.VI in the New section to open a new program. Figure 1.4 shows the two windows that open after you do that. One is called the Front Panel, and the other is called the Block Diagram. For the most part, NXT programs use only the Block Diagram. Click on the title of the Block Diagram window to make it active, or minimize the Front Panel window to get it out of the way.

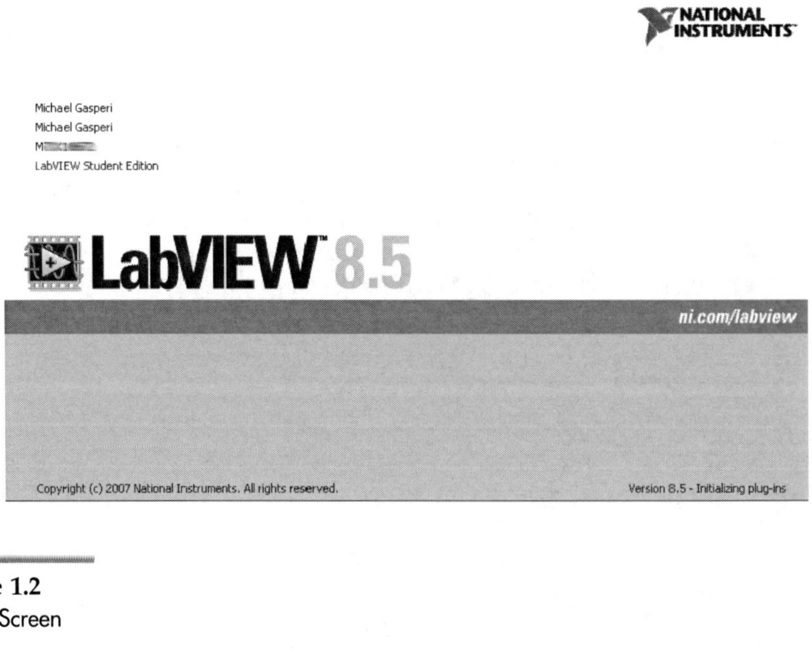

NATIONAL
INSTRUMENTS

Michael Gasperi
Michael Gasperi
M
LabVIEW Student Edition

ni.com/labview

Copyright (c) 2007 National Instruments. All rights reserved.   Version 8.5 - Initializing plug-ins

Figure 1.2
Splash Screen

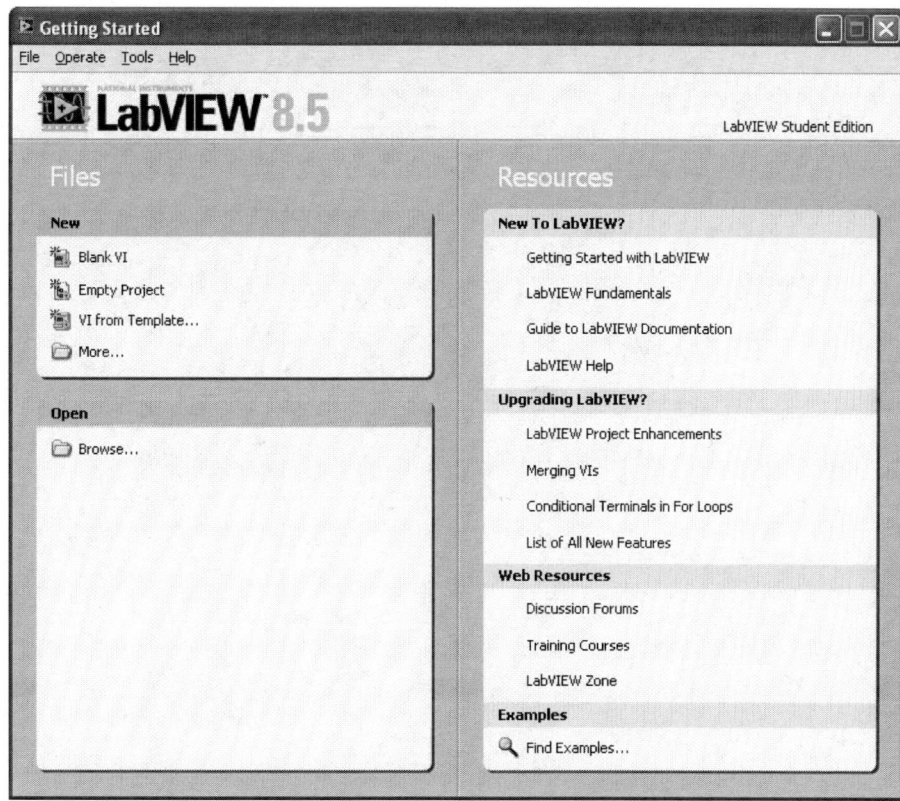

Figure 1.3
Getting Started Window

The Block Diagram

The block diagram shown in Figure 1.5 is where the program is developed. A Lab-VIEW program is made from blocks that are connected together. The blocks are called Function Blocks, because each one does a particular function. As we will see, a function block can be very simple or incredibly complex. Although the connections between blocks are called Wires, it is data that flows through them, not electricity. That data is generally the current value of a variable.

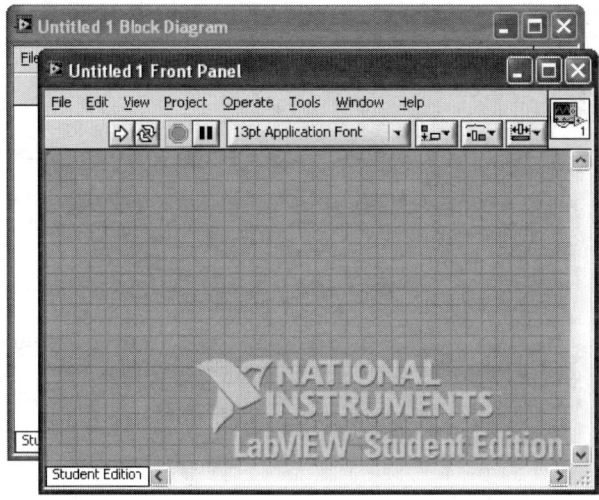

Figure 1.4
New File Windows

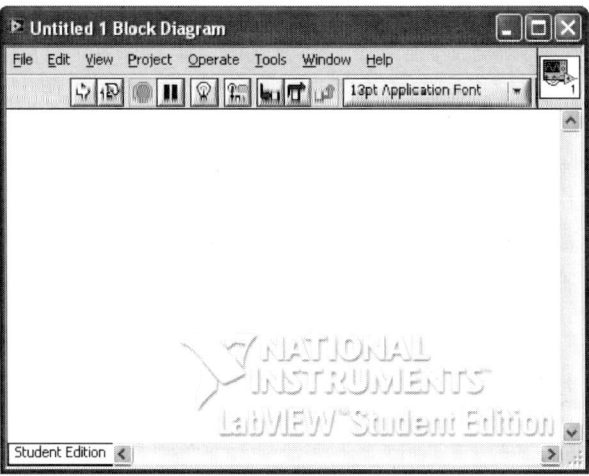

Figure 1.5
Block Diagram Window

The Functions Palette

Bring up the Functions palette by selecting it from the View pull-down menu as shown in Figure 1.6. Figure 1.7 shows the initial appearance of the palette. You will be concerned only with a small subset of functions found in the Addons area. Expand the palette by clicking the down arrow at the bottom and close the other unnecessary areas by clicking on the small triangles along the left side.

Figure 1.8 shows the appearance of the palette you are looking for. There are two sets of palettes for the NXT. The NXT Toolkit is for writing programs that run on the

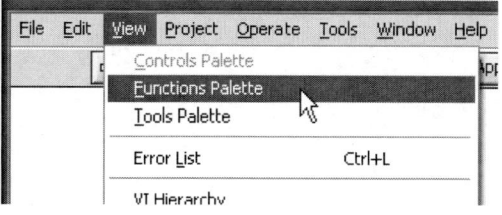

Figure 1.6
Opening the Functions Palette

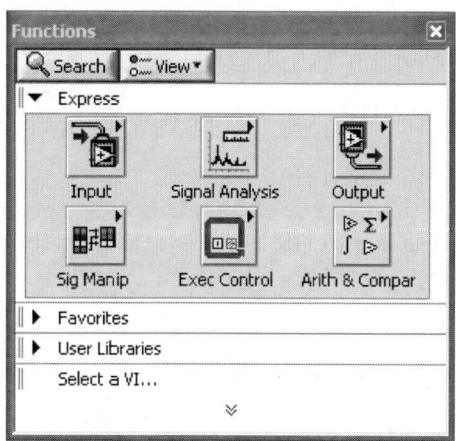

Figure 1.7
Initial Appearance of the Functions Palette

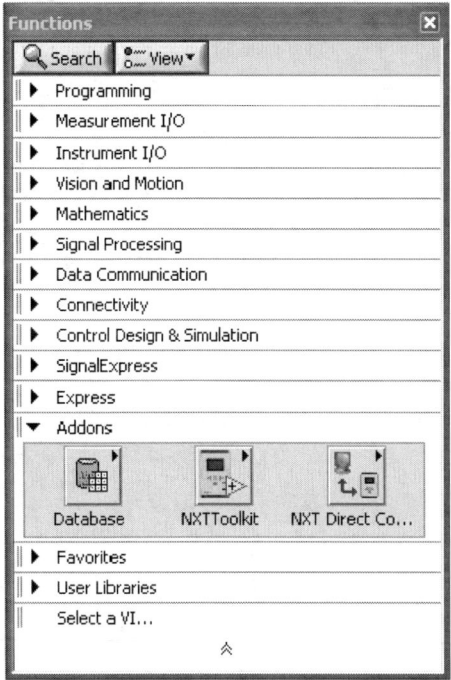

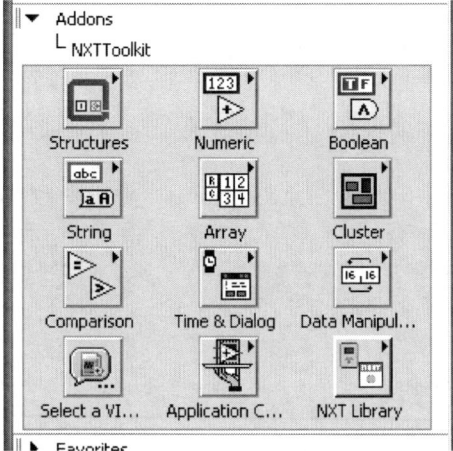

Figure 1.8
Addons Palette

Figure 1.9
NXT Toolkit Palette

NXT itself, and NXT Direct Commands is for writing programs that run on the PC and communicate to the NXT.

In the first part of this book, Chapters 1 to 13, we will be concerned only with the NXT Toolkit palette, which looks like Figure 1.9 when it is open. All the blocks you will use come from this palette. Other palettes throughout LabVIEW may have blocks that look like the ones in the NXT Toolkit, but stick with the ones in the Toolkit.

The While Loop

Each palette is a collection of related Function Blocks. For example, click on the Structures palette to open it. Figure 1.10 shows the four blocks that are a part of the Structures palette. To give you an idea of how much smaller the NXT toolkit is, the general LabVIEW Structures palette has 16 blocks in it.

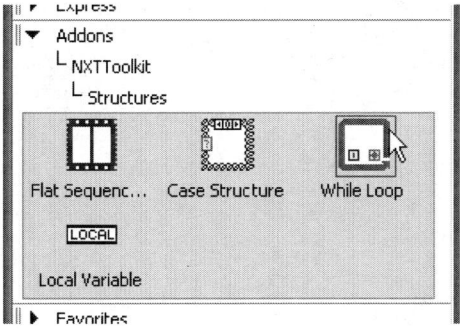

Figure 1.10
Structures Palette

Left-click on the While Loop block to select it and then move the cursor (which is now a little box with a circular arrow in the corner) over to the Block Diagram in the lower-left side, as shown in Figure 1.11. Holding the left button down and sweeping up and to the right will form a rectangle as shown in Figure 1.12.

Figure 1.13 shows the While Loop that appears as soon as you let up on the left button. As you move the cursor over the gray border (see Figure 1.14) of the loop, small blue squares called handles will appear on the corners and sides that can be used to resize the loop.

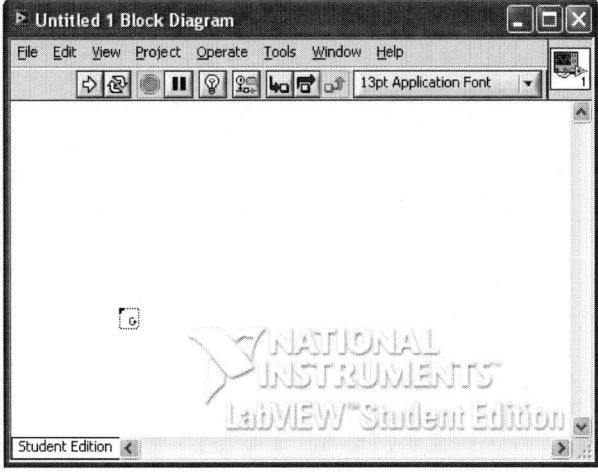

Figure 1.11
While Loop Step 1

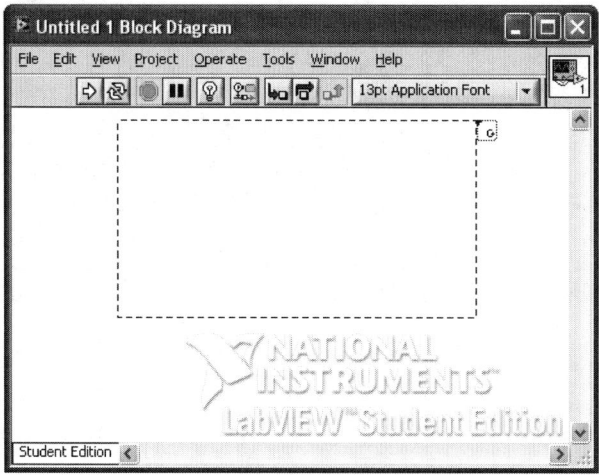

Figure 1.12
While Loop Step 2

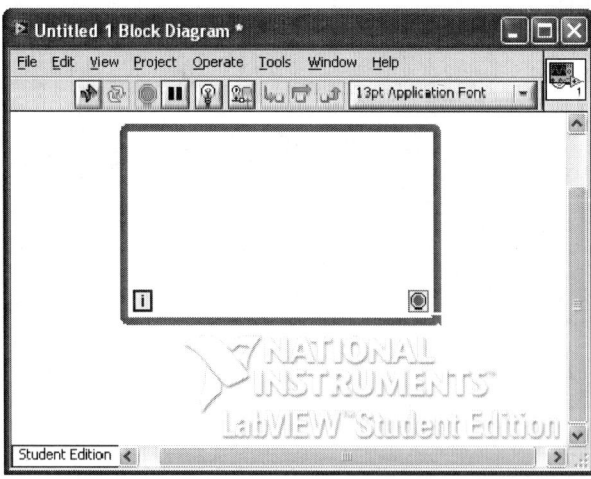

Figure 1.13
Finished While Loop

Figure 1.14
While Loop Handles

Two distinctive features of the loop are a blue box with a lowercase "i" inside on the left and a green box with a red circle on the right. I'll get to the blue box later, but for now, the green box is called the Loop Condition. The program will stay inside the While Loop until a condition has been met.

Three Tools

As you move the cursor over the Loop Condition it will change to signify three different tools that you use to move, change, or connect the function block. The Selection Tool is shown in Figure 1.15. With it you can hold down on the left mouse button and move the Loop Condition to a different location, as shown in Figure 1.16.

The pointing finger cursor is called the Operate Value Tool. Move the cursor over the Loop Condition so it looks like Figure 1.17, and by leftclicking you can toggle between the conditions needed to stop the loop. A False condition is indicated by the green circular arrow of Figure 1.18 and a True condition is indicated by the solid red circle. For now make sure you put the Loop Condition back to the corner and select the red circle, as shown in Figure 1.19.

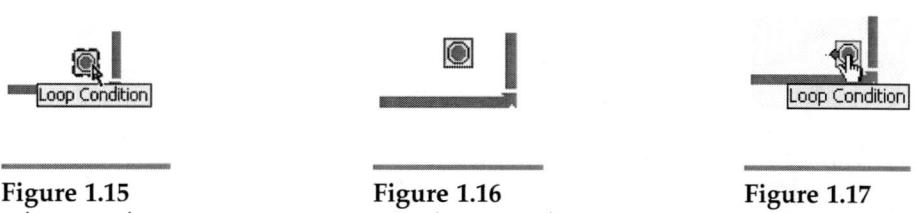

Figure 1.15
Selection Tool

Figure 1.16
Moved Loop Condition

Figure 1.17
Operate Value Tool

Figure 1.18
Stop on False Condition

Figure 1.19
Reposition the Loop Condition

Creating Constants

Move the cursor over the Loop Condition until the little spool of wire appears, as shown in Figure 1.20; it is appropriately called the Connect Wire Tool. Eventually we will be wiring blocks together with this tool, but for now just click the right mouse button. A menu will appear that looks like Figure 1.21. One of the choices in the menu is Create Constant. Select that line; when you let up on the right button, a False Constant block will appear already wired to the Loop Condition.

The False Constant block will look like Figure 1.22 with a light green T and blocked F. If you click inside the False Constant block with the Operate Value Tool, it will turn it into a True Constant block, but make sure you click it again to put it back. The type of variable that represents a value that can be only either True or False is called Boolean. Notice that the False Constant block and the short piece of wire connecting it to the Loop Condition are green. Only Booleans will be colored green.

We have made a While Loop that will loop forever, also called an Infinite Loop—well, at least until we stop the program with the stop button on the NXT. Anything we put inside the loop will be executed over and over again. This is handy where you need a robot to keep doing something until you turn it off.

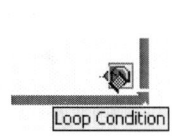

Figure 1.20
Wiring Tool

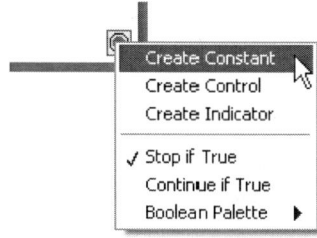

Figure 1.21
Creating a Constant

Figure 1.22
False Constant

Display Text

You're now ready to place your first NXT Function Block. In the Function Block palette, go to the NXT Library and then to the Display Function Blocks (see Figure 1.23). Locate the Display Text block, which has an uppercase T in the corner. The other blocks are used to display other types of graphics; we will get to them later.

Select the Display Text by clicking the left mouse button and then move the cursor into the While Loop on the Block Diagram. Place it toward the side (see Figure 1.24) of the loop by clicking the left mouse button again. Immediately the block's icon will change to the one shown in Figure 1.25. The little stubs sticking out are called

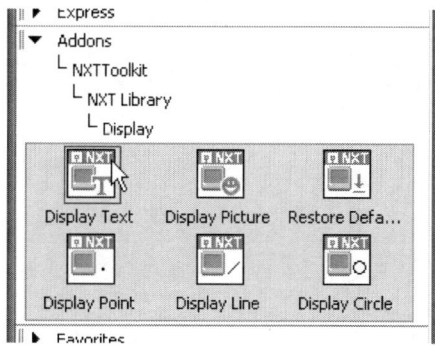

Figure 1.23
Display Palette

Figure 1.24
Placing the Display Text block

Figure 1.25
Icon Showing Connectors

Connectors. They represent the locations where connecting wires can be attach that lead to—or come from—other function blocks.

Figure 1.26 shows all the possible Display Text icon connections. We will get to what all these Connectors represent, but for now the only one we really need to deal with is the Text input. The type of data is called String, because it consists of a string of characters such as letters and numbers. This would be a good time to point out again that the type of data conducted by a wire is color coded. In this case, pink is for String.

Move the cursor over the Display Text icon until the Connect Wire Tool shows up and a box with the word Text appears, as shown in Figure 1.27. Now rightclick just as you did for the Loop Condition and select Create and then Constant. A pink block will appear like the one shown in Figure 1.28, which is, not surprisingly, called a String Constant block. Type the words Hello, World on the keyboard, and they will appear in the box.

Your first program is now complete and should look like Figure 1.29. All it does is write Hello, World to the NXT display over and over again until you press the stop button. Because it keeps writing exactly the same thing, you won't even be able to tell that it writes it more than once.

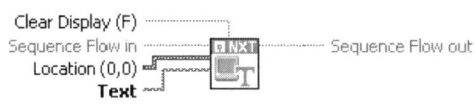

Figure 1.26
All Display Text Connections

Figure 1.27
Connect Wire Tool over Text Input

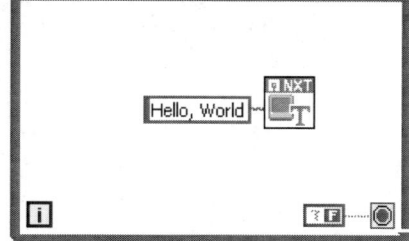

Figure 1.28
String Constant

Figure 1.29
Finished Hello World Program

Saving Files

This is a good time to save your work. It also is the time when you can give the program a meaningful name. As with most programs, go to the File menu (see Figure 1.30) and select Save As. The Name in the VI window will appear as shown in Figure 1.31.

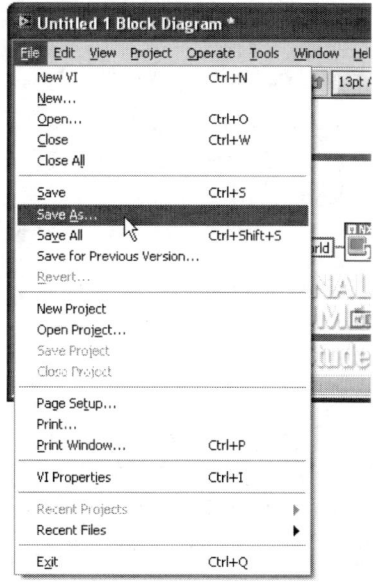

Figure 1.30
File Menu

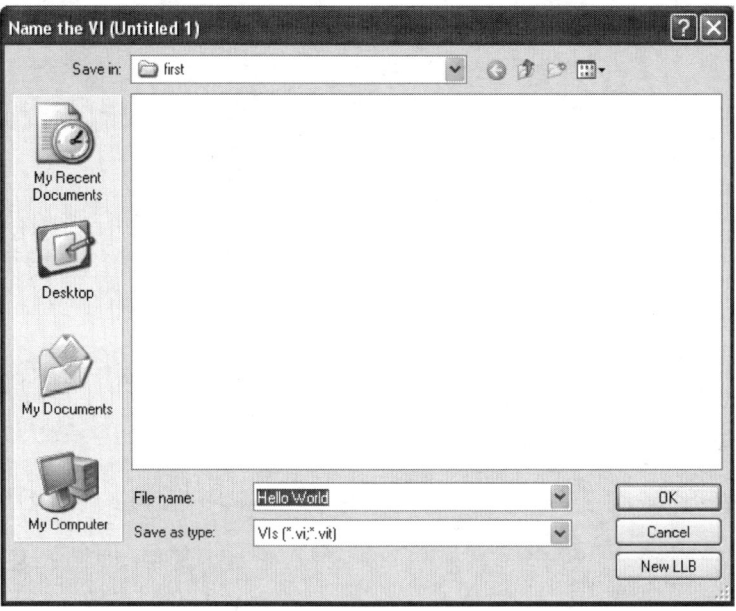

Figure 1.31
Name the VI Menu

Navigate to the directory where you want to keep the file and enter an appropriate name. It will be saved with the .vi file extension signifying it as a LabVIEW Virtual Instrument program.

NXT Terminal

Downloading and running LabVIEW programs on the NXT requires a special tool called the NXT Terminal. Go to the Tools pulldown menu, shown in Figure 1.32, and select the NXT Module. Within the module is the NXT Terminal, which looks like Figure 1.33. Make sure your NXT is connected to the computer and turned on. Although you can use Bluetooth to wirelessly communicate between the PC and the NXT, for now use the USB cable. If the NXT is turned off, the Status will be Not Connected.

In the title bar you should see NXT: NXT. The first NXT is to indicate just that this is the NXT Terminal window. The second NXT is actually the name of the NXT that is connected. NXT is the default name for all NXTs. The Status should be Idle, and that means the NXT is connected but not running any programs.

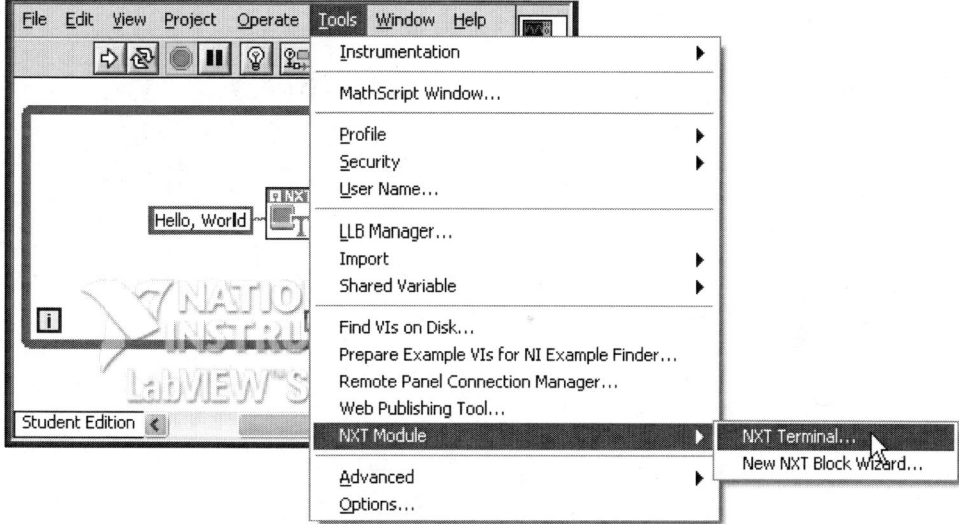

Figure 1.32
NXT Module

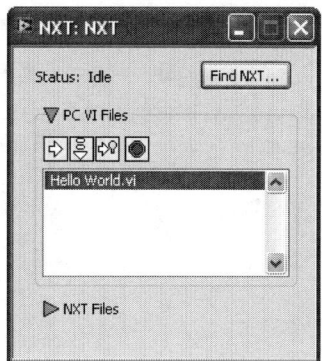

Figure 1.33
NXT Terminal

Now click on the Compile, Download, and Run button, as shown in Figure 1.34. LabVIEW will initialize, compile, and download the program, which can take a little while depending on the program's size. When the NXT has been told to run the program, it will make two short beeps. Because the program is in an infinite loop, you

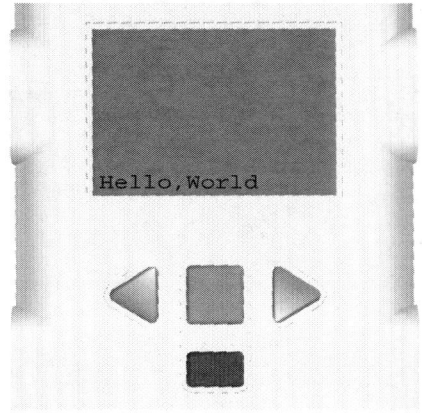

Figure 1.34
Compile, Download, and Run

Figure 1.35
NXT Display

will need to stop it with the NXT stop button. Figure 1.35 shows the screen of the NXT running the Hello World program.

Reflections

Congratulations: you have written your first LabVIEW program, saved it, and run it on the NXT. Just for fun, you might try changing the message to something else. In the following chapters I will take you through ever more complex programming concepts and the LabVIEW environment.

Let There Be Light

2

Better to light a candle than to curse the darkness.—Chinese Proverb

The Hello World program demonstrates only the output aspect of a computer program. Now let's write a program that has all three parts—input, process, and output. We can start with the Hello World program to save some time. If you already have LabVIEW running, close any files you have open and return to the Getting Started screen. Otherwise, launch LabVIEW and wait for the Getting Started screen, as shown in Figure 2.1.

Opening Files

In the Open area of the screen you should see the Hello World.vi file. Click on it, and the program will open. Only the Front Panel window of an existing file opens, because that is normally the program's user interface. You'll need to open the Block Diagram manually. In the Window dropdown menu pick Show Block Diagram, as shown in Figure 2.2.

Figure 2.3 shows the While Loop with the Display Text Function Block that represents the core of the Hello World program. The program only displays the same thing over and over again, which is pretty boring. Why don't we display something more interesting by showing the intensity of light as measured by the NXT Light Sensor?

Deleting

First we need to delete the String Constant block. Locate the cursor at a point to the left and above the block and, while holding the left mouse button down, drag a selection box over the whole block and some of its wire, as shown in Figure 2.4. Don't include

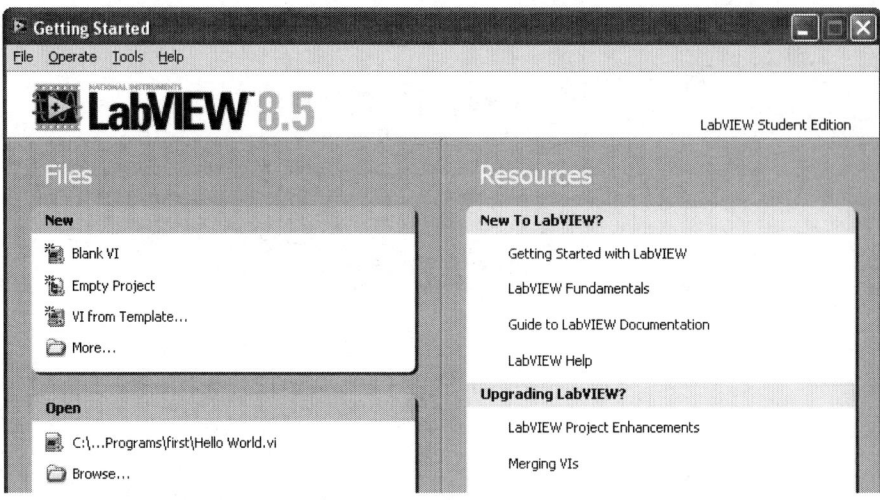

Figure 2.1
Getting Started Screen

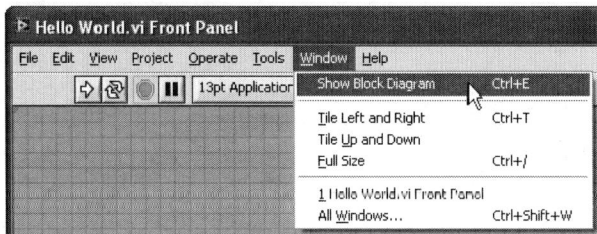

Figure 2.2
Showing the Block Diagram

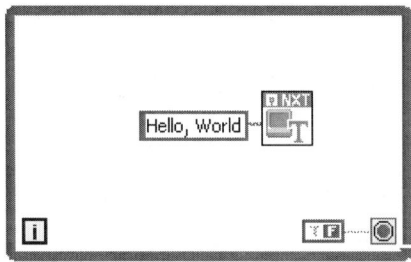

Figure 2.3
Hello World Program

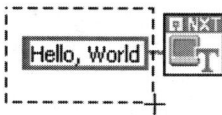

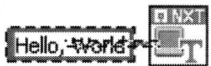

Figure 2.4
Selecting the Constant String Block and Wire

Figure 2.5
Selected Constant String and Wire

any of the Display Text block. When you let up on the button, the screen should look like Figure 2.5. You only need to hit the Delete key on the keyboard to delete both the block and the wire.

The Light Sensor

Connect the NXT Light Sensor to the NXT Sensor Input Port 3 with a cable, as shown in Figure 2.6. The NXT Light Sensor has a built-in red LED light source that can be used to reflect light off nearby objects to sense their presence or color. The sensor can't really detect different colors; it can only detect differences in how much light

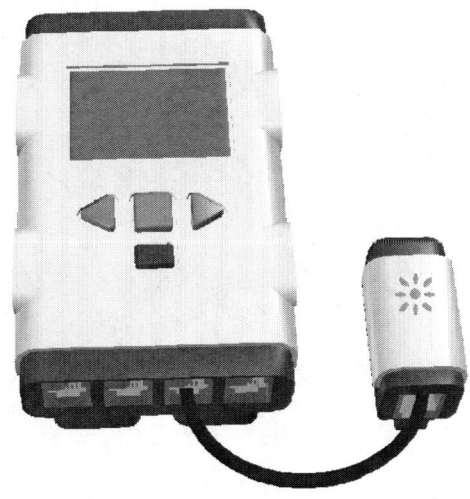

Figure 2.6
NXT Light Sensor Connected to NXT Sensor Input Port 3

reflects off an object. Closer objects are brighter than further ones, light-color objects are brighter than dark ones, and redder objects will seem brighter than blue ones. The LED can be turned off so that the sensor measures only the ambient light, like a photographic light meter.

The Light Sensor function block is located in the NXT Library Input palette, as illustrated in Figure 2.7. There are blocks for the other NXT Sensors as well as Legacy Sensors from the old LEGO MINDSTORMS RCX family.

All of the connections for the block are shown in Figure 2.8. You can see a connection for the Input Port Number, and you can determine whether to turn on the built-in LED with the Generate Light connection on the left. The default Input Port Number is 3, and you don't need to supply an input to this connection as long as you have the sensor plugged into Port 3. The default condition of the Generate Light is True, which means the LED will be lit while the program is running. The measured light level is the Intensity output connection on the right, and it will have Integer values from 0 to 100. Notice the wire color for Integer is blue.

Place the Light Sensor block in the While Loop, as shown in Figure 2.9, with some space between them. You can't directly connect the two blocks together, because the Light Sensor Intensity output is an Integer number and the Text Input to the Display Text Block is a String. We will need another function block to do the conversion.

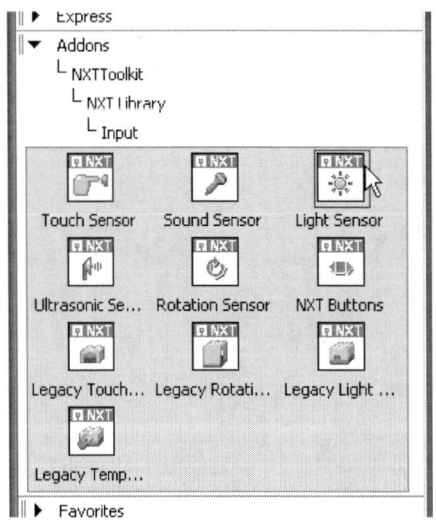

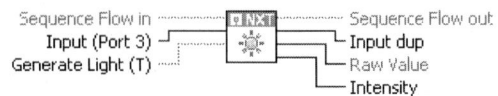

Figure 2.7
Input Palette

Figure 2.8
Light Sensor Block Connections

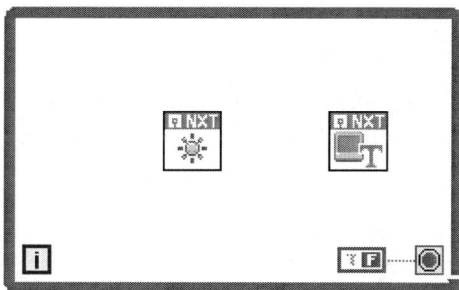

Figure 2.9
Place Light Sensor Block inside While Loop

Converting Numbers to Strings

Look in the String palette for the String/Number Conversion subpalette. It will look like Figure 2.10. There are blocks to convert Numbers to Decimal Strings and Decimal Strings to Numbers. The Decimal part of the name just means that the numbers are in base ten.

Pick the Number-to-Decima-String block and move it onto the Block Diagram. As you move the block around between the Light Sensor and Display Text blocks, LabVIEW might try to automatically wire connections. Be careful to place the conversion block only when the connection from the String output of the block is wired to the Text input of the display block (see Figure 2.11). Don't panic if the wire did not automatically connect. I'll show you how to manually wire blocks next.

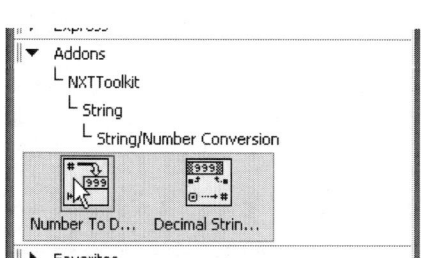

Figure 2.10
String/Number Conversion Palette

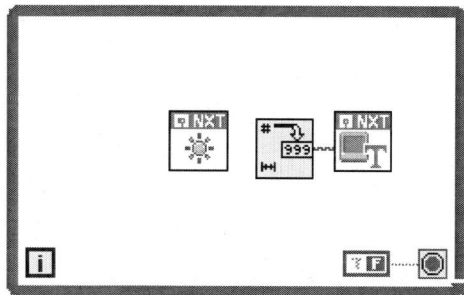

Figure 2.11
Conversion Block Automatically Wired

Manually Connecting Wires

Move the cursor around the Intensity output of the Light Sensor until it becomes the Connect Wire tool. Hold the left mouse button down and sweep up until the Connect Wire tool is over the Number input of the conversion block, as shown in Figure 2.12. Make sure you have not accidentally wired to the width input of the conversion block, as shown in Figure 2.13. If you did, move the Connect Wire tool near the wire and then hold the right mouse button to select Delete Wire Branch. When you are done, the three blocks will look like Figure 2.14.

This would be a good time to save the program with a new descriptive file name, such as Light Meter. When you are done with that, go to the NXT Terminal (see Figure 2.15) and Compile, Download, and Run the program.

Figure 2.16 shows what the NXT display should look like, except that the number will be different depending on your light level. The Display Text block is not erasing the display for each new number. It is only writing the new number over the old one. This is not a problem unless the number becomes 100. The units place "zero" will be left on the display even when the light level drops below 100. A cure for this would be to wire a True Constant block to the Clear Display input of the Display Text block.

The language that comes with the LEGO MINDSTORMS NXT is called NXT-G. Figure 2.17 shows the Light Meter programmed in NXT-G. You can see the similarity

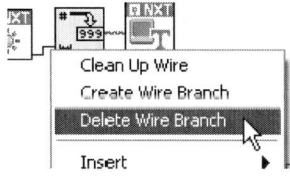

Figure 2.12
Wiring the Intensity Output to the Number Input

Figure 2.13
Delete the Wire If You Accidentally Connect It to the Width Input

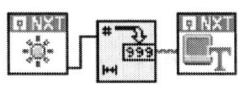

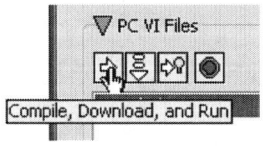

Figure 2.14
The Proper Wires

Figure 2.15
Compile, Download, and Run

Figure 2.16
NXT Display for the Light Meter

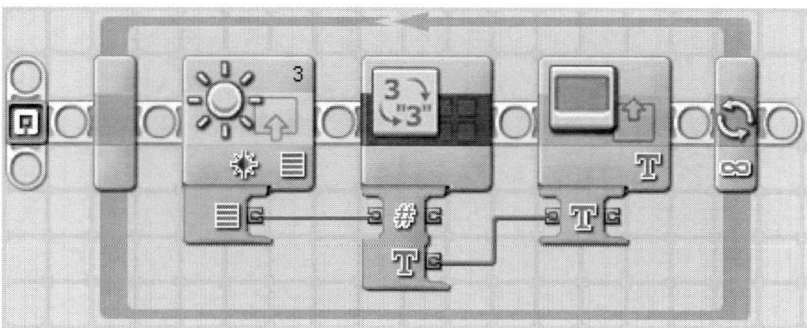

Figure 2.17
The Equivalent NXT-G Program

between this and your LabVIEW program. Now I'll give you a little taste of something you can't do in NXT-G.

Debugging

Debugging is the art of fixing problems with computer programs. Programs running on the NXT are particularly difficult to debug because the NXT has only a simple display to monitor values with. If you have ever written a complex NXT-G program, you'll know what I'm talking about. On the other hand, LabVIEW provides several handy tools for debugging using your computer.

Controls

Move the cursor over the Light Sensor block near the Generate Light input. When the cursor becomes the Connect Wire tool (see Figure 2.18), hold down on the right mouse button and the menu shown in Figure 2.19 will appear. Select Create and then Control. A gray box will emerge that is already wired to the Generate Light input. Your program should now look like Figure 2.20.

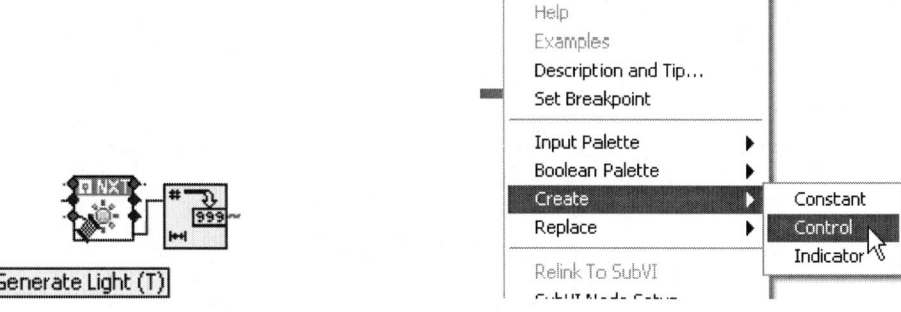

Figure 2.18
Connect Wire Tool Next to Generate Light Input

Figure 2.19
Adding a Control

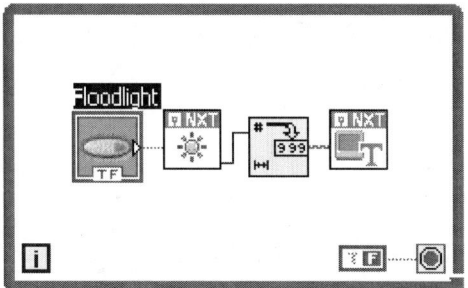

Figure 2.20
Control Added to the Program

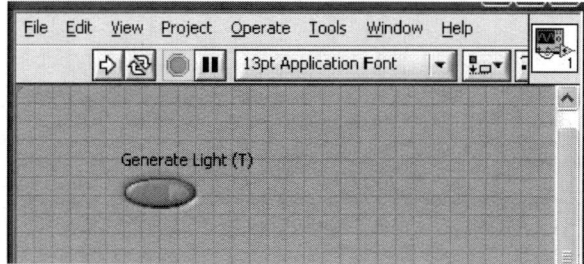

Figure 2.21
Pushbutton Control

Switch windows to the Front Panel (see Figure 2.21) and you will find that LabVIEW has automatically installed a pushbutton on it. Controls live on the Front Panel just as Function Blocks live on the Block Diagram. Pushbuttons are a Boolean type of input Control. They allow you to change the values of variables while the program is running. In this case, the state of the Generate Light input will be controlled by this pushbutton. There is even a simulated green LED to tell you the state of the button.

Indicators

On the Block Diagram, move the Connect Wire tool next to the wire connecting the Intensity and the Number input, as shown in Figure 2.22. Hold down the right mouse button (see Figure 2.23) and select Create and then Indicator. Another gray box will appear that is connected to the wire, as shown in Figure 2.24. The little ball at the intersection of the wires tells you that there is a connection; they are not just wires that happen to cross each other.

When you look at the Front Panel again, there will be a Numeric Indicator like that in Figure 2.25 on it. You can move it around if you want to align it with the

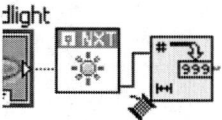

Figure 2.22
Connect Wire Tool Near Wire

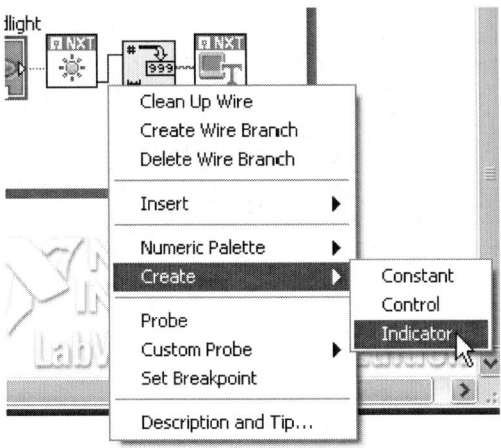

Figure 2.23
Create Indicator Menu

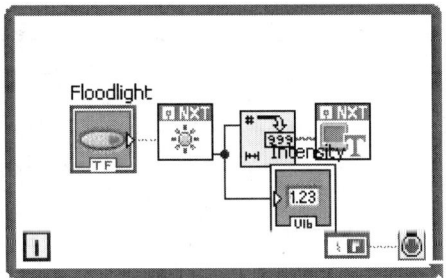

Figure 2.24
Control Added to the Program

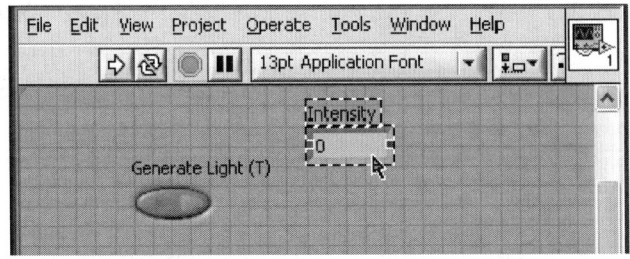

Figure 2.25
Moving the Numeric Indicator Control

pushbutton so it looks like Figure 2.26. This Front Panel is like a window into the NXT for debugging.

Instead of using the Compile, Download, and Run button on the NXT Terminal, use the Debug button as shown in Figure 2.27. Just as before, it will take a little while for the whole operation. When the NXT starts to execute the program, the Front Panel, shown in Figure 2.28, will show the same Intensity value as the NXT display, as illustrated by Figure 2.29.

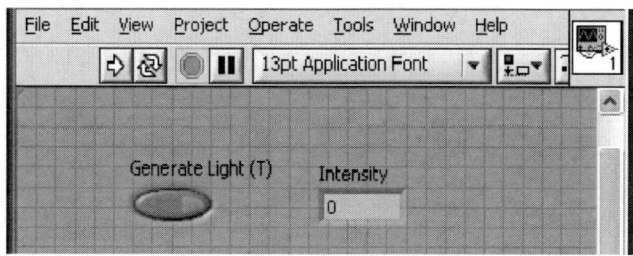

Figure 2.26
Final Debug Front Panel

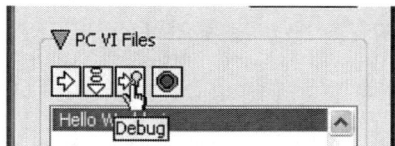

Figure 2.27
Start Debugging

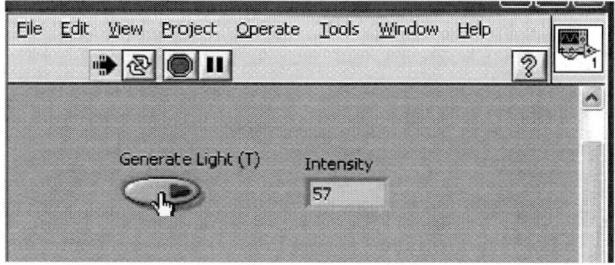

Figure 2.28
Front Panel While NXT Program Is Running

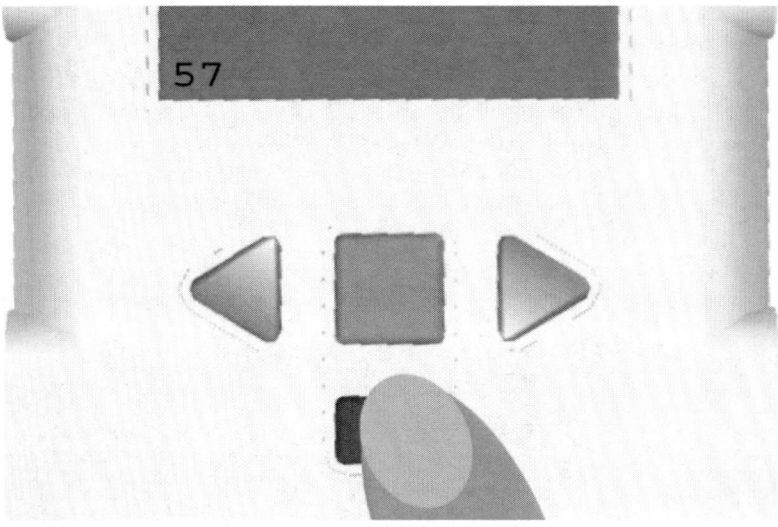

Figure 2.29
Stop the Program with the NXT Stop Button

Now click on the Generate Light pushbutton on the Front Panel with your mouse and the LED on the Light Sensor will go on and off. I know this isn't rocket science, but still that's pretty cool. There are many other Control types than can be used to change values in your program. You stop the program by pressing the Stop button on the NXT or the Stop button in the NXT Terminal, which is to the right of Debug.

Charts

On the Front Panel select the Intensity Numeric Indicator and then right-click to select Replace from the menu that appears. Replace will bring up a Tools palette (see Figure 2.30) from which you should select Graph Indicators and then Chart. A large graph-like display will replace the simple numeric one. In the NXT Terminal click the Debug button again. Now the Front Panel will display a graph of the light value while the program is running. I made the example shown in Figure 2.31 by passing my fingers in front of the Light Sensor with the LED turned on.

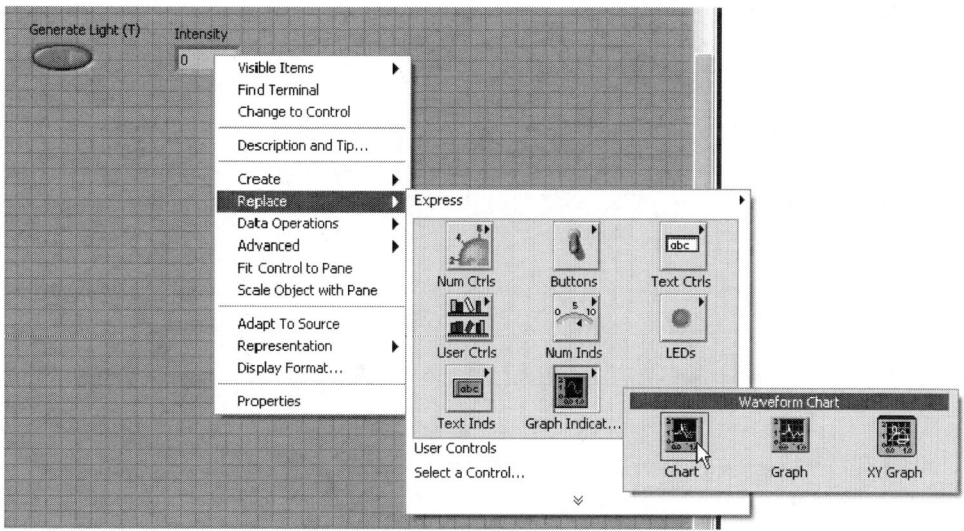

Figure 2.30
Replacing the Numeric Indicator with a Chart

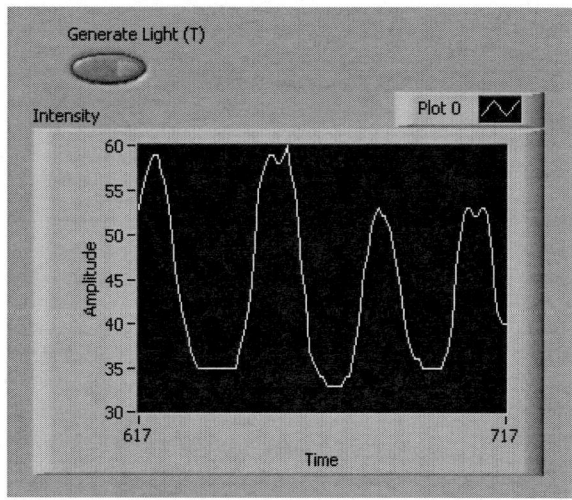

Figure 2.31
Front Panel with Chart

Reflections

In this chapter you have seen how to open existing programs, write programs that get input from sensors, and debug programs. I hope you were particularly impressed with debugging. We will be using it for a lot more than fixing programs. Now I'll show you how to get things moving with the NXT motors.

A Moving Experience

3

I find the great thing in this world is not so much where we stand,
as in what direction we are moving.—Oliver Wendell Holmes

In this chapter I'm going to show you how to program a mobile robot called Elmer. Elmer is a very compact and versatile little robot that will be used to demonstrate many LabVIEW programming concepts in this chapter and those that follow. The design is basically the LEGO TriBot robot that comes with the MINDSTORMS NXT kit with a few minor modifications.

Elmer

You will find the step-by-step building instructions for the TriBot in the Robo Center (see Figure 3.1) of the NXT software or it is readily available on the web by searching for Tribot building instructions. However, there are a few changes to the instructions you need to make. First, don't bother building Grabber, the down-pointing Light Sensor, or the Sound Sensor. Second, mount the Light Sensor where the Sound Sensor was supposed to go and connect it to Input Port 3 of the NXT. When you are done, Elmer will look like Figure 3.2. The connector wires have been left off to simplify the picture, but the Light Sensor is connected to Input 3 and the Touch Sensor to Input 1.

This robot shows off the ability of the NXT to control two motors synchronously. Synchronous operation means that the rotations of two motors are controlled at the same time. This is possible because NXT motors have built-in Rotation Sensors that constantly tell the NXT the amount the wheels have turned. Otherwise, one motor would naturally tend to rotate a little faster than the other, and the robot would tend to drift a little left or right instead of going perfectly straight. Synchronization also makes possible the coordinated action of steering, which requires the motors to rotate at different rates at the same time.

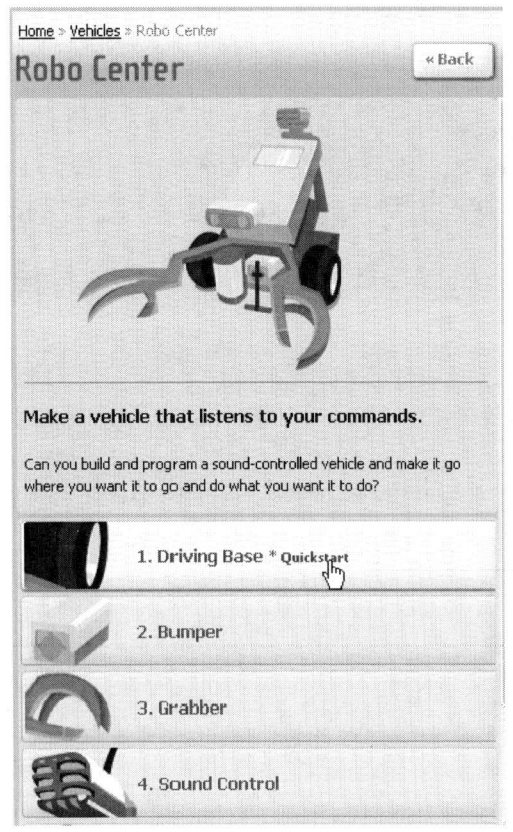

Figure 3.1
TriBot Instructions from the Robo Center

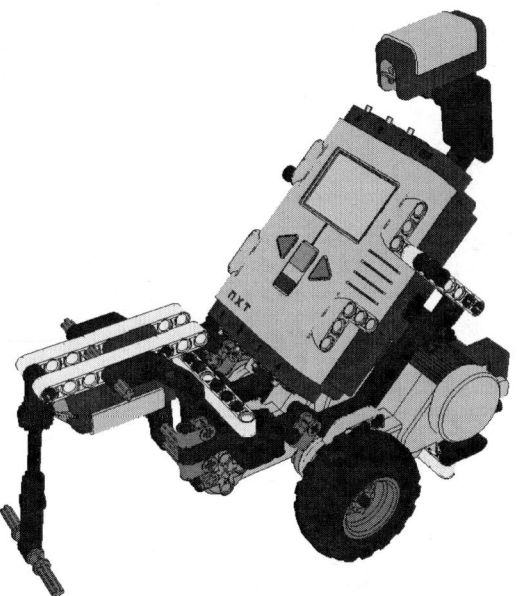

Figure 3.2
Elmer

Sync Unlimited

All of the motor-related Function Blocks are in the Output palette. The full Output palette is shown in Figure 3.3. The blocks that start with Motor control only a single motor. Blocks that start with Sync (short for Synchronized) are used to control two motors synchronously. We'll get to the other blocks in the Output palette later.

Sync Unlimited, as shown in Figure 3.4, turns two motors on, and the Sync Stop, as shown in Figure 3.5, is used to turn them off again. Usually Ports B and C are used for the right and left wheels of a robot such as Elmer or TriBot. You can override this by selecting different ports, but for now the more important inputs are for Power and Steering.

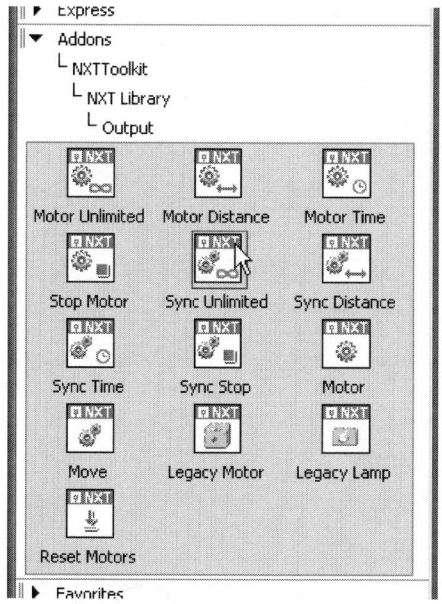

Figure 3.3
Output Palette

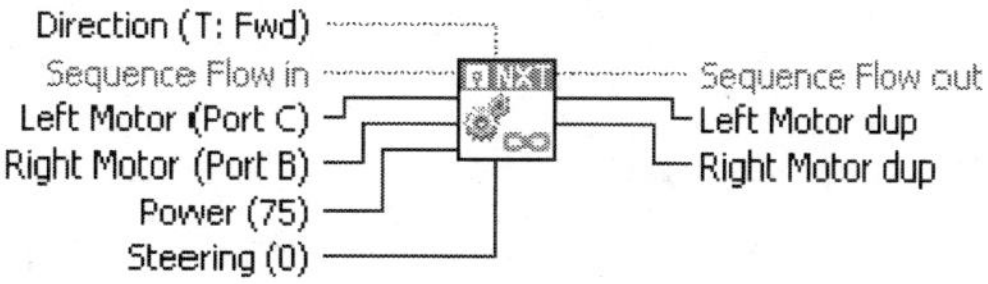

Direction (T: Fwd)
Sequence Flow in ⋯ Sequence Flow out
Left Motor (Port C) ⎤ ⎡ Left Motor dup
Right Motor (Port B) ⎤ ⎡ Right Motor dup
Power (75)
Steering (0)

Figure 3.4
Sync Unlimited

The Power input controls how fast the motors will turn. It is an Integer that can range from 0 to 100, with 100 being full speed. The default is 75, which is still pretty fast. Steering is also an Integer, but it has a range from –100 to 100. The value –100 will turn clockwise so hard it will stay in one place, and 100 will do the same thing only counterclockwise. Values between –100 and 100 are various degrees of turning with 0 going straight, and that is the default.

Place a Sync Unlimited on the left and a Sync Stop on the right of the Block Diagram, as shown in Figure 3.6. Make sure there is plenty of room between them to add some more blocks.

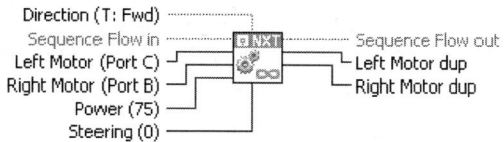

Figure 3.5
Sync Stop

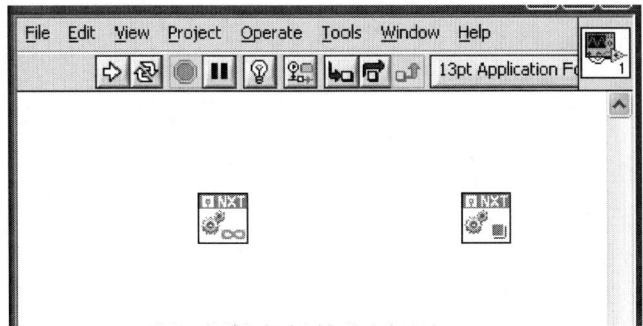

Figure 3.6
Sync Unlimited and Sync Stop on Block Diagram

Move Until Touched

Get a Touch Sensor block from the Input palette and place it between the Sync Unlimited and Sync Stop blocks. Figure 3.7 shows all the possible connections to a Touch Sensor. Elmer already has the Touch Sensor connected to Port 1, so you don't need to connect anything to that input. The Yes/No output is True when the Touch Sensor is being pressed. You should be able to add a While Loop around the Touch Sensor block and wire the Yes/No output to the Loop Condition (see Figure 3.8).

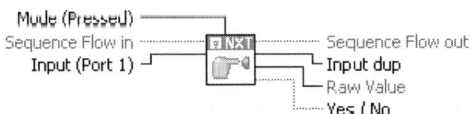

Figure 3.7
Touch Sensor

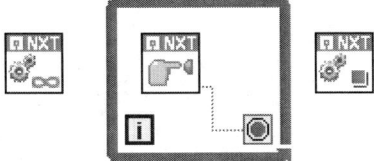

Figure 3.8
Wait-until-Touched Loop

Sequence Flow

We want the program to turn the motors on until something hits the Touch Sensor and then stop. You might think that the order in which the blocks in Figure 3.8 would be performed would be from left to right, like reading a book. However, there is actually no preference to order in a data flow language such as LabVIEW. As strange as it may seem, unless blocks have a need for data from previous blocks, they will all try to run at the same time. To control the order of performance, NXT blocks have Sequence Flow inputs and outputs.

Figure 3.9 shows how to use the Connect Wire tool to tie the Sync Unlimited block Sequence Flow output to the Touch Sensor block Sequence Flow input. Now the Touch Sensor won't run until the motors have been started. Next, tie the Sequence Flow output of the Touch Sensor to the Sequence Flow input of the Sync Stop. Now the motors will stop after the Touch Sensor While Loop has finished. The program should now look like Figure 3.10. The green boxes drawn in the walls of the While Loop where the wire goes through are called Tunnels.

As soon as the program starts running, Elmer will start moving forward, and he won't stop unless someone or something bumps the bumper switch. On the NXT Terminal you will want only to Compile and Download (see Figure 3.11) the program. That way you can safely unplug the USB cable before you push the orange enter button on the NXT to start it.

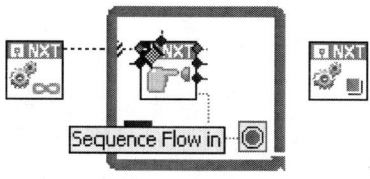

Figure 3.9
Adding Sequence Flow

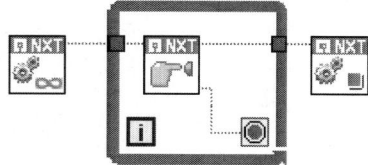

Figure 3.10
Finished Run-until-Touched Program

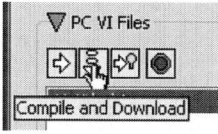

Figure 3.11
Compile and Download

Come to the Light

The Touch Sensor is either pressed or not, and that easily converts to a Boolean (True/False) variable that can be connected to the Loop Condition. What about the Light Sensor? Its output is Intensity with values from 0 to 100. To make a Boolean we need to compare this Intensity with another Integer value. For example; is the Intensity greater than 50? That question has a True/False or Boolean-type answer.

Comparisons

Let's add some blocks to make Elmer wait until the light is bright before he starts moving. The Comparison palette is shown in Figure 3.12. About half of these blocks have two inputs, and the top input is compared with the lower input. The rest of the blocks compare the number to zero, so they need only one input. Add the new blocks to create the program shown in Figure 3.13. You should connect the Intensity output of the Light Sensor to the top input of the Greater comparison first. Then create the Integer constant using the same right-click trick you've used to create all the other constants so far.

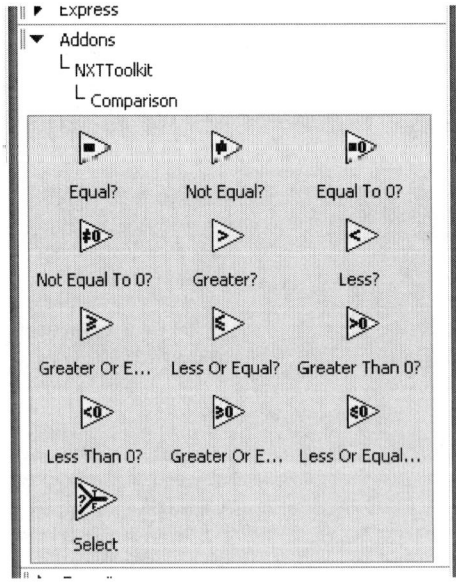

Figure 3.12
Comparison Palette

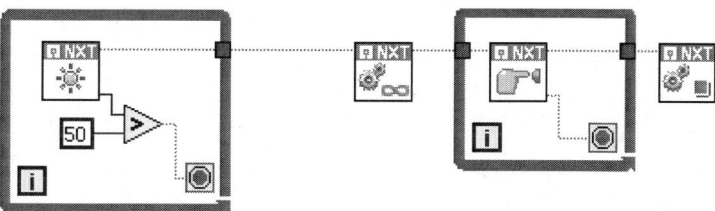

Figure 3.13
Come–to-the-Light Program

Reconnect the USB cable and Compile and Download the program as before. Unless you are in a pretty bright room, Elmer will just sit there after you push the enter button. He won't move until you shine a light at his Light Sensor. Then he will charge forward until his bumper is bumped.

Adding Labels

Sometimes it is difficult for someone other than the programmer to understand how a program works—after a while, even the programmer can't understand it. Suppose you had added a power input to the Sync Unlimited, as shown in Figure 3.14. There would be a number just hanging onto the side of the block, but what is it for? If you right-click on the constant, as shown in Figure 3.15, you can turn on a Visible Item called the Label. Figure 3.16 shows how the Label is automatically filled out to match the input that it was connected to. You can even click inside the Label and change the text if you want.

We can do the same thing for the Left Motor, as shown in Figure 3.17 and Figure 3.18. Even if you were using the default value of Port C, it makes it clear which port

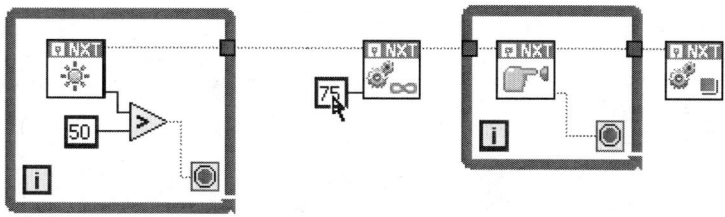

Figure 3.14
Adding Constant to Power

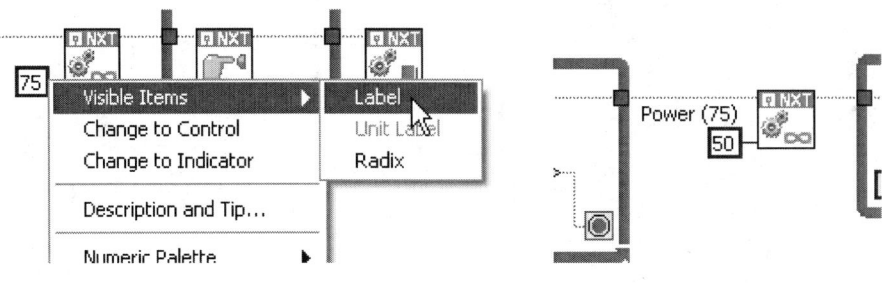

Figure 3.15
Making the Label Visible

Figure 3.16
Power Constant with Label

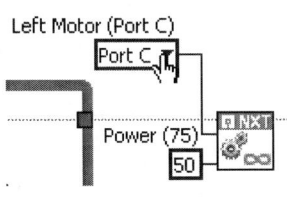

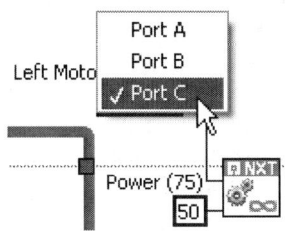

Figure 3.17
Adding Labeled Constant to Motor Port

Figure 3.18
Selecting Motor Port

you expect the motor to be connected to. You should have a labeled constant for every single input to every NXT block so there would be absolutely no confusion about what the program was using. I won't be doing that with the examples in this book since it tends to clutter the illustrations, but it is a really good way to document your program.

The Tools Palette

Another useful documentation tool is the comment. Comments are little messages that are stuck around the Block Diagram like Post-It Notes™ to tell people what the program is doing at that point. We need a new type of palette to add comments, and Figure 3.19 shows how you open the Tools palette with the View pulldown menu.

The Tools palette is shown in Figure 3.20. Some of the Tools should look familiar. For example, the Operate Value, Selection, and Connect Wire Tools are all there.

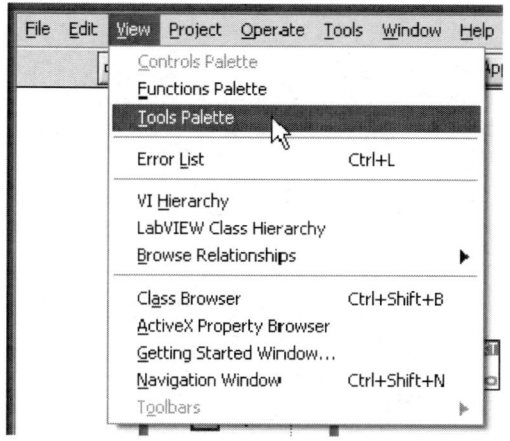

Figure 3.19
Opening the Tools Palette

Figure 3.20
The Tools Palette

We have been using a feature of LabVIEW that has been automatically selecting tools for us based on where the cursor is located. The green rectangle that appears lit up at the top of the palette signifies that Automatic Tool Selection is turned on.

Notice what happens when you left-click on the Edit Text Tool, as shown in Figure 3.21. The Automatic Tool Selection light turns off, and the Edit Text Tool turns dark to indicate that it has been selected. Now when you move the cursor back onto the Block Diagram, it has a different shape, as shown in Figure 3.22.

Move the Edit Text Tool under the first While Loop and left-click. Now you can type a comment about what the loop is doing, "Wait till Light>50." You can add comments

Figure 3.21
Selecting the Edit Text Tool

Figure 3.22
The Edit Text Tool Cursor

to the other stages of the program, as shown in Figure 3.23. Remember, the comments don't do anything but remind you about what the program is doing. If you changed the light compare value from 50 to 60, for example, you should also fix the comment.

When you're done adding comments, it is a good idea to turn Automatic Tool Selection back on by clicking on it in the Tools palette (see Figure 3.24). You can also add comments by simply double-clicking on any empty spot on the block diagram and then typing the comment.

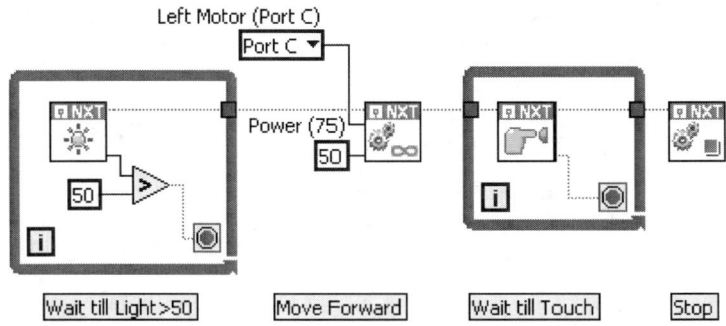

Figure 3.23
Program with Comments

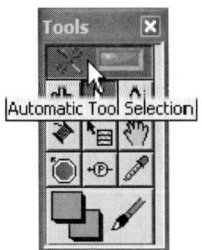

Figure 3.24
Reselecting Automatic Tool Selection

Fixing Broken Wires

Deleting a block from the Block Diagram doesn't automatically delete all the wires that were connected to it. Suppose we delete the Left Motor input, as shown in Figure 3.25. The wire will be shown as a dotted line with a red X in the middle, as shown in Figure 3.26, indicating an error. As you move the cursor over the X mark on the

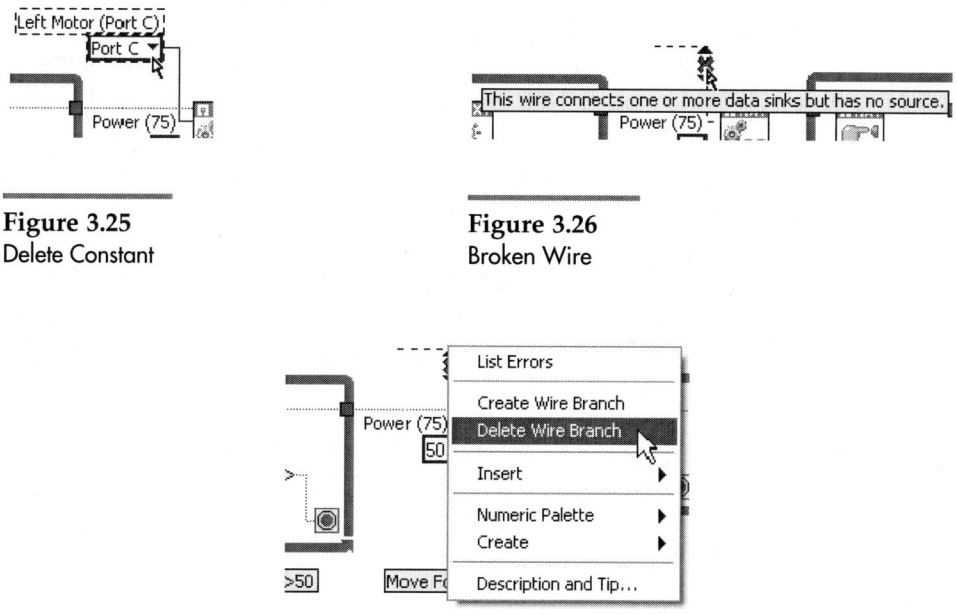

Figure 3.25
Delete Constant

Figure 3.26
Broken Wire

Figure 3.27
Delete Wire Branch

wire, a message will appear that tells you what the problem is. You can eliminate the entire broken wire by right-clicking and then selecting Delete Wire Branch from the menu that pops up. You can also use the keyboard shortcut of holding the Ctrl key down and typing the letter B. This will remove all of the broken wires on the whole diagram.

Loops within Loops

One last thing: the Come-to-the-Light program does its thing and then ends. But suppose you want the robot to keep cycling between waiting for light and waiting to be bumped without having to constantly press the Enter key on the NXT. We can put an infinite While Loop around the whole program, as shown in Figure 3.28. When the program reaches the Sync Stop it doesn't end. It starts over with the wait for the light, and only the Stop button on the NXT will end the program.

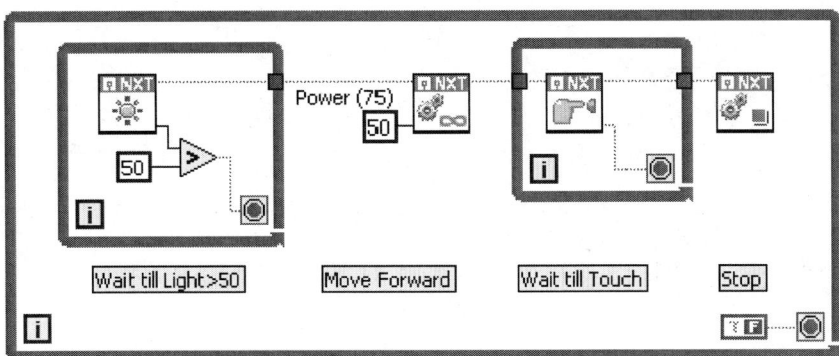

Figure 3.28
Endless Run to the Light

Reflections

There are a few things you should try before moving on to the next chapter. Try adding a constant to the Steering input of the Sync Unlimited. Experiment with how Elmer turns for different values such as 40 and 100. You might also change the light comparison value to make Elmer more or less sensitive to light. After that, we will learn how to make decisions.

Deciding to Decide

4

*Nothing is more difficult, and therefore more precious,
than to be able to decide.—Napoleon Bonaparte*

Inputs come and outputs go, but the heart of a program consists of the decisions it makes. So far we have decided only to wait for something. Now I will show you how to make more complex decisions in LabVIEW.

NXT Buttons

By now you should be able to build everything in Figure 4.1 without help. You might not recognize the NXT Buttons input (see Figure 4.2) that can be found along with the Touch and Light Sensors in the Input palette. Notice that the Right Button is being selected with a constant, not the default Enter button. You can pick the Action of these buttons to be Pressed, Released, or Bumped. Pressed or Released means that as long as the button is doing that, the Yes/No output will be True. Bumped is True only when the button has been just pressed and released.

The Case Structure

Go to the Structures palette (see Figure 4.3) to get a Case Structure and put it on the Block Diagram just as you have been doing with the While Loop. Click in the lower-left corner and drag up to the right in the open area inside the While Loop, as shown in Figure 4.4.

The Case Structure looks like a frame with a small green question mark on the left called the Case Selector and a rectangle on the top called the Selector Label. Because the Case Selector is green, you should have suspected it would be a Boolean-type input and that there would be two cases—True and False. You can slide the Case Selector up and down to make wiring easier.

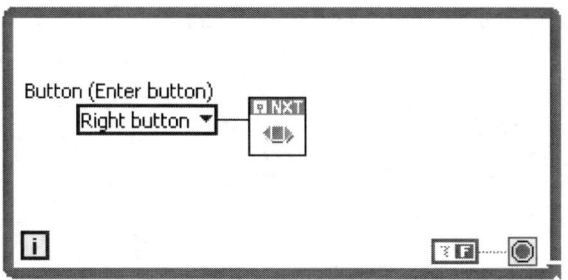

Figure 4.1
Program Starting Point

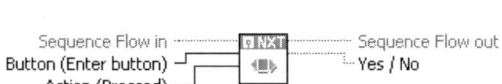

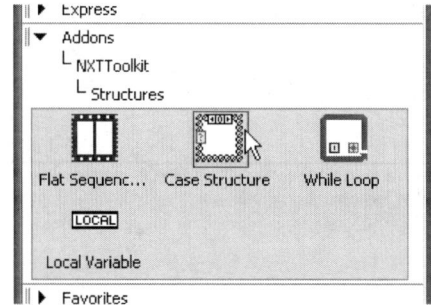

Figure 4.2
NXT Buttons

Figure 4.3
Case Structure in Palette

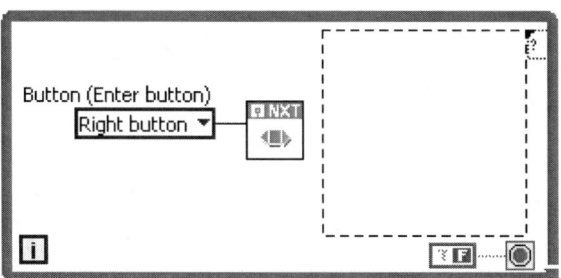

Figure 4.4
Add Case Structure to Program

Although there aren't any blocks in there now, you are looking at the True Case. Click the left mouse button when the Operate Value Tool is over the Case Label, as shown in Figure 4.5, and a menu will pop up like the one in Figure 4.6. Select the False Case, and now the Case Structure will look like Figure 4.7. You won't be able see both cases at the same time as you can with NXT-G in the flat mode.

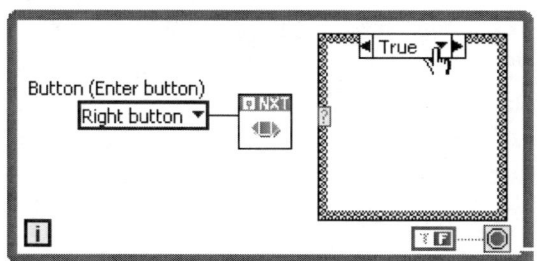

Figure 4.5
Operate Value Tool in Case Label

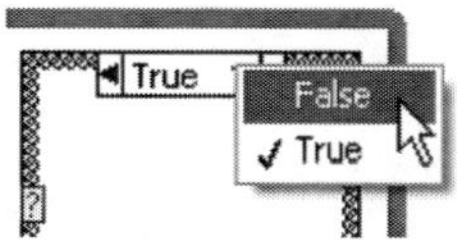

Figure 4.6
Select the False Case

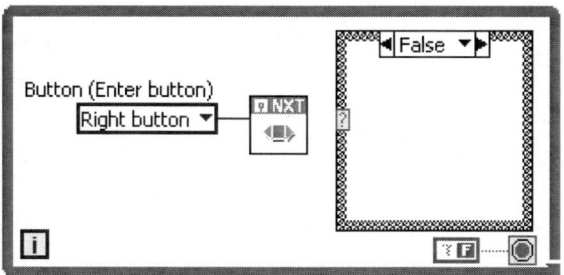

Figure 4.7
The False Case

Generating Sound

Generating sound is an exceptional feature of the NXT. The NXT can generate fixed frequency tones as well as play special sound files, much like an MP3 player. Not surprisingly, the sound function blocks are in the Sound palette in the NXT Library, as shown in Figure 4.8.

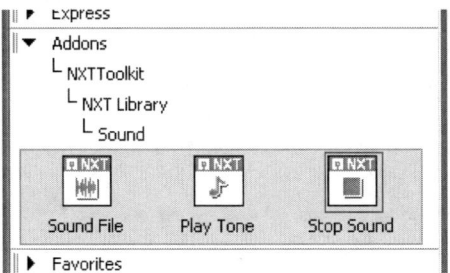

Figure 4.8
Sound Palette

Stop Sound

Pick a Stop Sound block from the palette and place it inside the False Case so it looks like Figure 4.9. No matter what type of sound the NXT is making, the Stop Sound block turns it off. Using the Operate Value Tool, switch the Case Label back to the True case. It will still be empty.

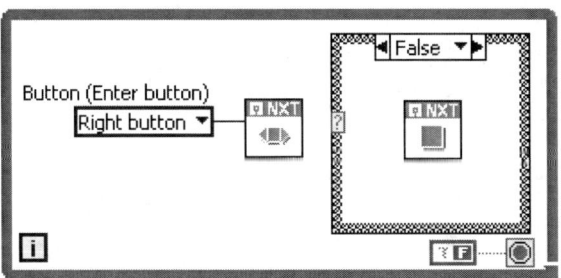

Figure 4.9
Add Stop Sound Block

Play Tone

Frequency is measured in units called hertz, which is abbreviated to Hz. Low frequencies have values like 200 Hz, whereas high frequencies have values like 4,000 Hz. The musical note A is 440 Hz. All of the connections to the Play Tone block are shown in Figure 4.10. The default is to play an A note for half a second.

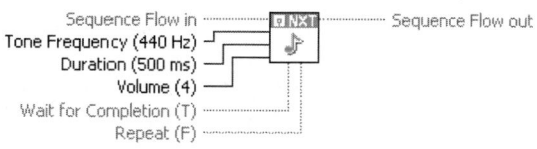

Figure 4.10
The Complete Play Tone Block

Place a Play Tone in the True case of the Case Structure like Figure 4.11. Now wire the Yes/No output of the NXT Buttons block to the Case Selector so that your program looks like Figure 4.12. When the button is not being pressed, a False is output from the NXT Buttons block to the Case Structure. This selects the False Case, which has

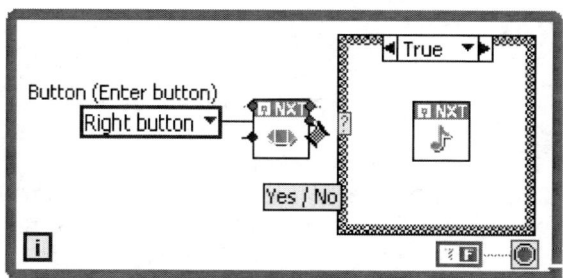

Figure 4.11
Add the Play Tone Block to the True Case

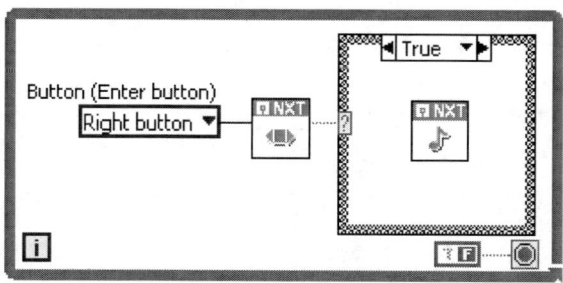

Figure 4.12
Doorbell Program

the Stop Sound block in it. When the button is pressed, a True selects the True Case, which has the Play Tone block.

Compile, Download, and Run the program using the NXT Terminal (see Figure 4.13). You just made your NXT into a rather expensive doorbell. As you push the Right button on the NXT, the NXT should produce a tone. When you let up, the sound will quickly stop.

Figure 4.13
Run the Program

The Select Block

There is another way to make Boolean decisions, called the Select block. You will find the Select block in the Comparison palette along with the Greater block we used in the preceding chapter. The Select block uses the Boolean input to choose between two values to send on to a later function block. Figure 4.14 shows the Doorbell program with the Select Block, where a constant has been created and connected to the True input.

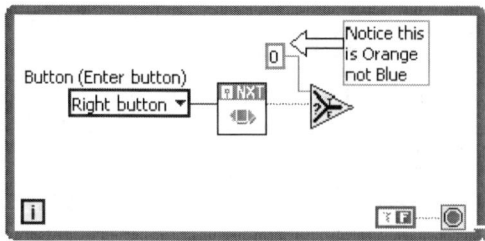

Figure 4.14
Select Block with Constant Input

Changing Representations

There is a little problem with the variable type that the Select decided to use here. Orange is for Floating Point, and we can't use Floating Point in NXT programs. We will need to change the variable type, which is also called its Representation, to an Integer. Using the right mouse button, bring up the pop-up menu shown in Figure 4.15. The current Representation of the constant is DBL, which stands for Double Precision Floating Point. Change it to U16, which stands for Unsigned Integer with 16 bits of precision, and the constant will turn blue.

When you create a constant for the False input, LabVIEW will already know you want it to be Integer. Enter values of 500 and 1000 for the constants and add a Play Tone block. Connect the output of the Select to the Tone Frequency input of the Play Tone; your program should then look like Figure 4.16.

When you Compile, Download, and Run this program it will start making the 1000 Hz tone. When you push the Right button on the NXT the tone will drop to 500 Hz. The Select can be used in similar ways to change values based on the results of comparisons and other Boolean functions.

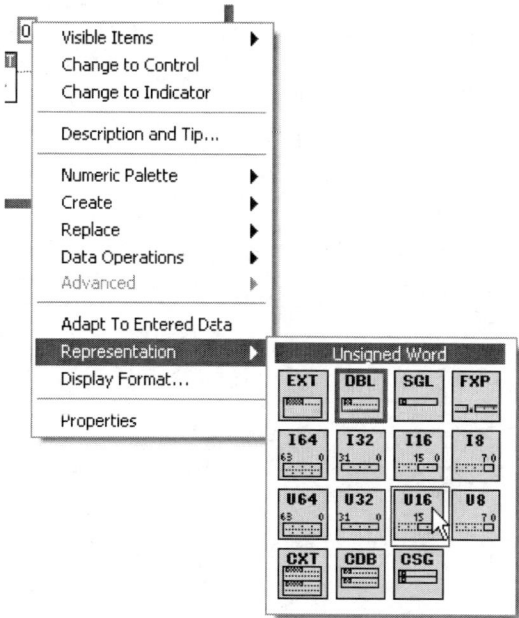

Figure 4.15
Change the Representation of the Constant

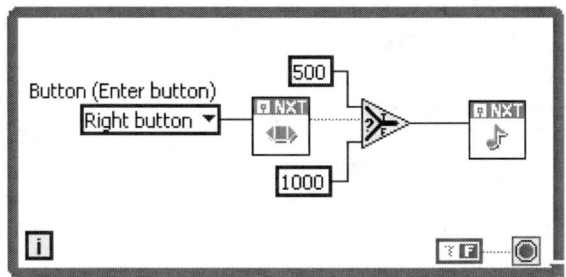

Figure 4.16
The Complete Select Program

Numeric Cases

Most decisions boil down to True/False cases, but sometimes it is necessary to create more than just two cases. Let's make Elmer's behavior more complex by combining the values from both the Light and Touch Sensors to determine the case. First, build the program shown in Figure 4.17.

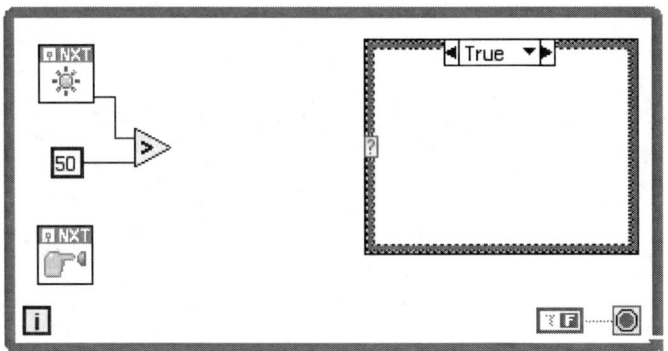

Figure 4.17
Program Starting Point

Boolean to (0...1)

We have already seen a function block that converted an Integer into a String back in Chapter 2. Conversion from a Boolean-type variable to an Integer is done with the suitably named function Boolean to (0...1). If the Boolean is False, then the output of the function is an Integer zero, and if True, then the output is one. You find the function in the Boolean palette, as shown in Figure 4.18.

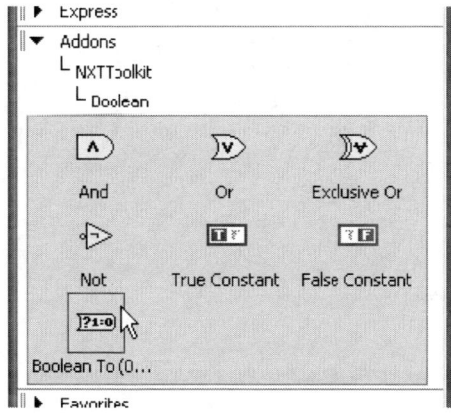

Figure 4.18
Boolean to (0...1) Block in Boolean Palette

Multiply and Add

The arithmetic functions are found in the Numeric palette (see Figure 4.19). All the simple two-input functions such as the Add and Multiply are found there. Simpler one-input functions such as increment and decrement are found there as well. Our old friend the Numeric Constant is also available, and it is conveniently already set to Integer type.

Build the rest of the program as shown in Figure 4.20. As you connect the output of the Add block, the Case Selector Label will change to reflect the new type of variable controlling it. You will find that there is a 0, Default Case and a 1 Case. As you might expect, when the Case Selector value is 1, the 1 Case will execute. When the value is 0, or anything else for the matter, the 0, Default Case will execute.

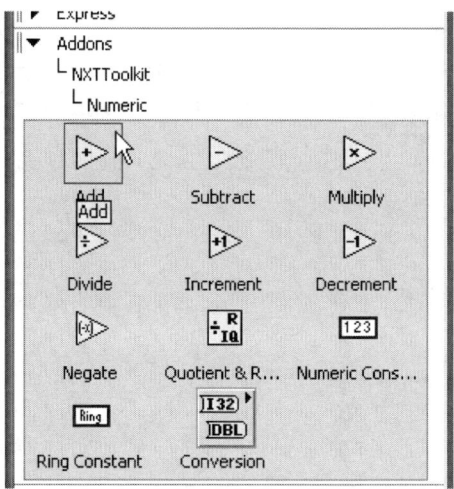

Figure 4.19
Add Block in Numeric Palette

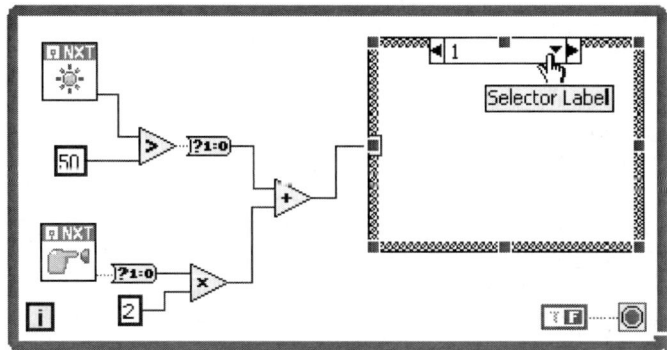

Figure 4.20
Case Label Will Change to Numeric

Adding Cases

We will need two more cases to cover all the possibilities; 0 = Dark and Not Touched, 1 = Light and Not Touched, 2 = Dark and Touched, and 3 = Light and Touched. Using the Operate Value Tool, set the Selector Label to the 1 Case (see Figure 4.20).

Now right-click, and a menu like the one in Figure 4.21 will pop up. Select Add Case After, and a new 2 Case will be created. Repeat this again to create the 3 Case.

In the 0, Default Case we want Elmer to slowly spin around in one place looking for a bright light. Get a Sync Unlimited and program it as shown in Figure 4.22. Do the same thing for the other three cases as shown in Figure 4.23, but remember you can see only one case at a time. Now when Elmer sees light, he quits turning and starts going forward. Because both cases 2 and 3 are exactly the same, no matter what he is doing, if he bumps something he will back up and turn.

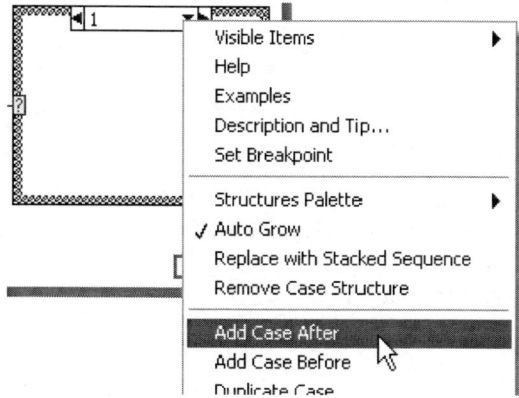

Figure 4.21
Adding Cases

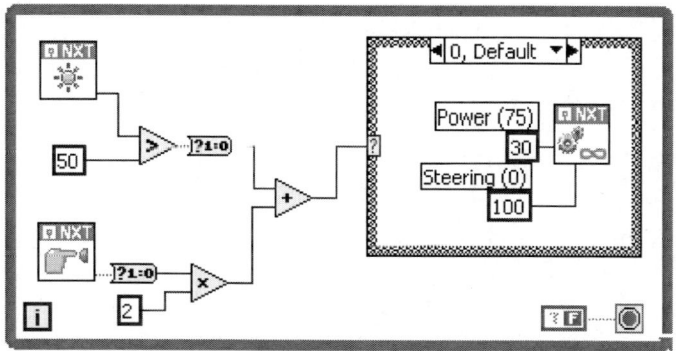

Figure 4.22
Compete Elmer Program

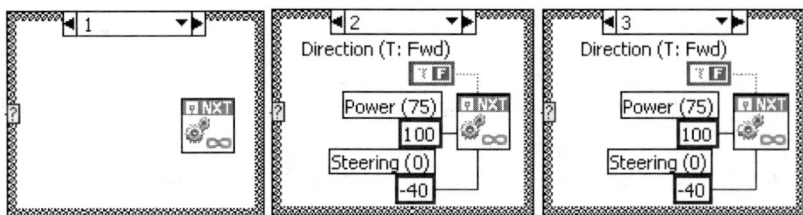

Figure 4.23
The Other Three Cases

Compile and Download

Because Elmer might get tangled in the USB cable, use only the Compile and Download button (see Figure 4.24) in the NXT Terminal. Unplug the USB cable and then push the orange Enter button on the NXT. You might need a flashlight to shine at the Light Sensor to get Elmer to react.

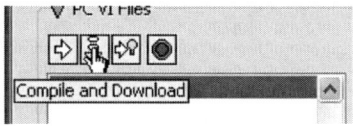

Figure 4.24
Compile and Download Then Run with NXT Button

Printing

Making a hard copy of your program is easy with LabVIEW. The Print command is found in the File menu, as shown in Figure 4.25.

A window like the one in Figure 4.26 will come up with two options. You can either print the current VI or print many VIs at the same time. Just take the default and click the Next> button. NXT programs generally don't have front panels so you will want to select the Icon, description, panel, and diagram options from the Print Contents window shown in Figure 4.27. Figure 4.28 is roughly what the printed page will look like. Notice how the different cases are printed out below the main program.

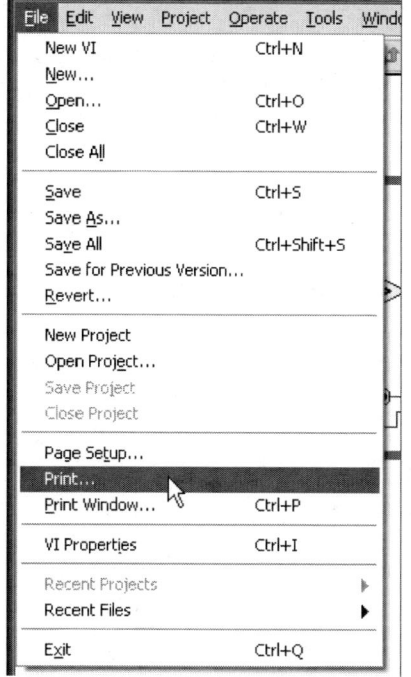

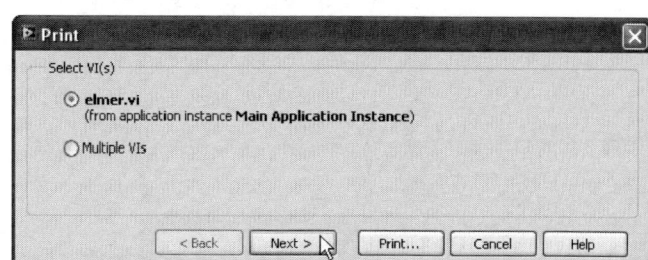

Figure 4.25
File>Print Menu

Figure 4.26
Select VI Window

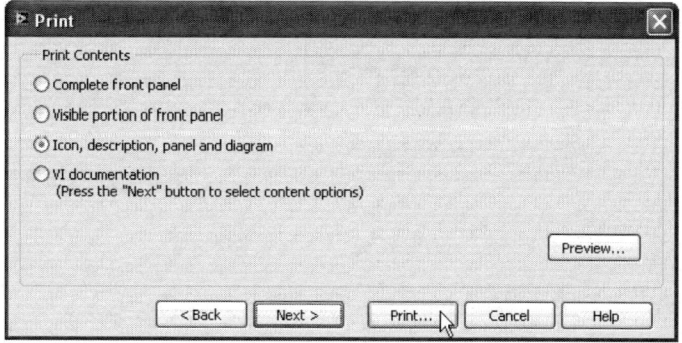

Figure 4.27
Print Contents Window

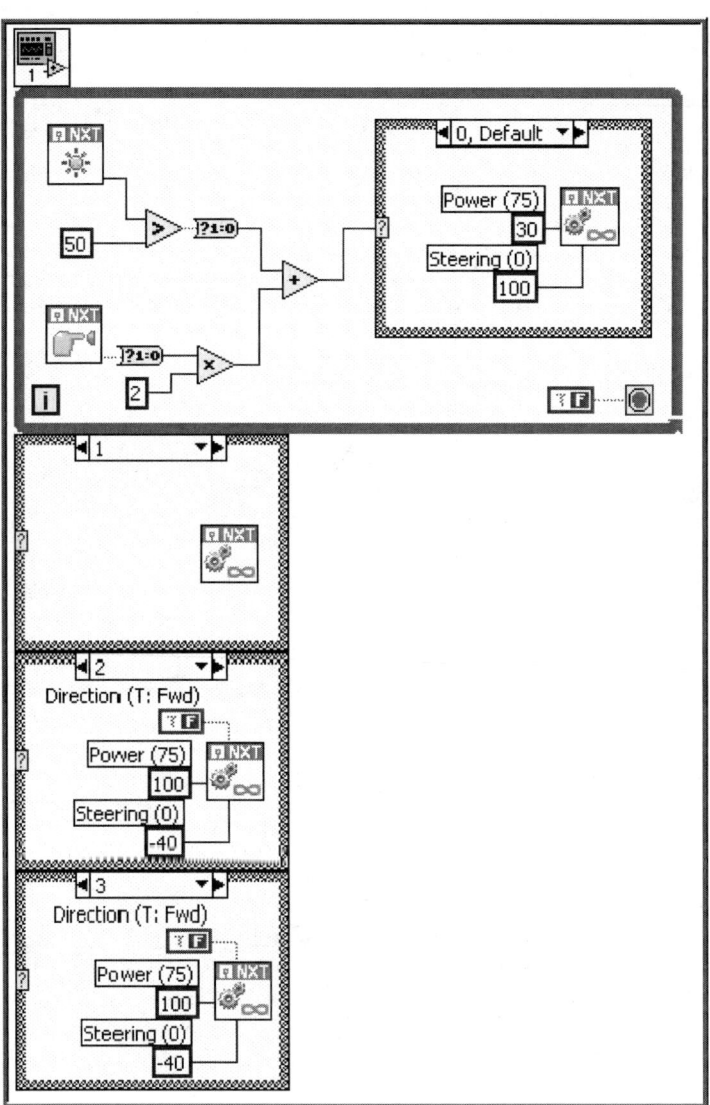

Figure 4.28
Sample Printout

Reflections

Right now Elmer reacts the same way to bumping something regardless of how much light there is. You could modify the program so that he does something different when he is bumped in the dark than when he is bumped when the light is bright. Don't take Elmer apart yet. We will get back to him in a few chapters, but for now are going to get to know some of the more internal functions of the NXT.

Taken It Easy File Functions

5

Garbage in, garbage out.—George Fuechsel, an early computer programmer

The programs you've been downloading to the NXT are examples of files. However, computer programs can also use files to store and retrieve data. The NXT has special files to store pictures that it can display and sounds that it can play. In this chapter you will learn how to make and use your own files with LabVIEW programs.

Data Logging

You can use the NXT to input sensor measurements, output the values to the NXT display, and then write the values by hand into a logbook. But what if the time between samples was so short that you couldn't write the numbers down fast enough, or what if they were an hour apart and you had to sit by the NXT for days? That is where data logging comes to the rescue.

Data logging is the automatic recording of data by a computer. Let's examine a simple program that records a number of data samples with a fixed time between the samples. By now, you should know how to build almost everything you see in the Data Logging block diagram of Figure 5.1. The new blocks are from the File Access palette shown in Figure 5.2. We are using the "Easy" file blocks because, big surprise, they are easier to use than the other file type blocks I will cover in Chapter 8. There is also a Wait block, which is in the NXT Library.

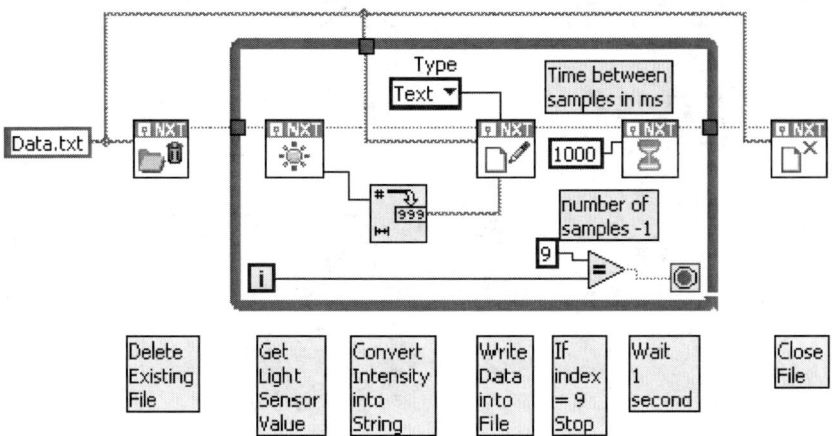

Figure 5.1
Data Logging Program

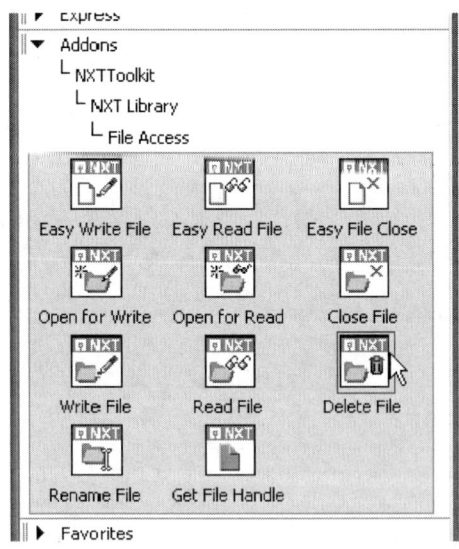

Figure 5.2
File Access Palette

Delete File

When the NXT writes to a file that already exists, it appends the new data to the end of whatever is already in the file. If the file doesn't already exist, the NXT will create a new file and then start writing to it. At the start of a new experiment it is a good idea to delete any file that already has the same name as the file you will be using. Nothing special happens if you try to delete a file that isn't there, and that way you will not accidentally append data from a new experiment onto the results of an old one. That is what is going on with the first block in the Data Logging program, which is the Delete File block shown in Figure 5.3.

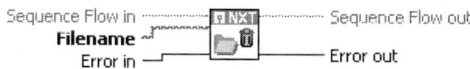

Figure 5.3
Delete File Block

Easy Write File

Easy Write File (see Figure 5.4) can input either String or an Integer (Type = Text or Number) variables. I always use Text and convert numbers to Strings myself rather than depend on the block to do it for me, but that's just my choice. Each time the block is used, it writes a String to the file with two special characters stuck on the end that are basically like hitting the Enter key on your keyboard. Those characters will make reading the file easier later. You really don't need to worry about file size, because the software will automatically expand the file if it runs out of room. However, that can take some time, and if you know the file will end up large, you might want to start out by having it bigger.

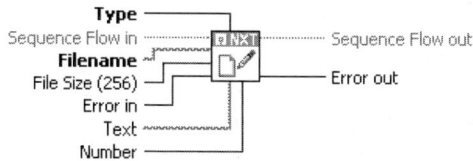

Figure 5.4
Easy Write File Block

Easy File Close

The Easy File Close (see Figure 5.5) is like telling the NXT to save the file at the end of a program. If you don't Close the file there is some chance that some of your data will be lost. It is also a good idea to Close files that you were only using to Read.

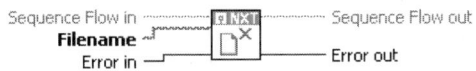

Figure 5.5
Easy File Close Block

Notice that the same filename is wired to all three file blocks. That way if you change the name of the data file, it will be automatically used by all three blocks. Using the .txt file extension will make reading the file with other programs easier.

Wait

Without the Wait block, the program would still work, but the time between the data points would only be a fraction of a second. The Wait block (see Figure 5.6) is used to force the program to sit still for a fixed amount of time. The Wait input time is in units of milliseconds (ms), which is 1/1,000 of a second. That means one thousand ms is one second or 60,000 ms would be one minute. I'll explain the millisecond timer value output in Chapter 9. The Wait block is in the NXT Library, as shown in Figure 5.7.

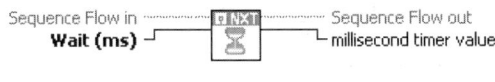

Figure 5.6
Wait Block

Loop Interation

Another thing that is new on the Figure 5.1 block diagram is the connection to the Loop Interation. That is the little blue box with the lowercase "1" in it shown in Figure 5.8. This block outputs a value of zero the first time the loop executes and then counts up

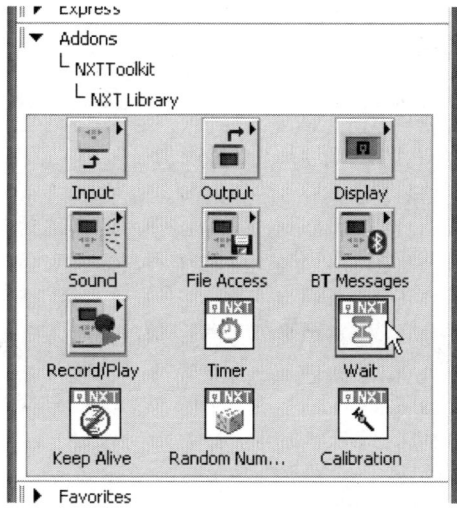

Figure 5.7
Wait Block in the NXT Library

Figure 5.8
Loop Interation

by one for each successive loop. You can use these values to repeat the loop an exact number of times by comparing the value with a constant and then terminating the loop when the comparison is True. Because the Loop Interation starts with zero and not one, the constant must be one less than the number of times you need the loop to execute.

Compile, Download, and Run the Data Logging program using the NXT Terminal. While the program is running, move your finger in front of the Light Sensor to change the light intensity from data point to data point. The program takes 10 data points that are one second apart, so it will only take 10 seconds to run.

Sending Files to the PC

The NXT Terminal has a separate area near the bottom to see the names of the files stored in the NXT. Normally the area is minimized, and you need to click in the gray triangle next to the words NXT Files to see it. There might be a lot of files already in your NXT, but one of them should now be Data.txt. Select the Data.txt file and click the Send File(s) to PC button as shown in Figure 5.9. This same window can be used to run programs or delete files on the NXT if you run out of memory.

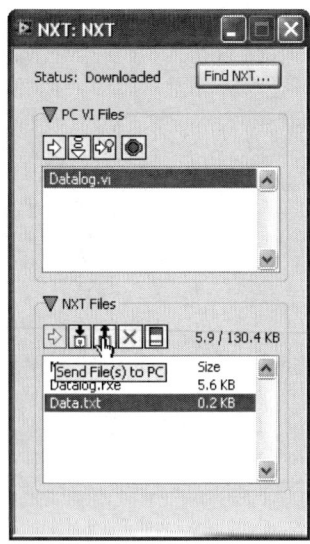

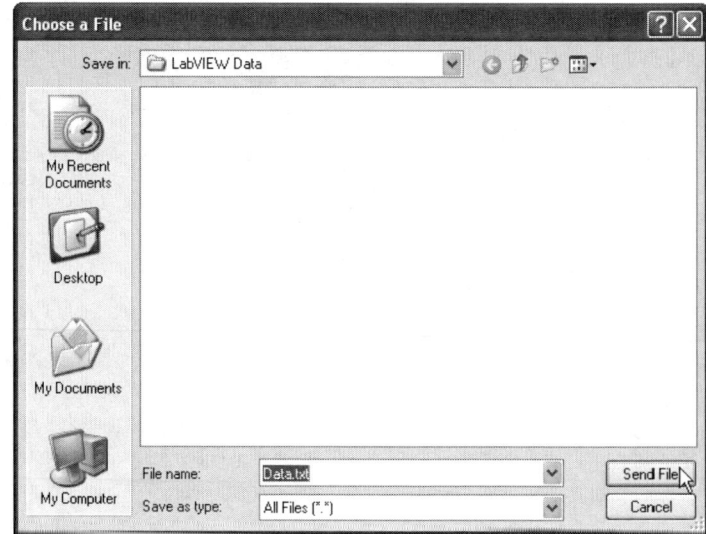

Figure 5.9
NXT Terminal with Files Open

Figure 5.10
Choose a File Window

A window will appear that looks like Figure 5.10. This window allows you to select the location on the PC at which the file will be stored. Clicking the Send File button will move the file up to the PC.

Dealing with Data Files

With a text editor such as Notepad (see Figure 5.11) you can look at the data inside the file. There will be 10 numbers, and the two special characters that Easy File Write added account for why each value is on a separate line. Of course your values won't be the same as the ones shown here. Spreadsheet programs such as Excel

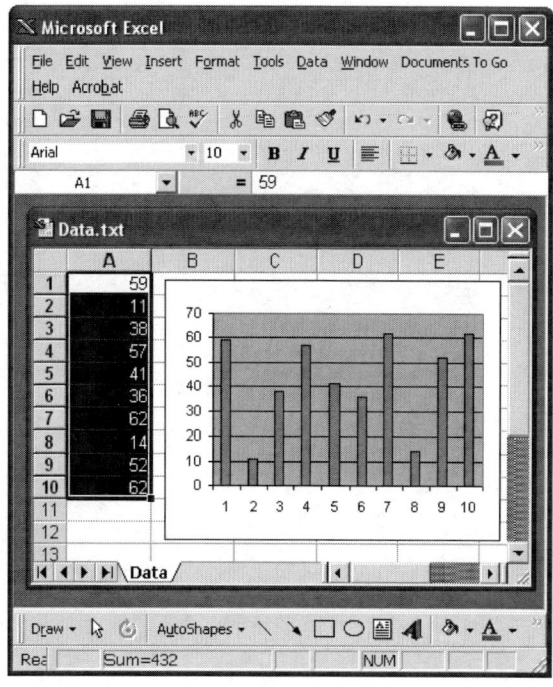

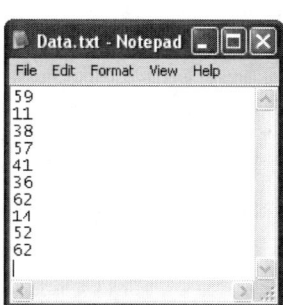

Figure 5.11
Data File in Notepad

Figure 5.12
Data Analysis in Excel

(see Figure 5.12) can be used to read or import the numbers in the file so they can be analyzed or plotted.

The Data Logging program is just a starting point. It can be easily modified to use other sensors. The number of samples and time between samples can also be easily adjusted. However, if you plan to record data over a long period of time, you will need to set the Sleep feature of the NXT to Never. This is done with the Settings Menu on the NXT itself. There is an NXT block to keep it alive also, but we will get to that later.

Music Box

Data files can be read by the NXT as well—even data files that the NXT didn't create itself. The data might be sequence of instructions or values used by a program. An entertaining example of this is a music box in which the notes of the song are stored in a file.

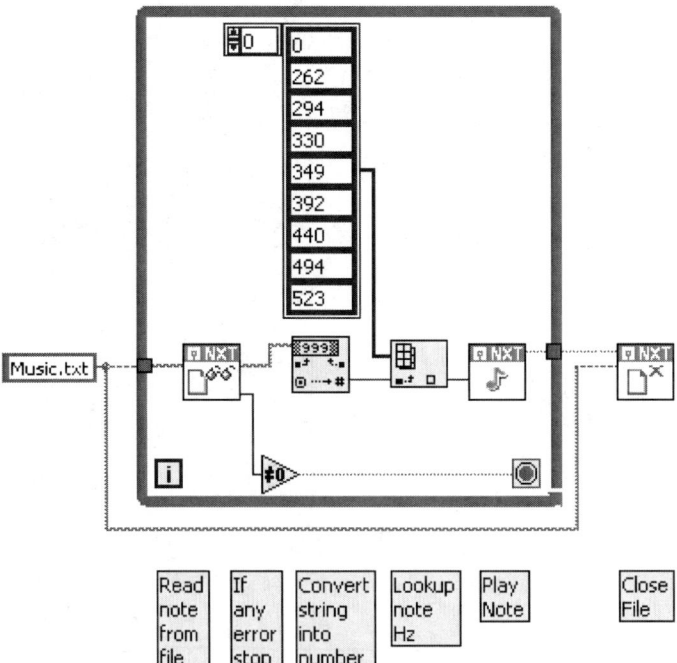

Figure 5.13
Music Box Program

The Music Box program is shown in Figure 5.13. The new items in the program are the Easy File Read block from the Files palette, the Decimal String to Integer from the String/Number subpalette of the Strings palette, and the Array-related parts. The error output of the Easy File Read is zero if the last value read from the file was alright. As the program reaches the end of the Music.txt file, the last read will report an error (not equal to 0), and we use that to terminate the loop.

Easy File Read

Remember the special characters I said Easy File Write stuck on the end of the String before it wrote it into the file. Now Easy File Read, shown in Figure 5.14, reads a String back out of the file until it sees those special characters. It also takes a crack at converting the String to a Number, but if you didn't put a number in the file in the first place that probably won't turn out well. I also have a habit of converting my Strings back to Numbers in my program rather than depending on the block to do it.

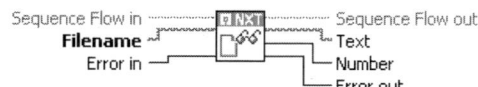

Figure 5.14
Easy File Read

Arrays

Arrays are like a long list of variables where individual values, called Elements, are accessed with a single number called the Index. In LabVIEW the Index starts with the number zero. In the Music Box program an array is used to store the tone frequencies for the notes it can play. For example, 6 is the A note, and it has the frequency 440Hz. The Index Array block is found in the Array palette shown in Figure 5.15. The top input is the Array, the bottom is the Index, and the output is the value of the individual Array Element (see Figure 5.16).

After placing the Index Array block, go to its Array input and create a constant as you have been doing for other blocks. The initial appearance of the Constant Array looks like Figure 5.17. The little box on the left with up and down arrows next to it is the Index, and the box on the right is the value of the Element accessed by that Index. You will notice it is orange for Floating Point, so we will need to fix that eventually.

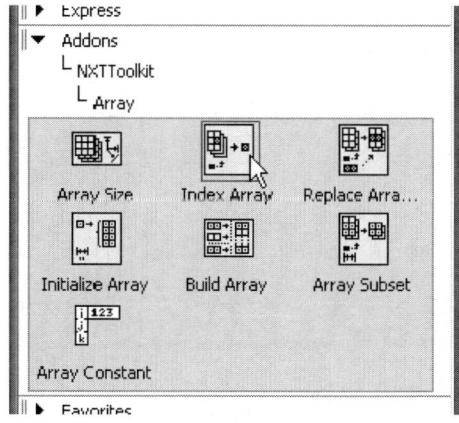

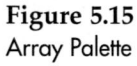

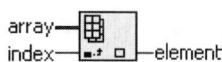

Figure 5.15
Array Palette

Figure 5.16
Index Array

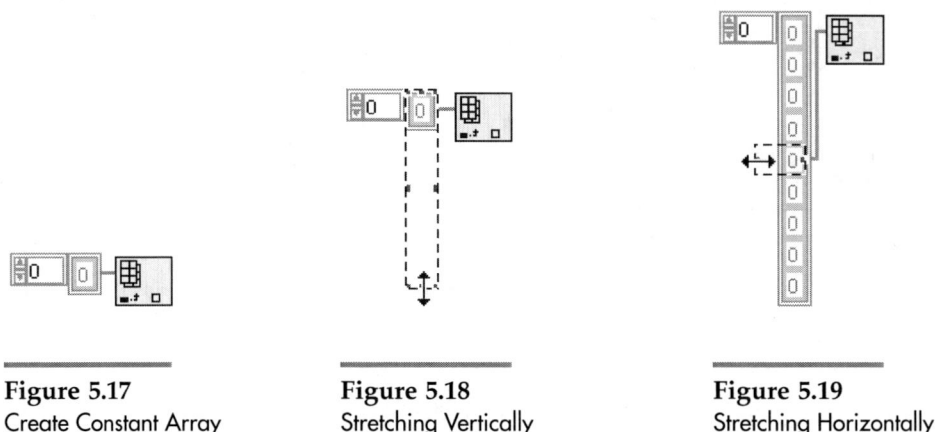

Figure 5.17
Create Constant Array

Figure 5.18
Stretching Vertically

Figure 5.19
Stretching Horizontally

It can be fairly tedious looking at only one element at a time. Fortunately, you can stretch the Constant vertically to see more than one element, as shown in Figure 5.18. You should also stretch it horizontally (see Figure 5.19) so you can see more than single-digit numbers. Finally, you will need to change the Representation to U16 so it is blue and looks like Figure 5.20. Now you can start entering the values shown in Figure 5.13.

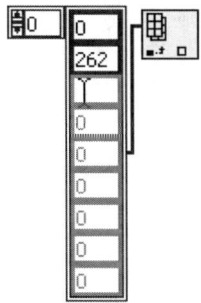

Figure 5.20
Change to U16

Preparing the Music File

The song will be stored in a file as a sequence of numbers that represent the individual notes in the song. Figure 5.21 shows the note number, letter, and location in the musical scale. The program doesn't have sharps or flats, I'll leave that enhancement up to you. The zero Note is 0Hz which doesn't make any sound.

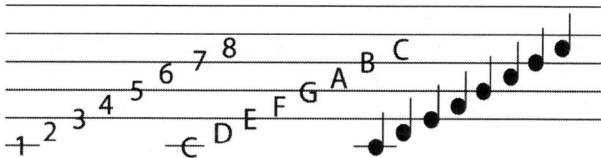

Figure 5.21
Note Number, Letter, and Scale

The notes in the song are stored one per line. Notepad is a good program for entering these, because it doesn't add any special document formatting information to the file. It does add those two special characters that Easy File Read is looking for to separate the data. You can use a word processing program such as Word, but you will need to save the file as Plain Text with a .txt file extension. Copy the numbers exactly as shown in Figure 5.22. I'll let the tune be a surprise.

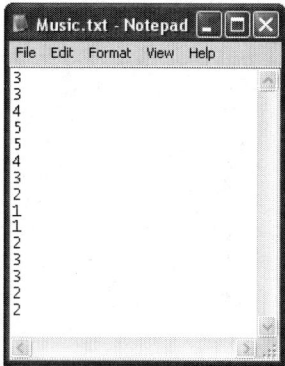

Figure 5.22
Music File Music.txt

Sending Files to the NXT

Before you can run the Music Box program, the Music.txt file must be downloaded to the NXT. Open the NXT Terminal and select Send File to NXT, as shown in Figure 5.23. A Select File window will appear like the one in Figure 5.24 that you use to navigate to the location where you stored the file. After the file has been downloaded, you should be able to find it in the NXT Files window (see Figure 5.25).

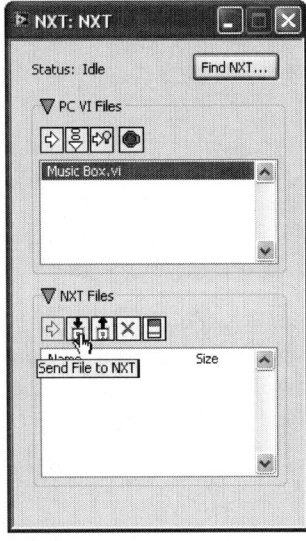 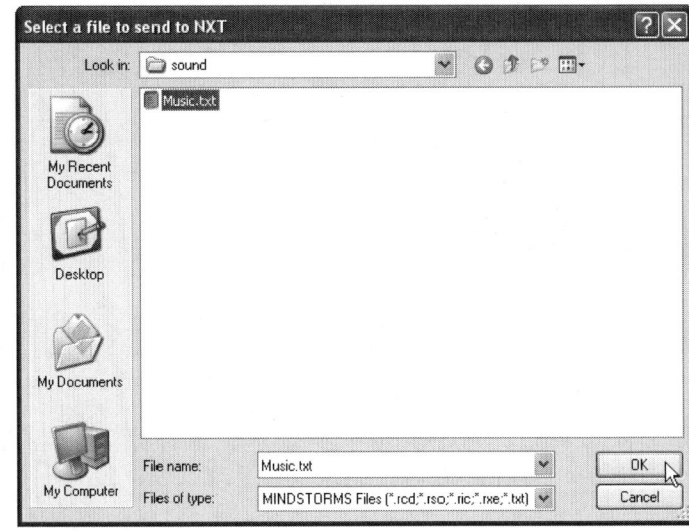

Figure 5.23
Send File to NXT in NXT Terminal

Figure 5.24
Select File Window

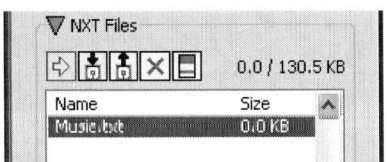

Figure 5.25
Uploaded Music.txt file

Now Compile, Download, and Run the program, and the NXT should play a little familiar tune. The Music Box program is just a starting point for a more elaborate program. You could add a wider range of notes by extending the size of the Array. You could also adjust the length of each note by entering a value for the Play Tone duration.

Record/Play

You can create a long sequence of actions for a robot by programming a series of individual motor related blocks that control turning and going forward. However, the program would be large and time consuming to debug. The Record Action block

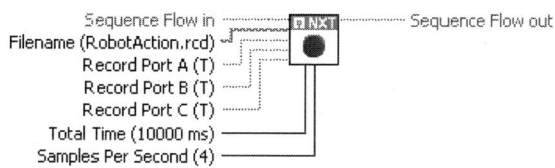

Figure 5.26
Record Action

(see Figure 5.26) keeps track of the values of the Rotation Sensors over a period of time and saves them in a file. You can use it to "teach" a robot a sequence of actions by actually forcing it through them once by hand.

The default is to record four samples of all the Rotation Sensors every second for 10 seconds and save the recording into a file named RobotAction.rcd. Record Action is almost an entire program by itself. In fact, try running a program that has only a single Record Action block in the Elmer robot. During the 10 seconds it takes the program to run, push Elmer around. Make sure you push down hard enough that the wheels don't slip on the floor. After the program has finished, you should find the RobotAction.rcd file in the NXT memory.

The Play Action block (see Figure 5.27) plays back the recorded file. It tries to move the motors so that they are in exactly the same place at the same time as the recording. It doesn't really make sense to just play back the recording, but just as with Record Action, Play Action can be a program by itself. Write a new program that contains only a single Play Action block and run it on the Elmer robot. Elmer will move around reproducing the original "taught" movements. A more practical program would use several different recorded action files, and the program would decide which file to play based on inputs or other conditions.

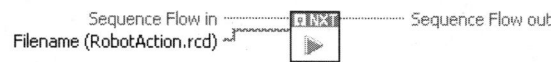

Figure 5.27
Play Action

Play Sound File

As long as we are working with files, we should look at the Play Sound File block (see Figure 5.28). You'll find it in the Sound palette along with Play Tone and Stop Sound. The convention is to use the .rso extension for sound files. You have inputs to

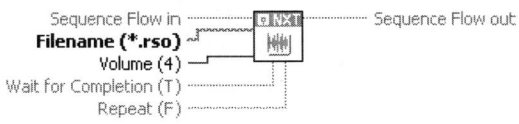

Sequence Flow in .... Sequence Flow out
Filename (*.rso)
Volume (4)
Wait for Completion (T) ....
Repeat (F) ....

Figure 5.28
Play Sound File Block

control the Volume level and if the program should Wait for Completion of the sound or allow the program to do other things while it is playing. The block can also be setup to Repeat the sound over and over until a Stop Sound shuts it up.

The LEGO software ships with a wide range of sound files that can be found in the folder C:\Program Files\LEGO Software\LEGO MINDSTORMS NXT\engine\ Sounds. Using the NXT Terminal, download the sound file Hello.rso as shown in Figure 5.29. Figure 5.30 is the Doorbell program from Chapter 4 with the True case modified to have a Play Sound File block with the file name Hello.rso as a constant String input. Running the program and holding the Right button down will make the NXT repeatedly play the Hello file.

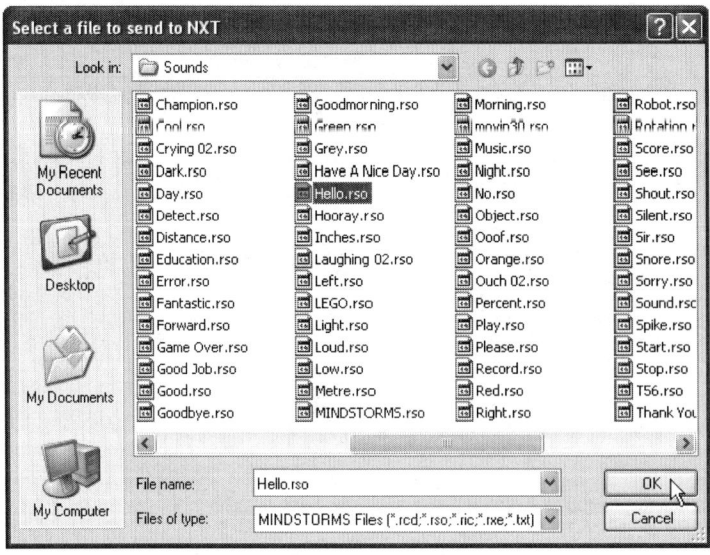

Figure 5.29
Folder of NXT Sound Files

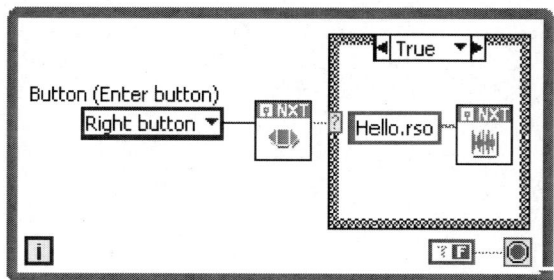

Figure 5.30
Play Sound Program

Reflections

In this chapter we learned about the Easy File functions, Record/Play, and Play Sound File. This may be everything you thought you ever wanted to know about the File functions, but there will be even more in Chapter 8. For now, let's take some drawing lessons.

Drawing Conclusions

6

I sometimes think there is nothing so delightful as drawing.—Vincent van Gogh

So far, we have only written text on the NXT screen, but you can also display a variety of shapes and even special image files. The display consists of 6,400 black and white pixels arranged as 64 rows by 100 columns, as illustrated in Figure 6.1. In this chapter you will see how to turn individual pixels on with the Display Point block and learn some new tricks for the Display Text block. Most importantly, you will also learn how to create your own function blocks.

Simple Sketch

Figure 6.2 shows a simple program that uses the NXT display and two Rotation Sensors to simulate an Etch A Sketch™. Pushing the Right Button on the NXT is like turning it over and shaking to erase the screen. One Rotation Sensor controls the horizontal and the other the vertical movement of the drawing pen. Remember, the Rotation Sensors are built into the NXT motors; mounting tires on the motor shafts will make them easier to operate. Also, make sure you connect them to Output Ports B and C. I'll leave the details of constructing the rest of the project to your imagination.

The Rotation Sensor

Rotation Sensors keep track of the rotation of the NXT motors. Normally they are used, as discussed in Chapter 3, to regulate the speed and synchronization of motors. However, they can also be used just as sensors. Figure 6.3 shows the Rotation Sensor block and all its inputs and outputs. The Degrees output is the total amount of rotation since the last time the sensor was reset with the Reset input. The Direction output tells you whether the Direction of rotation was forward or reverse. Because the Rotation

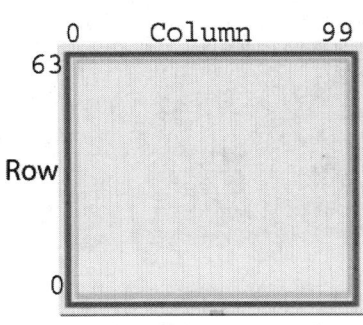

Figure 6.1
NXT Screen Coordinates

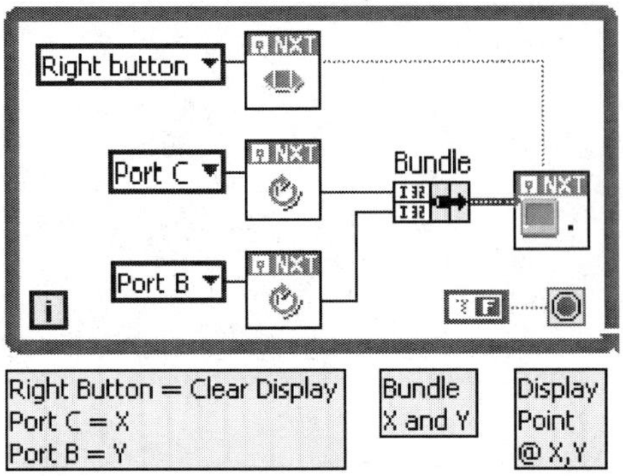

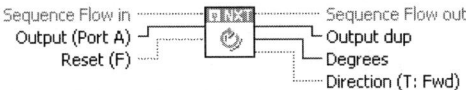

Figure 6.2
Simple Sketch Program

Figure 6.3
Rotation Sensor

Sensor is really part of a motor, it is connected to an Output Port, you can see in Figure 6.2 how Ports C and B have been selected and not the default Port A.

Display Point

The more interesting new block in Figure 6.2 is the Display Point block. You find it in the Display palette along with the Display Text block that you have already been using. Shown in Figure 6.4, it does exactly what you would expect. With the Clear

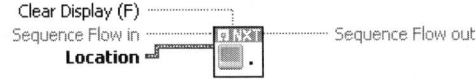

Figure 6.4
Display Point Block

Display input you have the option of erasing the entire screen before it turns a single pixel at the Cluster called Location to black, but what is a Cluster?

Clusters

The Display Point block, along with other display type blocks, uses a Cluster to combine or Bundle the Row and Column variables into a single input wire. Notice the unique pattern and reddish color of the Cluster wire. Clusters merge related variables together to avoid needing too many connections to a function block. It probably wasn't all that necessary to go to the trouble of making a Cluster for Location, but Clusters also simplify the appearance of a block diagram by cutting down the total number of wires on it. The Bundle is found in the Cluster palette, as shown in Figure 6.5. Placing it on the Block Diagram and wiring it is straightforward, but you should connect both inputs of the Bundle before connecting the Cluster output to the Display Point block.

Now Compile, Download, and Run the Simple Sketch program. You will find that rotating one motor causes the pen to draw back and forth, whereas the other controls up and down. The Degrees output of the Rotation Sensor block is always a positive number because it has a separate Direction output. That is why if you try to move the pen too far to the left or down, it will just start moving to the right or up again.

Figure 6.6 is an example drawing I made on the NXT. Just as with the real toy, diagonal and curved lines are tricky to draw without practice. An easy improvement to the program would be to divide the Degrees output by a small number. Then it would take more rotation of the knobs to make the pen move by the same amount. I'll discuss some challenges with division in the NXT a little further on.

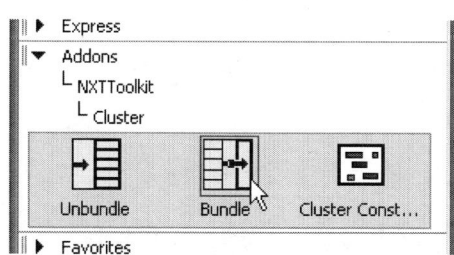

Figure 6.5
The Bundle

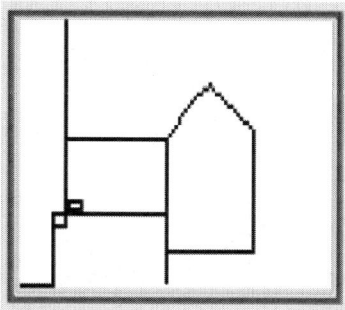

Figure 6.6
Example Drawing

Creating SubVIs

Most computer languages have subroutines, but LabVIEW has SubVIs. SubVIs provide a way for you to build your own function blocks. They let you reuse common arrangements of blocks and make large programs easier to understand by hiding some of the details. For example, I like to display the values of important variables on the NXT screen while it is running. This can be tricky, because the Number-to-String conversion block adjusts the length of the String to the size of the number. Digits of old values can be unintentionally left on the screen, leading to confusion about the real value. It also takes a separate block to include a descriptive text label for the value.

The NXT display can accommodate eight lines of text (see Figure 6.7) where each letter is eight pixels high. There is also room to print 16 letters across. Let's create a SubVI that writes a text label and a numerical value to a particular line on the display. We should also make sure the line is erased before we write anything new.

Figure 6.8 is the starting point for the SubVI. The Line number input has to be multiplied by eight to convert it into a Row value. Erasing the line involves simply writing a String Constant with 16 spaces in it. The second Display Text writes the Text constant starting on the far-left side for the label. Then the value of the variable is written a little more than halfway across the screen with the last Display Text. A Sequence Flow has been wired between the blocks and extended with a constant to the left and an indicator to the right.

Select just the area shown in Figure 6.9 and not the constants or the indicator. When you have done that, the selected elements will have blinking dotted lines around them and will look like Figure 6.10. If you make a mistake, just reselect the region until you get it right.

Now go to the Edit menu and select Create SubVI, as shown in Figure 6.11. All of the selected blocks will collapse into a single block, as shown in Figure 6.12. This block is the new SubVI, and it will always have this default icon with a small number in the lower-right corner.

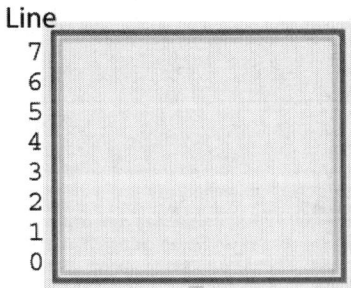

Figure 6.7
Text Lines on NXT Display

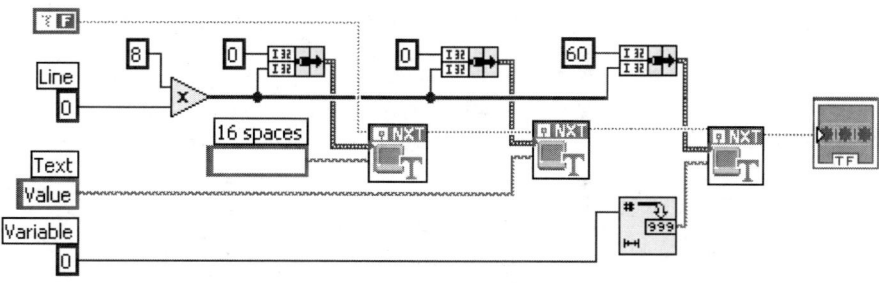

Figure 6.8
Display Variable SubVI Starting Point

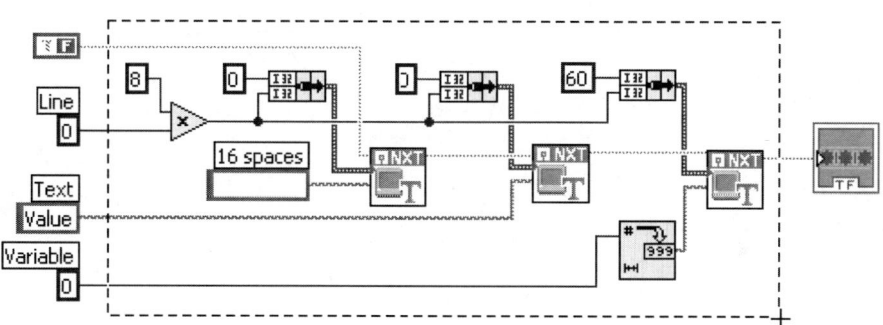

Figure 6.9
Select Blocks

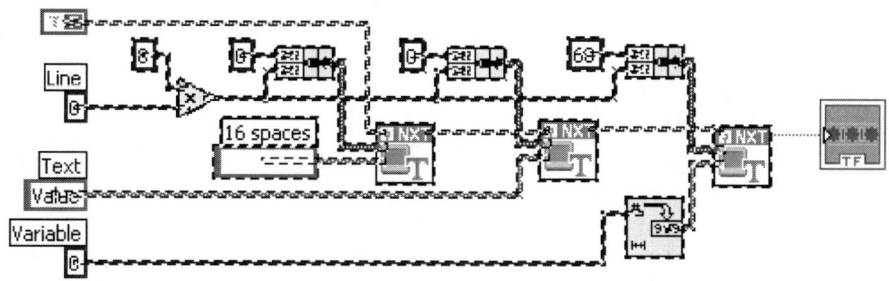

Figure 6.10
Appearance of Selected Blocks

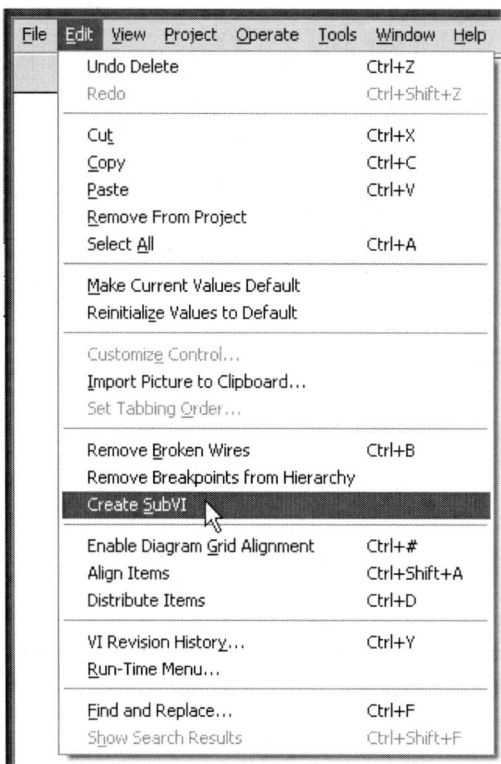

Figure 6.11
Create SubVI

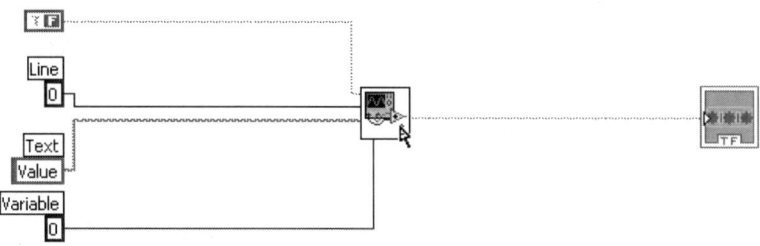

Figure 6.12
Appearance of SubVI after Creation

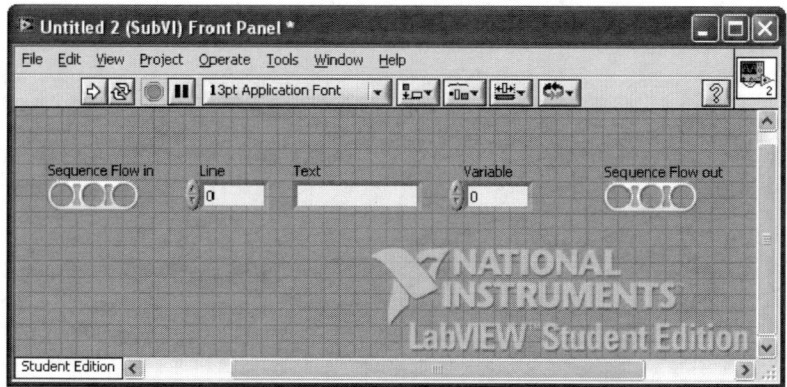

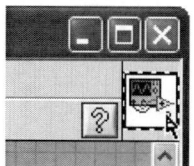

Figure 6.13
SubVI Front Panel

Figure 6.14
Edit Block Icon

Double-click on the icon and you will see the SubVI's Front Panel window, as shown in Figure 6.13. The placement of the controls and indicators are automatic, so your Front Panel may not look exactly like this. In the upper-right corner (see Figure 6.14) you will find the icon for the block. Clicking here will bring up an editor, like the one in Figure 6.15, in which you can change the appearance of the icon. The tools

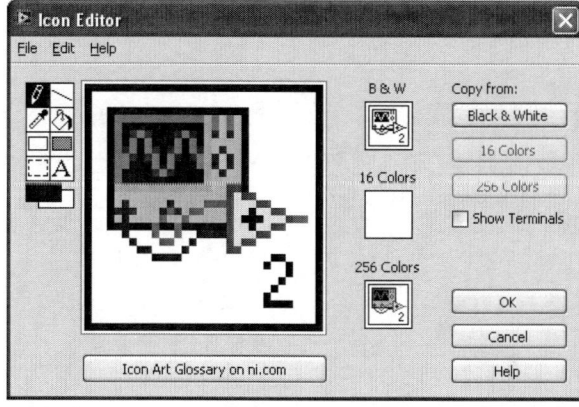

Figure 6.15
Icon Edit Tool

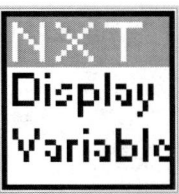

Figure 6.16
Display Variable Icon

are pretty simple, and I won't go into the details of drawing icons. I made up the icon in Figure 6.16 so the block would look something like the official NXT blocks.

Go to the Window menu and select Show Block Diagram to see the SubVI Block Diagram shown in Figure 6.17. Notice that it is identical to the original starting point VI in Figure 6.8, except that the constants are now controls. All we need to do now is save the SubVI to give it a proper name. Go to the File menu and select Save As, as shown in Figure 6.18, and the Name the VI window shown in Figure 6.19 will pop up to allow you to enter a name. In this case I entered Display Variable with a space between the words, and I also put it in a folder called math. You don't need the original starting point VI any more. Its work is done, and it can be thrown away.

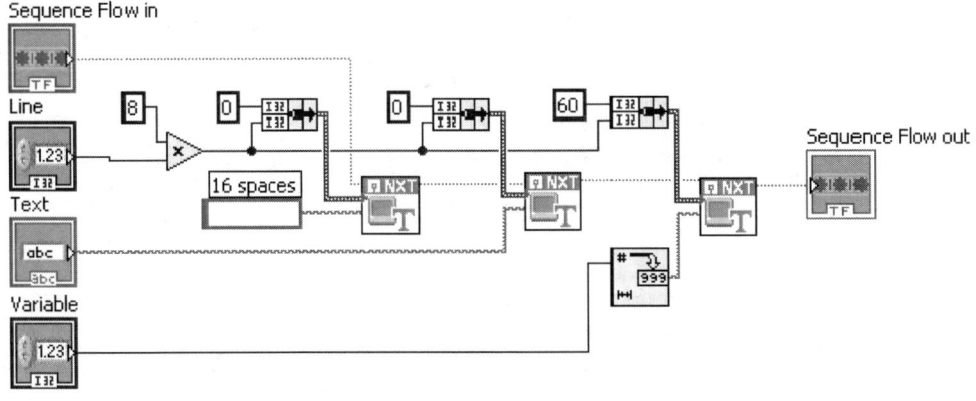

Figure 6.17
SubVI Block Diagram

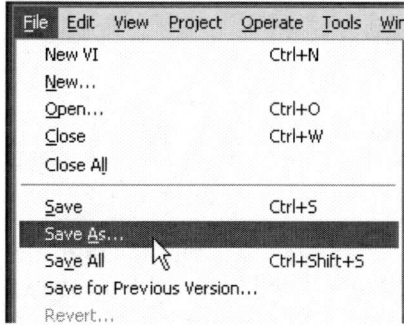

Figure 6.18
Saving the SubVI

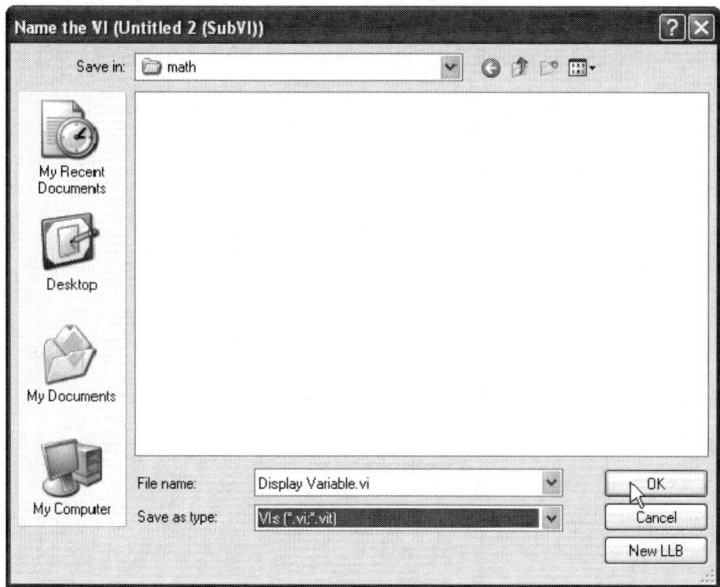

Figure 6.19
Giving SubVI a Name

Using the New SubVI

Open a new Blank VI from the Getting Started screen of LabVIEW. On the Block Diagram you will want to add the function block for the Display Variable SubVI by going to the Functions palette and selecting Select a VI..., as shown in Figure 6.20. A Select-the-VI window will show up as shown in Figure 6.21, and the directory will most likely already be set for the folder you just saved it in. If it isn't, navigate to the directory and select Display Variable, as shown in Figure 6.21.

When you place the Display Variable block, you will see the connectors for the four inputs and one output, as shown in Figure 6.22. Create the three constant inputs and the empty While Loop, as shown in Figure 6.23. All the While Loop is doing is keeping the program from ending so that you can see the results on the NXT display. The screen should look like Figure 6.24 if everything is working. You press the Stop button on the NXT to stop the program.

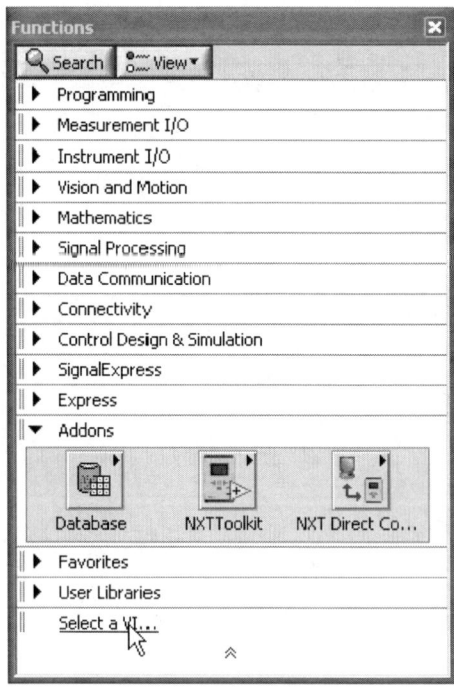

Figure 6.20
Adding a User-Created SubVI

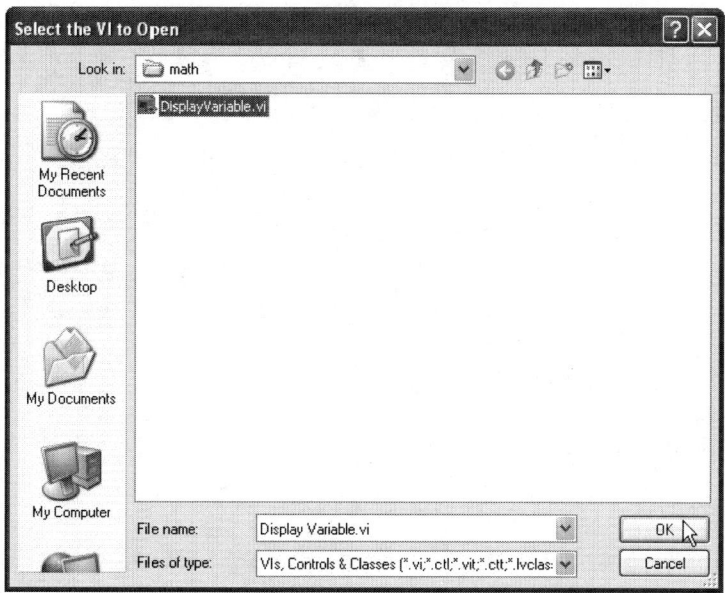

Figure 6.21
Selecting Display Variable SubVI

Figure 6.22
Appearance of the Display Variable SubVI

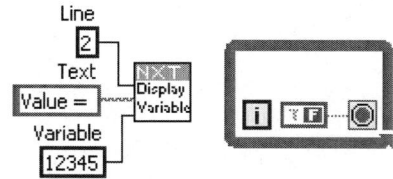

Figure 6.23
Testing the Display Variable SubVI

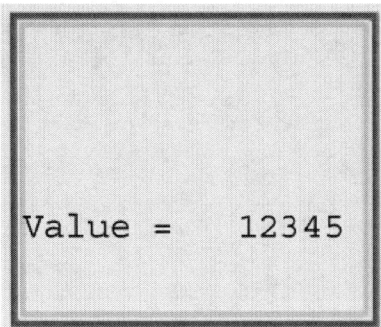

Figure 6.24
Test NXT Screen

Quotient and Remainder

When you first learned to divide numbers in elementary school you used Integer
division. Division was carried out only to a whole number (the Quotient), and then you
were left with a Remainder. Later you leaned how to handle decimal point arithmetic,
which is called Floating Point in computers. For example, in Integer arithmetic, 71
divided by 13 is 5 with a remainder of 6. Not 5.4615..., as you would get using a
calculator. In LabVIEW you can use a Divide block, but it was really designed for
Floating Point arithmetic. The better choice is a block called Quotient and Remainder,
shown in Figure 6.25, because it outputs both the Integer Remainder and Quotient.

We can write a little program to compare the two division-type blocks and show
off our new Display Variable SubVI. The program is shown in Figure 6.26. The While
Loop contains a Display Variable that will show the value of the Loop Interation. It
also has a Wait block to slow the looping down enough that the numbers aren't a
complete blur.

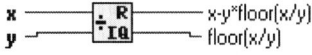

Figure 6.25
The Quotient and Remainder Block

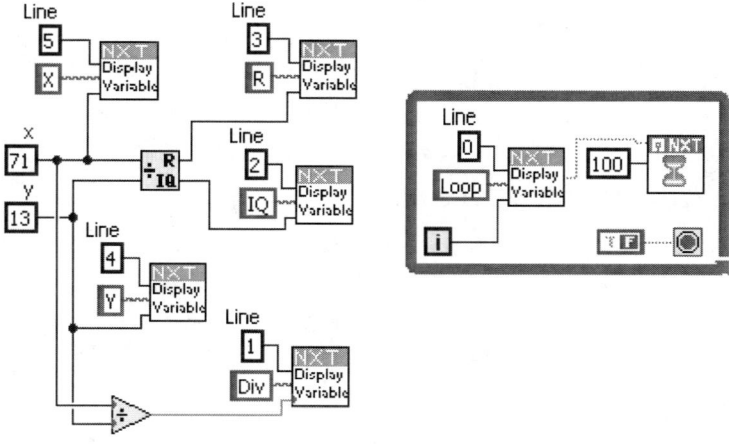

Figure 6.26
Math Test Program

Coercion Dots

Right away you should notice something strange about the inputs to the Division block and the bottom Display Variable Block. There are small red spots called Coercion Dots (see Figure 6.27) on them. These dots are LabVIEW's way of warning you that it is automatically converting a variable's Representation at these locations. This is a nice feature for LabVIEW programs running on the PC, but it can lead to some problems for programs that run in the NXT.

When you Compile, Download, and Run the program with the NXT Terminal you will get the warning message shown in Figure 6.28. Because it is only a warning, the program will still run, as can be seen in Figure 6.29. Notice that the Integer Quotient and Division results are the same, but from here on you should use only the Integer

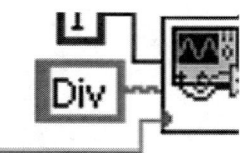

Figure 6.27
Coercion Dot

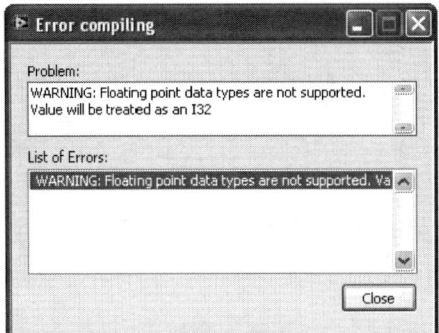

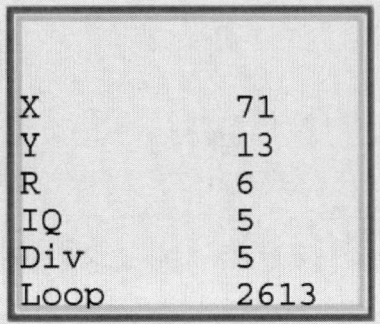

Figure 6.28
Floating Point Warning

Figure 6.29
NXT Screen

Quotient and Remainder block to avoid seeing the Floating Point warning about
Division.

Reflections

We have only scratched the surface of the NXT Display type functions. In the following
chapter you will learn about Display blocks for pictures, lines, and circles. We will
plot data on the NXT screen in real time and even create another SubVI.

Uncharted Territory

7

Life is uncharted territory. It reveals its story one moment at a time.—Leo Buscaglia,
author and lecturer on creating loving relationships

We have already seen how to make charts on the PC using the Debug feature of the NXT Terminal and the Chart Graphical Indicator. The NXT screen could also be used to plot data in real time, and that might come in handy when you can't connect the NXT to a computer. In this chapter you will learn a few more display-related function blocks along with an important feature of While Loops called the Shift Register.

Simple Chart

Figure 7.1 is the simplest chart-drawing program I could think of. The Light Sensor's Intensity output ranges from 0 to 100, which maps almost perfectly to the Column number that ranges from 0 to 99. There is a slight problem when the Intensity is 100, because the point will be off to the right side of the display. The Quotient and Remainder block we learned about in the previous chapter takes care of creating a value that keeps sweeping through the Rows over time. The Remainder of a division by 64 is always between 0 and 63 and the Loop Interation provides a continuously increasing dividend.

Figure 7.2 shows the NXT display when the Simple Chart program is running. The screen is never cleared, and it is difficult to tell what is going on after a short time. It's a little annoying that the plot sweeps from bottom to top of the screen, which seems backwards, and it would also be nice to be able to adjust the time between points.

Improved Chart

Figure 7.3 is only a little more complicated, but it shows several nice improvements. First of all, it scales the Intensity of the Light Sensor to the same 0 to 63 range of the Row. That way the plot never goes off the screen. It also sweeps from left to right, which is

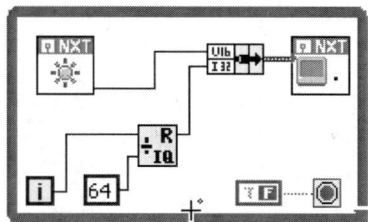

Figure 7.1
Simple Chart

Figure 7.2
NXT Display for Simple Chart

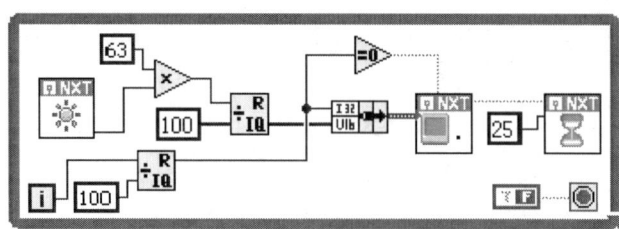

Figure 7.3
Improved Chart

more natural, and every time the plot is about to restart in Column 0, the display is automatically cleared. Finally, the addition of a Wait block allows for adjustment of the time between points. In this case the delay is 25 ms.

The appearance of the NXT display is shown in Figure 7.4. Unfortunately, there is an undesirable side effect of clearing the screen at the start of each sweep. The last points plotted on the screen are shown for only a short time before they are cleared and they look pale or become invisible.

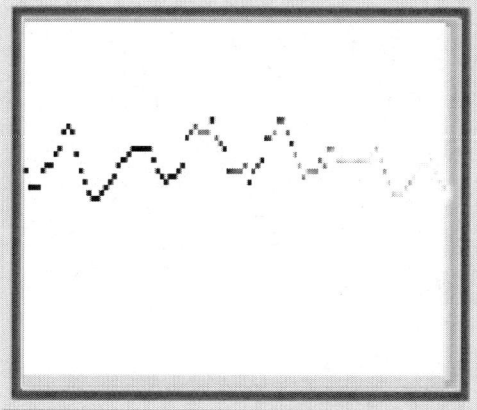

Figure 7.4
Effect of Clearing the Display

Selective Screen Clearing

One rather serious shortcoming of NXT graphics is that you can set individual pixels to black but you can only clear the entire screen. This forces us to use some rather unusual methods for clearing selective parts of the screen. The NXT can display images that are stored in special files, and those images contain white as well as black pixels. Suppose we had an image that was only a single column of white pixels. Then, when we are about to plot a new point, we could display that image and effectively erase anything that was already in that column without disturbing the rest of the display.

How do we go about getting this magic image? A program called nxtRICedit by Andreas Dreier (http://nxtasy.org/wp-content/uploads/2006/10/nxtRICedit.zip) allows you to create NXT image files by hand. To make a white vertical line, start with a new blank image and save it. Figure 7.5 shows the Save RIC Image window from nxtRICedit and the Add Borders settings, which give you a one-column-wide and 64-row-high all-white image. Save it with the filename line.ric. The files are stored by default in a folder along with the other pictures that shipped with the LEGO NXT

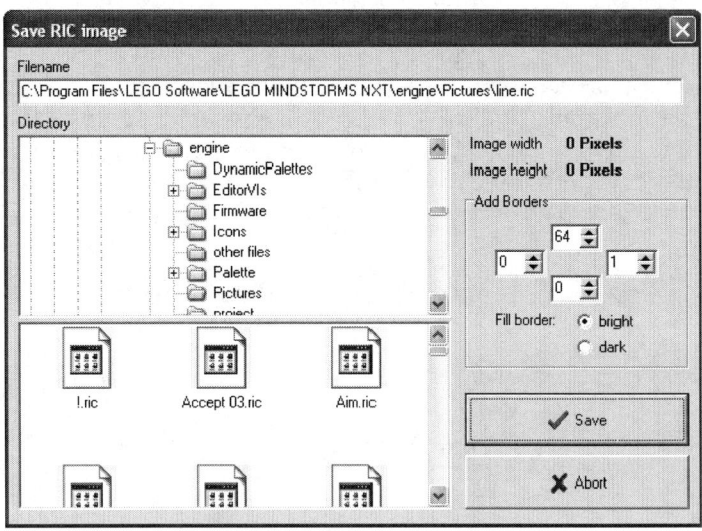

Figure 7.5
Making a Vertical White Line

software. Obviously, this file needs to be downloaded to the NXT before you can use it, and you already know how to do that with the NXT Terminal.

Display Picture

The Display Picture block is shown in Figure 7.6. The name of the file to display is input as a string, and the convention is to use the .ric file extension for image files. The NXT image file is rather involved and goes well beyond just storing simple bitmap images. It has features that make it work more like a program, and that is why there is a Variables input. The Location input defines the lower-right corner of the image.

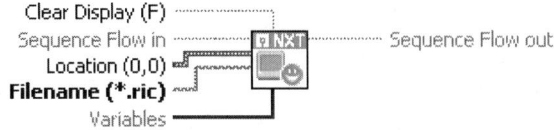

Figure 7.6
Display Picture Block

Better Chart

Notice how the Display Picture block in Figure 7.7 is wired with the Sequence Flow to always precede the Display Point. That guarantees that the column will be cleared before the new point is added. Also notice how the filename line.ric is input with a String Constant. Figure 7.8 shows the appearance of the display when the Better Chart program is running. It looks better, but something that would make it even

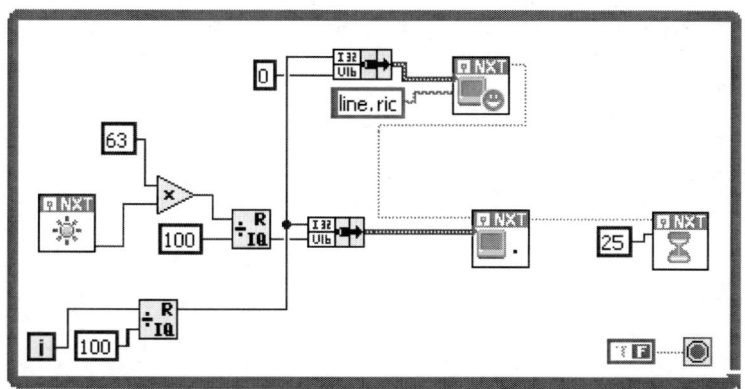

Figure 7.7
Better Chart

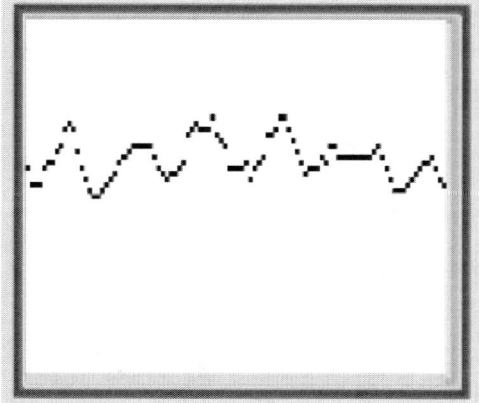

Figure 7.8
Better-Looking Chart

easier to look at would be to draw a line between consecutive data points rather than just plotting them as disconnected dots.

Shift Registers

Shift Registers add memory to While Loops. With a Shift Register, the last value of a variable is available within the loop as well as the current value. For example, we need the previous data point value to draw a continuous line from the old point to the new point. To get a Shift Register, move the cursor over the edge of the While Loop structure, as shown in Figure 7.9. Now right-click and a menu will pop up like the one in Figure 7.10 from which you select Add Shift Register. A pair of rectangles with down and up arrows will now appear on opposite sides of the While Loop. You can move them vertically to make connecting wires easier, but both rectangles will move together.

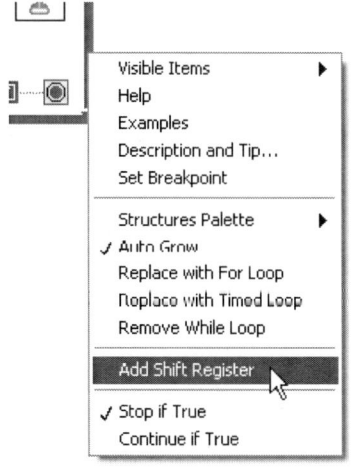

Figure 7.9
Selecting the While Loop

Figure 7.10
Adding a Shift Register

Best Chart

The Display Line block connects any two points with a straight line. A Shift Register will be used to store the previous data point value, but there is no previous data point for Column 0. Actually there is, but it is on the opposite side of the screen, and you

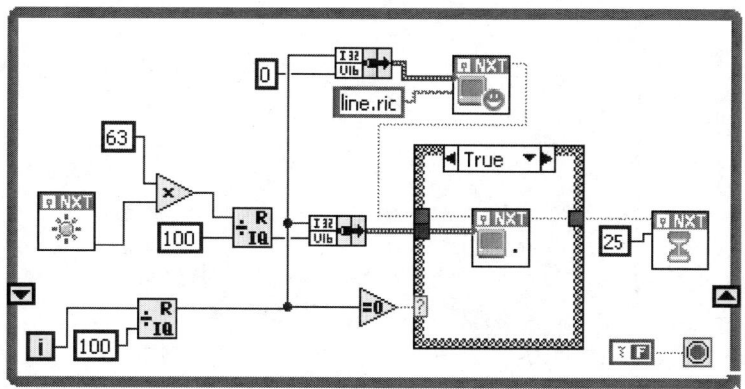

Figure 7.11
Adding Column 0 Case

really don't want to draw a line to it. That is the special case shown in Figure 7.11 where, if the Column is 0, we still use the Display Point, as shown in Figure 7.7.

Display Line

Display Line (see Figure 7.12) requires two Location inputs. One is called the Start and the other the End, but it doesn't really matter in which direction the line is drawn. It simply draws a line between the two coordinates, and it will look the same either way.

Figure 7.13 shows additional wiring for the False Case. The old value is retrieved from the left Shift Register. The current value is brought over to the right Shift Register, and you should notice that the tunnel through the Case Statement is hollow, indicating a problem. LabVIEW is telling us that we forgot to produce a value for this wire in the True Case. Figure 7.14 shows you how to fix it.

We've come a long way to get Figure 7.15. The direction of the flow is good, the trace is dark, and the data points are connected. If all we ever wanted to do was make

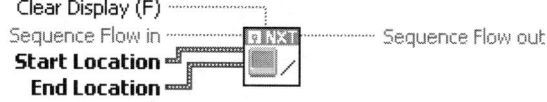

Figure 7.12
Display Line Block

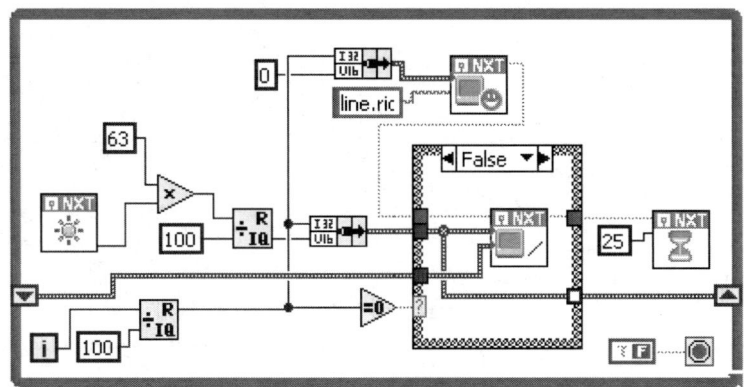

Figure 7.13
Wiring the False Case

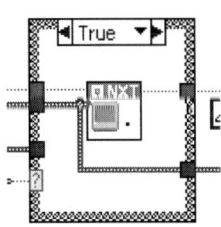

Figure 7.14
Fixing the True Case

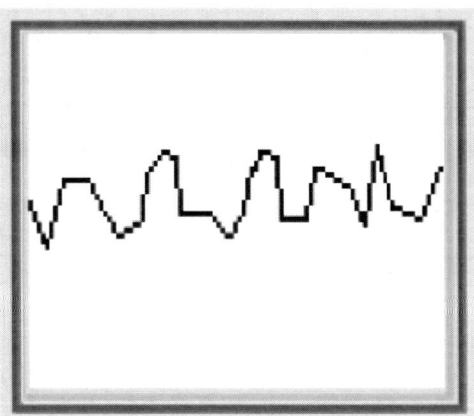

Figure 7.15
Chart Output

charts of some sensor value over time we would be done. However, charting should be a SubVI that can be used within a bigger program.

Chart SubVI

I think we can leave the vertical scaling of 0 to 100, but we will need to pull the Light Sensor block out. Another thing we won't need inside the SubVI is the Wait block and its constant. That would be the job of the higher-level program. Pull both blocks out and put them on either side of the While Loop. Then rewire the Intensity and a Sequence Flow to them, as shown in Figure 7.16.

The Loop Interation was taking care of producing the column number, but we will need something else to remember the column number from point to point. That sounds like a Shift Register to me. Add another Shift Register and wire it as shown in Figure 7.16. The triangular block with a +1 inside is an Increment block, and it adds one to the old column number and feeds the new value to the right Shift Register. You'll find the Increment bock in the Numeric palette. LabVIEW will maintain the column value from call to call, because there is no initial value wired to the left input.

We don't need a While Loop any more, but we still need the Shift Registers. That can be fixed by changing the Boolean Constant for the Loop Condition to True so that the While Loop executes only one time. You do that with the Operate Value Tool by clicking on the T inside the constant. Make sure your constant looks like the one shown in Figure 7.16.

Select everything except the Light Sensor and the Wait Block. Use the Edit menu and Create SubVI to create a SubVI just as we did for Display Variable in the previous chapter. The Front Panel of the new SubVI will look like Figure 7.17. It is a good idea to add a comment about the need for the line.ric file so future users of the block will know how to use it. You can edit the icon to make it look pretty and then save the SubVI with the filename Chart.

A little program to plot light intensity over time is shown in Figure 7.18. The output of the program looks the same as the one in Figure 7.15. You might try charting

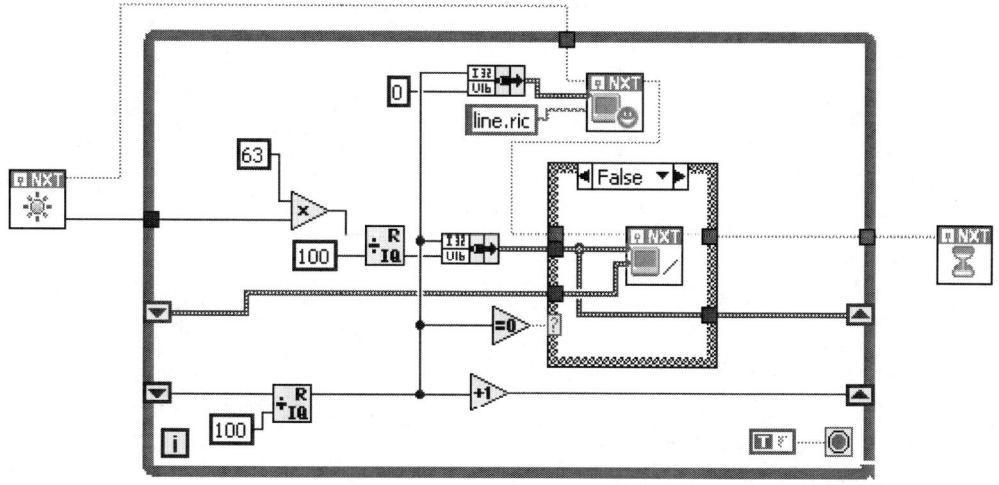

Figure 7.16
Preparing Chart SubVI

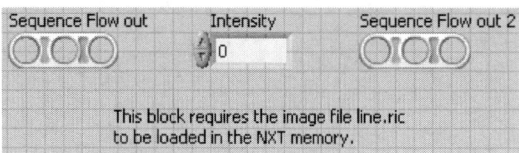

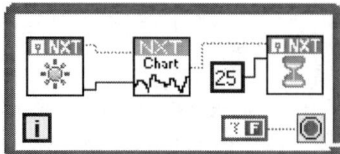

Figure 7.17
SubVI Front Panel

Figure 7.18
Chart Light

the Volume output of the Sound Sensor, since it has the same range as the Light Sensor, or you might change the time between points to get a chart for a longer period of time.

Restore Default

Restore Default is an unrewarding display block. Its icon, shown in Figure 7.19, has no inputs or outputs besides the obligatory Sequence Flow. This underachiever makes the NXT screen look exactly the same as a program that didn't have any graphics in the first place. In other words it makes the display look like Figure 7.20. It can be used as a backdoor way to clearing the screen, but other than that I don't see the need for it.

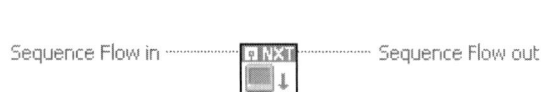

Figure 7.19
Restore Default

Figure 7.20
Default Display

Display Circle

Display Circle (see Figure 7.21) is the last function in the Display Palette. It draws a one-pixel-thick circle at the Center Location with a specified Radius. You will probably find yourself using the function to draw circles only a few pixels in radius rather than big-diameter happy faces, because it is useful for drawing little balls for video games.

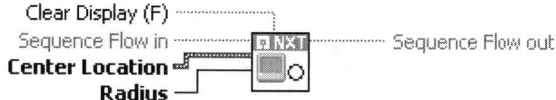

Figure 7.21
Display Circle

Bouncy Ball

I'm not going to explain all the Physics in the Bouncy Ball program shown in Figure 7.22. However, there are a couple interesting new function blocks worth noting. The triangle with a –1 inside is the Decrement block, and the triangle with the (–X) is the

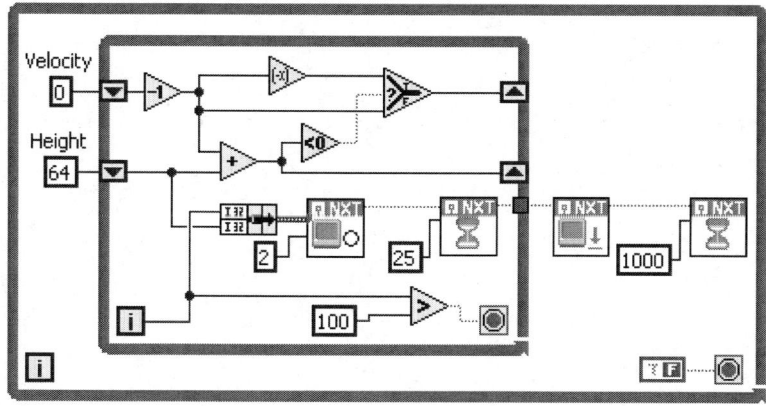

Figure 7.22
Bouncy Ball Program

Negate. Both blocks are in the Numeric palette. Two Shift Registers are being used to keep track of the ball's vertical Height and Velocity. Should the Height of the ball drop below the screen, which is detected with the Less Than 0? Block, the Velocity is reversed. That takes care of simulating the bounce off the floor.

The Restore Default was thrown in just to show you what it does. The animated ball will drop on the screen as shown in Figure 7.23, and then the default Figure 7.20 screen will appear for a second before everything starts over. You might try erasing the ball so it doesn't leave a trail.

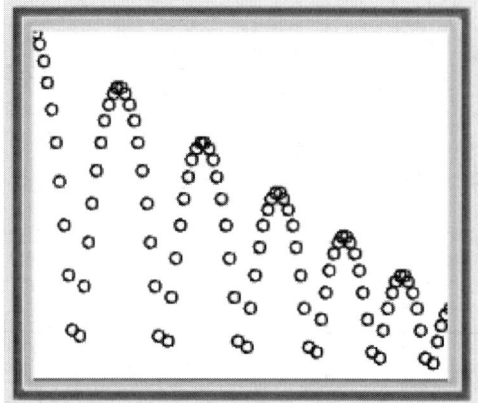

Figure 7.23
Bouncy Ball Display

Reflections

Now we have visited every block in the Display palette. You could probably write a pretty decent Pong™ -like game if you put your mind to it. There are plenty of blocks left to discover. In the following chapter we'll take a look at the "hard" file blocks.

It's Not Easy Files

8

It's not easy being green.—Kermit the Frog

You could probably live with only the Easy File–type function blocks we learned about in Chapter 5, but since we just learned about NXT Picture files, I thought this would be a good time to look at the not so easy File–type blocks. Unfortunately, we can't sneak up on these blocks by learning them one at a time as we did for the Display blocks. They work together, and I'll introduce five of them before even getting to the example program. If this stuff seems a little scary, don't panic. It'll be over before you know it.

Open for Read

Opening a file for Read (see Figure 8.1) causes the NXT operating system to check to see whether Filename exists and that you're not already doing something with the file. You can only read or write a file at any given time. File Handle is just a reference number that will be used by later function blocks instead of the Filename. The Error out output will be zero if the open went alright. If the Error input is anything but zero, the block won't do anything. That way, if an error occurred earlier in the program, you can automatically prevent later file actions from taking place by wiring the Error flows together.

Open for Write

Opening a file for Write (see Figure 8.2) is a little more complex. If the file doesn't already exist, the operating system will create a new one with the specified File Size. You *do* need to worry about the File Size, because the software will *not* automatically expand the file as it did for the easy file functions. If the file already exists, the operating

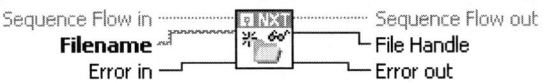

Figure 8.1
Open for Read

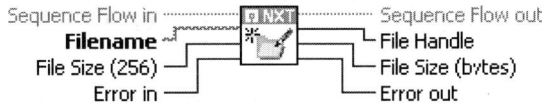

Figure 8.2
Open for Write

system will prepare to append to it and report the amount of space left in the old file with the File Size output. File Handle and Errors are the same as the Open for Read. I doubt you will ever run into this limit, but you can have only four files open for writing at the same time.

Read File

When you Read from a file, you provide the File Handle that was generated by the Open and specify how many bytes you want to read (see Figure 8.3) with the Length input. The output of the Read File is called the Buffer, and it is in the form of a String. However, it is composed not just of letters of the alphabet like the ones you have been dealing with up to this point. It is a raw sequence of 8-bit bytes. The block also tells you the actual number of Bytes Read in case it was different from what you wanted. The Error output will be zero unless there was an error. You can use this output compared to zero as an input to a While Loop Condition to keep reading until you reach the end of the file.

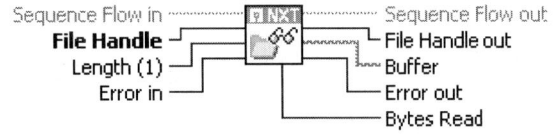

Figure 8.3
Read File

Write File

Write (see Figure 8.4) is actually a little simpler than Read. The advantage of using String variables is that you don't have to keep track of their size. LabVIEW automatically does that, and there is even a String Length block you can find in the String palette. Write File tells you the actual number of Bytes Written along with the usual Handle and Error outputs.

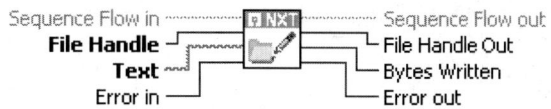

Figure 8.4
Write File

Close File

Closing a file is the essentially the same as saving a file, except that you should do it even when you were only reading a file. If you don't Close a file you were writing, chances are some or all of your work will be lost. That makes five new function blocks in a row. Let's get to an example.

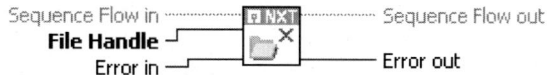

Figure 8.5
Close File

Make Icon

I've combined the new File function blocks into one program called Make Icon, shown in Figure 8.6. It makes—modifies might be a more honest description—a small NXT Picture file about the size of an icon. It starts with a file named Square.ric and copies all but eight Bytes out of the middle of it into a new file called MyIcon.ric. Those eight Bytes are the bitmap of an 8-by-8 pixel image or icon. The 20 Bytes before and 20 Bytes after the bitmap are other parts of the NXT Picture file format. We'll skip that detail for now.

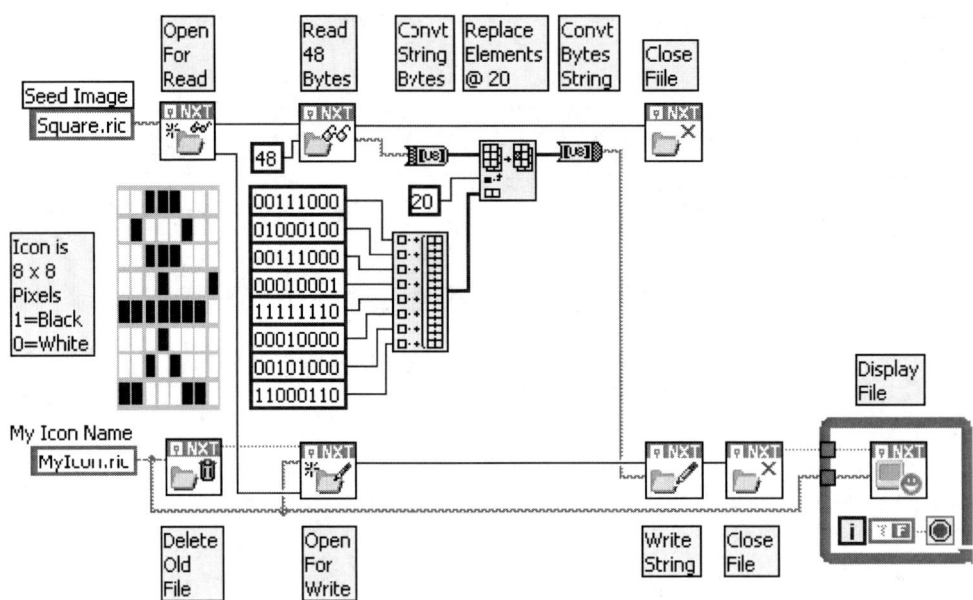

Figure 8.6
Make Icon Program

Notice the way the Error output of the Open for Read has been wired to the Error input for the Open for Write, as shown in Figure 8.7. That way if something goes wrong with the Open of Square.ric, you won't end up with a messed-up MyIcon.ric. Also notice how the Sequence Flow forces the Delete File to operate before we try to Open for Write MyIcon.ric. Finally, there is a Sequence Flow between the Close File for MyIcon.ric and when we try to use the file with the Display Picture block as shown in Figure 8.8.

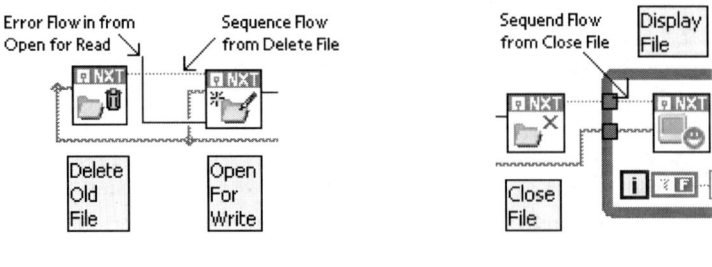

Figure 8.7
Critical Flow Wiring

Figure 8.8
More Critical Flow Wiring

Now let's focus on the flow between the Read and the Write. First, the String Buffer is converted into an Array of Bytes. That function block and its converse are found in a subpalette of the String palette called String/Array/Path Conversion. Bytes 20 through 27 are where the actual bitmap is stored in the file, and the Replace Array Subset block allows you to change just those bytes without changing the rest. When that has been done, we need to convert the Byte Array back into a String.

Display Format

The constants started out as Numeric Constants from the Numeric palette. Their Representation was changed to U8 for Unsigned 8 bit, which is a good choice for bytes. The Display Format for the Numeric Constants has been edited as shown in Figure 8.9 to be Binary with 8 zero-padded digits. You get to this window by right-clicking on the constants and selecting Display Format from the pop-up menu. Ones will be black pixels and zeros white. My icon is a little person stick figure, and I even pasted a picture of it on the Function Block Diagram for reference.

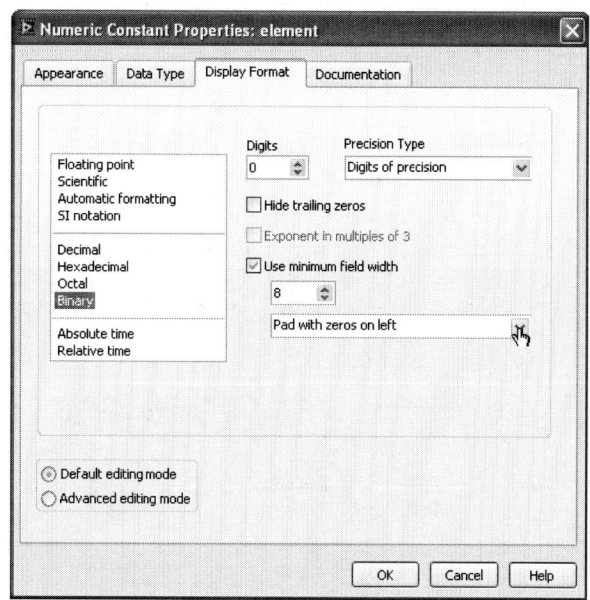

Figure 8.9
Display Format

Build Array

The constants need to be combined into an Array. This is done with the Build Array block. When you first place the Build Array, it will look like Figure 8.10. As you move the cursor over the block, handles will appear so you can stretch the block and increase the number of inputs. Figure 8.11 shows the Build Array with the eight inputs we need to feed the eight constants into.

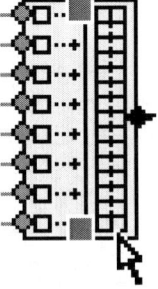

Figure 8.10
Initial Appearance of Build Array

Figure 8.11
Stretched Build Array

Making Square.ric

Before you use Make Icon you need the Square.ric Picture file, and that is another job for nxtRICedit. Figure 8.12 shows the 8-by-8 all-black square drawn with the program. Saving it is as simple as giving it the proper filename, as shown in Figure 8.13. Make sure the Image width and height are 8 pixels and don't add any borders to it either. You should try reopening the Square.ric Picture file (see Figure 8.14) with nxtRICedit

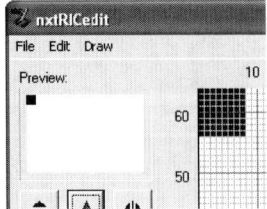

Figure 8.12
Making Square in nxtRICedit

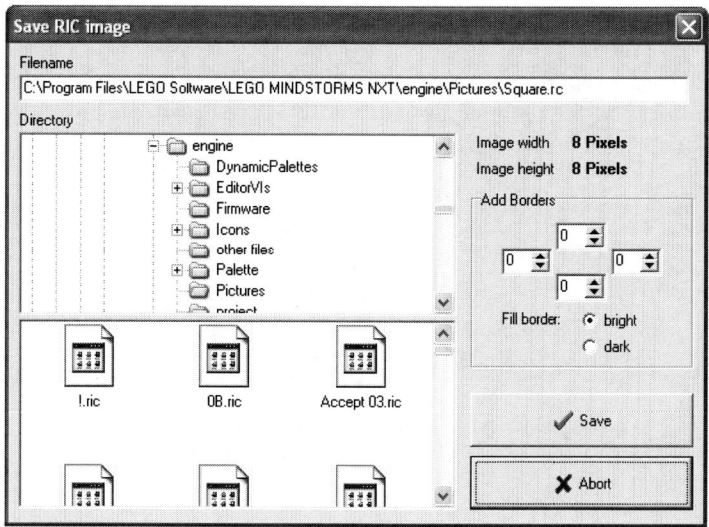

Figure 8.13
Saving Square.ric

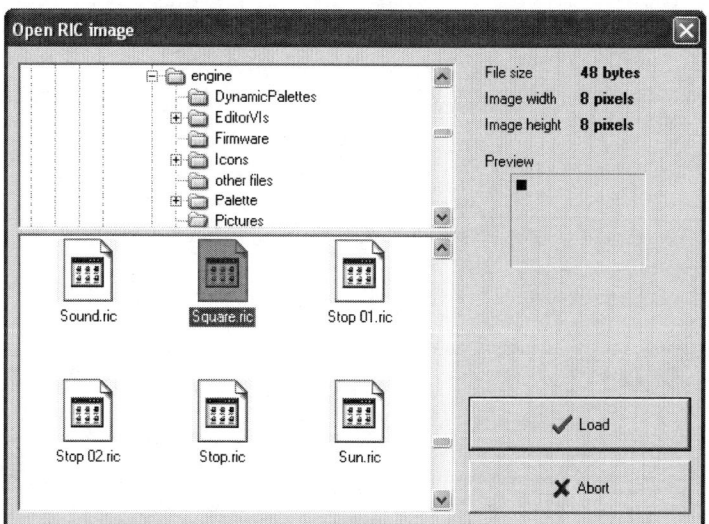

Figure 8.14
48-Byte File Size

to see that the file size is in fact 48 bytes. Remember to download it into the NXT with the NXT Terminal.

The program runs very quickly, and it finally displays the finished icon in the lower corner of the NXT screen, as shown in Figure 8.15. You can upload MyIcon.ric to the PC and check it out with nxtRICedit.

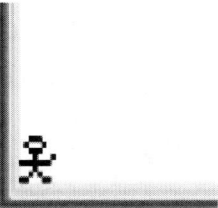

Figure 8.15
Icon

Rename File

Rename File shown in Figure 8.16 isn't one of those blocks you use very often. It is helpful when you need to expand the size of a file. First you Rename the file you need to expand to something temporary, open a new file with the original's filename but with a larger File Size, copy the contents from the temporary file into the new file, and then delete the temporary file.

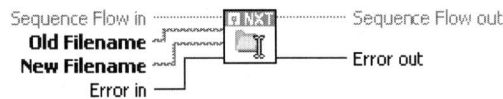

Figure 8.16
Rename File

Get File Handle

Maybe your dog ate your File Handle and you need to know what it was. Who knows why, but if you need to get a file's Handle for some reason, Get File Handle (see Figure 8.17) does just that. It will even tell you whether the file is already Open for Read or Write.

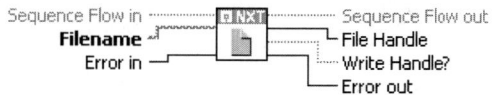

Figure 8.17
Get File Handle

Dissecting a Text File

When we were learning about the Easy File Read, I told you that there were two special characters added to the end of the Strings so that the block could figure out where one read ended and the next one began. The program in Figure 8.18 reads the first 12 bytes out of the Music.txt file that was used for the Music Box program described in Chapter 5 and puts the bytes into an Array. The block connected to the Shift Register builds a String by adding, or Concatenating, one element at a time. It is called the Concatenate String block from the String palette. We are going to use the Debug feature of the NXT Terminal to look at the values in that Array to figure out what just what is inside the file, including those extra characters.

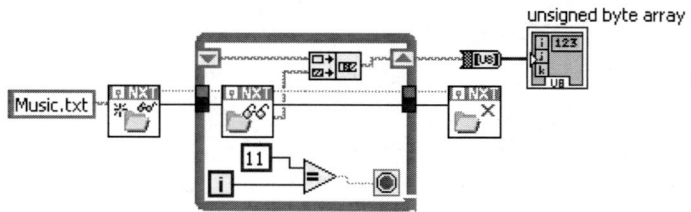

Figure 8.18
Look File Program

Array Indicator

Move the cursor over the String to Byte Array block output until the Wire Tool appears. Then right-click and a menu like the one in Figure 8.19 will show up. This is the same method you have been using to create constants. Select Create Indicator, and when you look at the Front Panel you'll find that an Array Indicator like the one in Figure 8.20 has been added. The number on the left is the Array Index, and you could look at the Array Elements one at a time by just using that, or you can stretch the Array to

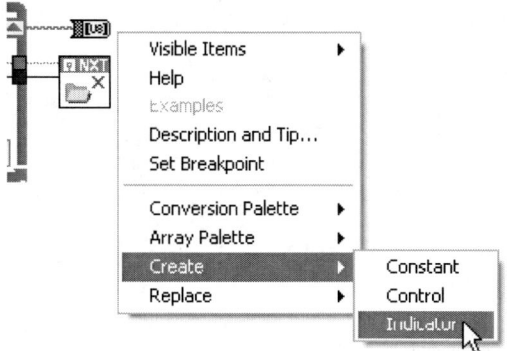

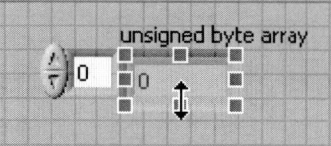

Figure 8.19
Array Indicator

Figure 8.20
Array Indicator on Front Panel

show more than one Element at a time. Move the cursor till the handles appear and pull down 11 more elements, as shown in Figure 8.21.

Naturally, you still need to have the Music.txt file loaded in your NXT for this to work. Using the NXT Terminal, select Debug as shown in Figure 8.22. The program

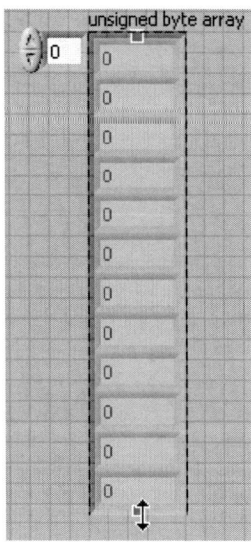

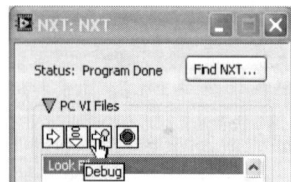

Figure 8.21
Stretched Array Indicator

Figure 8.22
Debugging Program

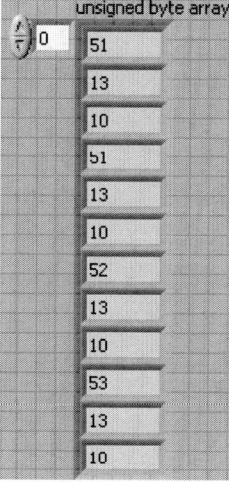

Figure 8.23
Contents of Array

will run, and the first 10 values of the Array will be displayed on the Front Panel, as shown in Figure 8.23. Make sure you use Debug, not Compile, Download, and Run.

ASCII

The beginning of the Music.txt file looks like Figure 8.24. The first number entered in the file was a 3, but the first Element in the Array has a value of 51. The 51 is called an ASCII code, and Table 8.1 has all the codes for the numbers. ASCII codes are necessary not so much for numbers like this but for letters of the alphabet and symbols. LabVIEW has a handy table of all 128 ASCII codes; just look in the Help Index for ASCII Codes.

The next two Array Elements are the characters that were added. Table 8.2 has the ASCII codes for values from 0 to 13, and it appears as though 13 is a CR and 10 is

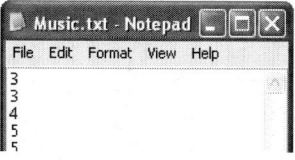

Figure 8.24
Content of Music.txt

Table 8.1   *ASCII Codes for Numbers*

Number	Code
0	48
1	49
2	50
3	51
4	52
5	53
6	54
7	55
8	56
9	57

Table 8.2   *ASCII Codes for Control Characters*

Number	Code
NUL	0
SOH	1
STX	2
ETX	3
EOT	4
ENQ	5
ACK	6
BEL	7
BS	8
HT	9
LF	10
VT	11
FF	12
CR	13

an LF. CR is short for Carriage Return, and LF is short for Line Feed. Historically, computers used something like an electronic typewriter for output. Separate codes were devised not only to print symbols but to command the typewriter to return to the start of the line—called Carriage Return—and to advance to the next line—called Line Feed. Hitting the Enter Key in a text editor usually adds both a CR and a LF to the file, and that is what Notepad has done after typing the 3.

Binary Files

The most efficient way to store values into a file is called Binary. This means that if the variable took up four bytes in memory like an I32, then you store the four bytes "as is" in the file. For example, a 32-bit Integer variable could be a number as large as 2,147,483,648. That takes 12 digits or ASCII codes to store, including a CR and an LF. On the other hand, an I32 takes only four bytes to store as a binary number, and that is one-third the space. Scaled sensor values have a range from 0 and 100 and could be stored as a single byte, which would take about one-fourth the space.

Let's look at a little example of how to store numbers in a Binary file. Figure 8.25 is a program that Opens a file named Data.dat and puts the numbers 0, 1, 2, and 3 into it in binary form. The Loop Interation is an I32 variable, and the Flatten to String block knows that is four bytes, so it creates a String that is four characters long for the Write to File to save. Flatten to String is found in the Data Manipulation palette along with its counterpart Unflatten from String, as shown in Figure 8.26. Then the program Closes the file.

To see what ended up in the file we need to modify the Look File program to use Data.dat (see Figure 8.27) and run it in Debug with the NXT Terminal. Figure 8.28 is what the Front Panel of Look File will show. The first four bytes are the four bytes from the first I32 number that was zero. The next four bytes are for the next number, and so on. The numbers are stored with the lowest byte first by default, and that is why the one is first followed by three zeros, since the value is only one.

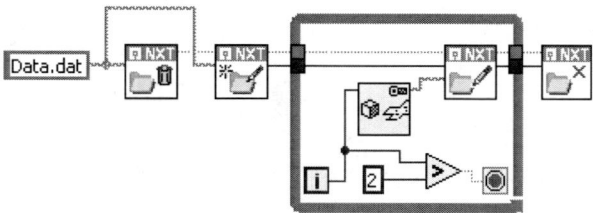

Figure 8.25
Write Binary File

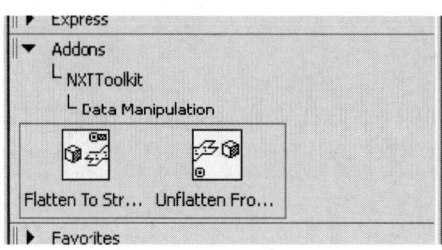

Figure 8.26
Data Manipulation Blocks

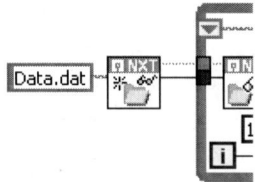

Figure 8.27
Change Filename in Look File

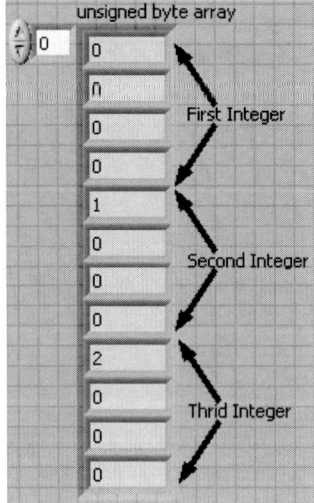

Figure 8.28
Values of Bytes in Data.dat

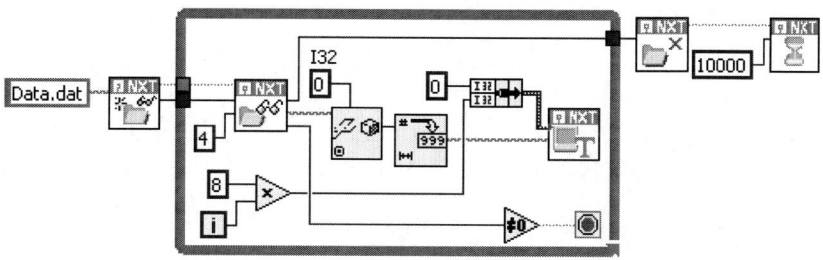

Figure 8.29
Read Binary File

Figure 8.29 is a program that reads the Data.dat file we just made and displays the values on the NXT screen. The Unflatten from String can reconstruct the value for any type variable, but you have to give it an example of the variable for it to work. That is what the I32 constant labeled I32 is for. If you were Unflattening a byte, you would use a U8 for unsigned 8-bit number. Unflatten from String doesn't use the label or value of the constant, only its type or Representation. In this case an I32 is four bytes, and that is also why we are reading only four bytes at a time from the file. The program immediately converts the value into a text string for the display you can see in Figure 8.30.

The program reads from the file until there is an error. It actually tries to read past the end of the file where there isn't another value but still tries to convert a value from nothing. This is why there is an additional 0 on the display. It would be simple enough to prevent the error with some extra blocks, but that would unnecessarily complicate the program.

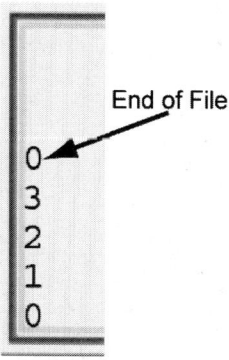

Figure 8.30
Display of Data.dat

Reflections

Practically speaking, you will probably need to use only the Easy File blocks. The reason for using these lower-level blocks is primarily for storage efficiency. If you stored each pixel for a bitmap for the NXT screen as individual values, it would take 19,200 bytes. Efficiently stored as one bit per pixel, it only takes 800 bytes, which saves a lot of memory and time. Speaking of time. . .

Time Flies

9

Time flies like an arrow, fruit flies like a banana.— Groucho Marx

In this chapter you will learn how to tell, wait, measure, record, defeat, and stop time. Okay, you aren't really going to become a superhero; we'll only defeat the Sleep timer and Stop programs. There are a variety of time-related functions in LabVIEW, but they are scattered in several different palettes. We have been using the Wait block since Chapter 5, when we paced the time between samples in data logging; now let's get to know the rest of the time family.

Keep Alive

The NXT has a built-in Sleep feature to save battery life. It automatically shuts itself off—or goes to sleep—when there hasn't been user interaction with it for a period of time. Surprisingly, this feature works even if the NXT is running your program. This can be really annoying when the NXT shuts itself off during a long data logging experiment. You can change the time duration on the NXT under Sleep in the Settings Menu. The options are for 2, 5, 10, 30, 60 minutes, or Never. Setting it to Never seems like a good idea until you find your NXT with dead batteries because you accidentally left it on.

The Keep Alive block, shown in Figure 9.1, resets the sleep timer just as though there were some user interaction. If you call it periodically within your program, then the NXT won't ever go to sleep. The output of the block tells you the time in milliseconds (ms) you have selected for the duration. For example, 5 minutes is 300,000 ms. If you run the little program shown in Figure 9.2, you'll see your NXT's sleep time setting on the display.

Figure 9.1
Keep Alive

Figure 9.2
Sleep Time

Tick Count

Tick Count (see Figure 9.3) gives you the number of milliseconds that have elapsed from when the NXT was turned on. It uses a 32-bit Unsigned Integer and can count up to 4,294,967,296. That works out to over 1000 hours or 50 days! I doubt you have to worry about ever running out of Ticks unless you have the NXT plugged in and always turned on. The Tick Count block is in the NXTToolkit under the Time & Dialog palette, as shown in Figure 9.4.

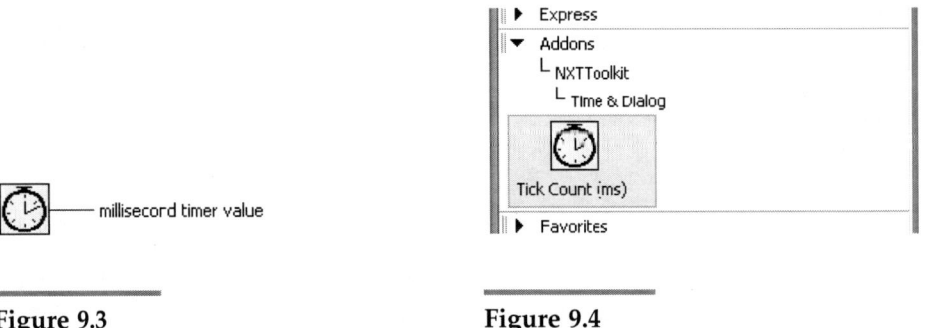

Figure 9.3
Tick Count

Figure 9.4
Time & Dialog Palette

Hour Clock

Figure 9.5 shows a 24-hour clock program that uses the Tick Count to generate the seconds, minutes, and hours for a time-of-day display. There isn't any AM or PM; it keeps time in military time, so 3 o'clock PM is 15 hours. The Keep Alive block you just learned about is inside the While Loop to prevent the NXT from going to sleep.

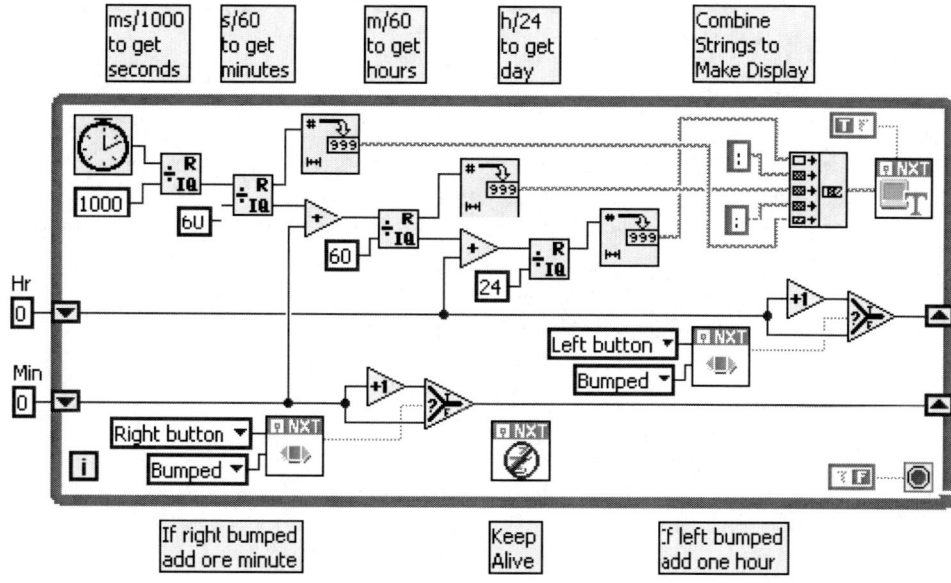

Figure 9.5
24-Hour Clock Program

The NXT display looks like Figure 9.6 while it is running. When the program starts, the display will show a time based on the elapsed time from when the NXT was turned on. Every time you bump the Left Button the hours will increment up by one, and when you bump the Right Button the minutes will advance. Something that isn't obvious from Figure 9.5 is that all the Numeric Constants have had their Representation changed to U32 for Unsigned 32-bit Integers to prevent any Coercion Dots.

Figure 9.6
Clock Display

Concatenate String

About the only new programming feature of the 24-Hour Clock program is the way the String for the display is being created. First, each of the Hours, Minutes, and Seconds values are converted into short Strings themselves. Then they are combined with the Concatenate String block along with the colons. The Concatenate String block is in the String palette, as shown in Figure 9.7. When you first put the block on the Block Diagram, it will have only two inputs (see Figure 9.8). As you move the cursor over it, handles will appear, and you can stretch it to have as many inputs as you need. In this case we need five, as shown in Figure 9.9.

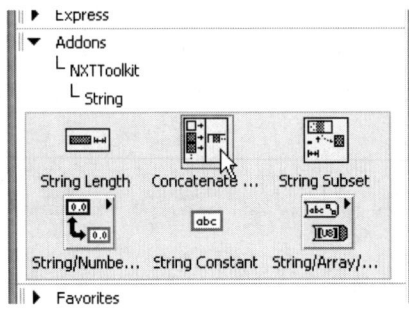

Figure 9.7
Concatenate String in the String Palette

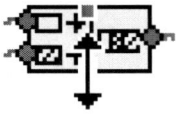

Figure 9.8
Initial Appearance of Concatenate String

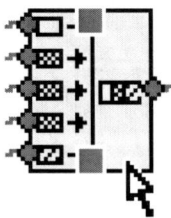

Figure 9.9
Concatenate Stretched for Five Inputs

Wait

We have been using the Wait block (see Figure 9.10) for a long time without really getting to know what it does. It waits a given amount of time in milliseconds, so a Wait of 1000 will be one second. I'm not sure why you would need the value of the Tick after the Wait, but it is available as the millisecond timer value output.

It is important to understand what happens to the rest of your program when part of it enters a Wait block. Build the little block diagram shown in Figure 9.11 and then select it, as shown in Figure 9.12. Now type Ctrl-C on the keyboard to copy the block and Ctrl-V to paste the copy back on the Function Block diagram. Move the new While Loop over and modify the Column and Wait time entries so that the display looks like Figure 9.13.

Compile, Download, and Run the program. After a short while, the display will look something like Figure 9.14. It should be apparent that the NXT is multitasking, because both loops are running in parallel. Because the Wait time for the second loop is shorter, the count for the upper number will grow faster. The Waits are affecting only the loops they are inside of, not the entire program.

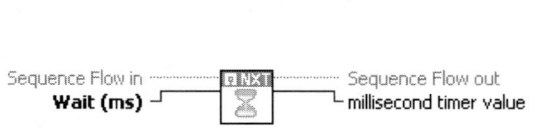

Figure 9.10
Wait Block

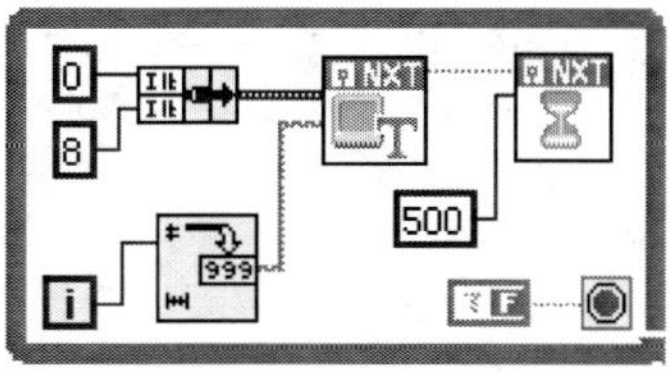

Figure 9.11
First Step

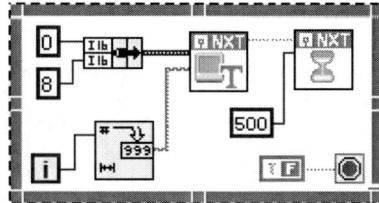

Figure 9.12
Select and Copy

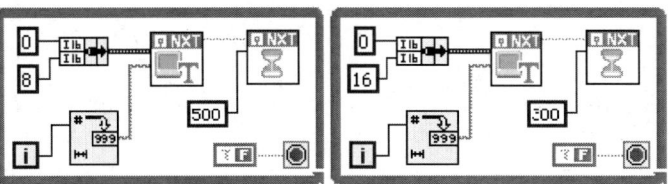 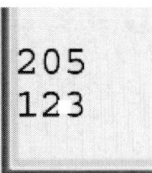

Figure 9.13
Paste and Modify

Figure 9.14
Two Loop Display

Event Time Logging

You already learned about data logging in Chapter 5. That involved periodically recording the value of some input. Suppose you really didn't care about the value of the input as much as when it changed. You could record a lot of samples very close together in time and then pick through the data later to figure out when it changed. As you can imagine, that would waste a lot of memory storing all that data. A better strategy would be to record only the time when the input changed or another event occurred.

Let's take our 24-hour clock program and add a time-logging loop to run in parallel with it. The time-logging part will record only the time when a bright light is detected by the Light Sensor. We start by adding an Indicator to the text String that is being displayed. You should know how to create an Indicator and change the label to Time, as shown in Figure 9.15.

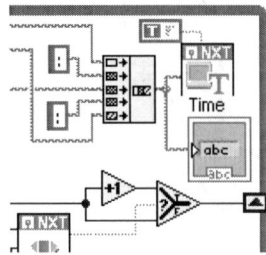

Figure 9.15
Add an Indicator to Clock24

Local Variables

That Indicator and its label allow the value of the String to be available as a Local Variable called Time outside the 24-hour clock While Loop. Figure 9.16 shows the Time Logging program that needs to be built just below the Clock24 on the same block diagram. Everything on the diagram should be familiar except the box with the word Time inside. That is the Local Variable that will be receiving the value of Time from the Indicator we previously added.

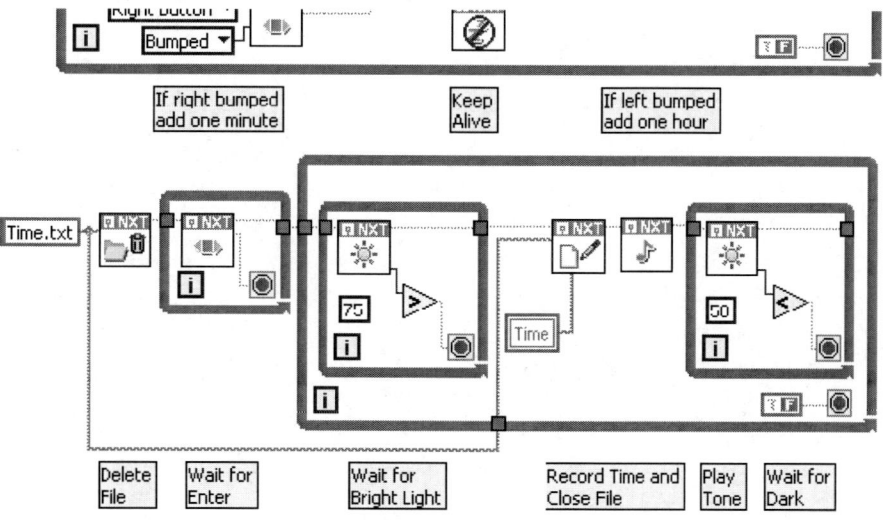

Figure 9.16
Time Logger Added below the Clock24 Loop

Go to the Structures palette (see Figure 9.17), get a Local Variable block, and place it below the Easy File Write, as shown in Figure 9.16. When it is first placed, it will be gray and it will have a question mark inside. When you left-click on it, a list of possible Local Variables will show up, but Time will be the only one available in this program. Select Time, and it will show up inside the box. By default the Local Variable is a Write type, so right-click on it and Change to Read, as shown in Figure 9.19. Now wire it to the Text input of the Easy File Write.

Save the program as Time Datalog and then Compile, Download, and Run it. When the program starts, you can adjust the hours and minutes just as with the 24-hour clock program. When you have the correct time, press the Enter button. The light on the Light Sensor should light up, indicating that the program flow has dropped into the Wait for Bright Light Loop. Now flash a bright light into the Light Sensor. Wait a while and repeat this a few times. Every time a data point is recorded, the NXT will make

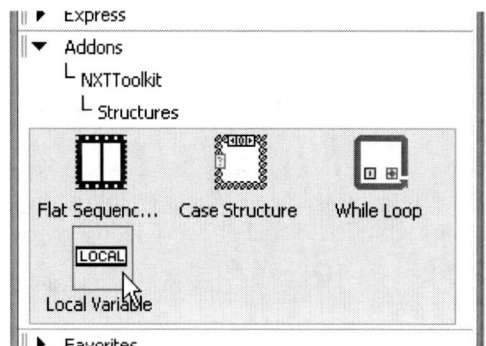

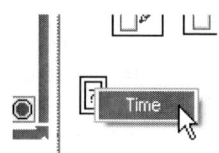

Figure 9.17
Local Variable in Structures Palette

Figure 9.18
Adding Local Variable

a beep to let you know. It is safe to stop logging with the Stop button on the NXT, because the file will be automatically closed by the NXT operating system.

Retrieve the Time.txt file from the NXT using the NXT Terminal as you did for the data files. Now you can look at the time values with a program such as Notepad, as shown in Figure 9.20. From this file you can see that a light was flashed at 13 s, 16 s, 4 min and 23 s, 8 min and 27s, and 21min and 36 s.

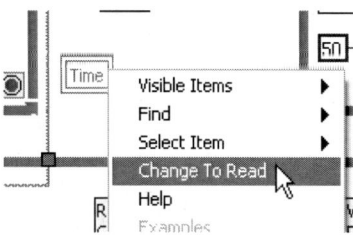

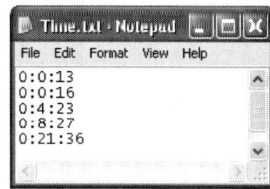

Figure 9.19
Changing to Read

Figure 9.20
Time.txt in Notepad

Reaction Timer

Figure 9.21 is a program to measure how quickly you can react to a sound that has started and push a button. The time delay before the sound starts is random, so you can't anticipate when it will start. You also can't cheat by just holding down on the

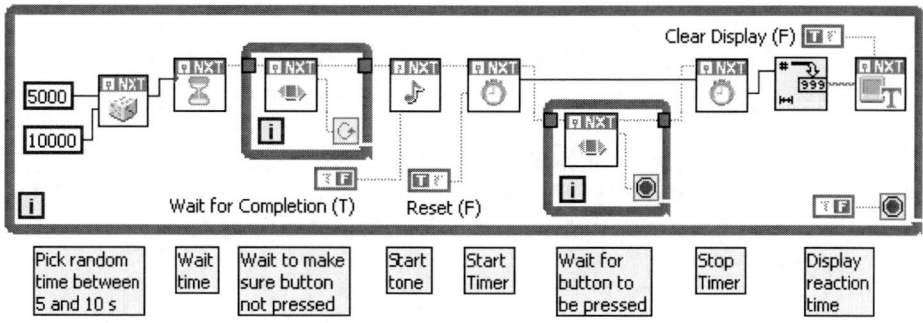

Figure 9.21
Reaction Timer

Enter button, because it must be in the released position before the tone is started. Right now the program just keeps testing over and over; a nice enhancement would be to record the data in a file or keep other statistics. You might also see whether the reaction time to a visual input on the display is faster or slower than the reaction time to a sound input.

Random Number

The Reaction Timer program uses the Random Number block, shown in Figure 9.22, to generate a range of unknown delay times. The block has two inputs to set the Minimum and Maximum value the Number output will have. All of the values between and including the Minimum and Maximum have the same probability of occurring. You could simulate flipping a coin by setting a Minimum of zero and a Maximum of one, because Number will be zero or one with equal probability.

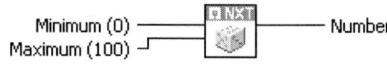

Figure 9.22
Random Number

Timer

The NXT has four Timers, and they are controlled with the Timer Block, shown in Figure 9.23. Timer Blocks are generally used in pairs. First the Timer is Reset by setting the Reset input to True. Later the value of the Timer Value is read with the Reset input set to False. Essentially, the Time Value is the current Tick Count minus the Tick Count when the Timer was Reset. You can read the Time Value as many times as you need.

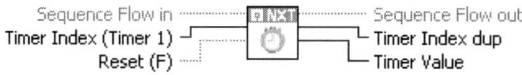

Figure 9.23
Timer Block

Wait for Completion

There is another subtle time-related thing going on in Figure 9.21. The Wait for Completion on the Play Tone block is set to False. Otherwise the block would make the program wait until the tone had completed, and the default duration of a tone is half a second. By not waiting, the Tone is started, but the program immediately continues with Resetting the Timer and waiting for the button to be pressed. The Wait for Completion is also an input for some Output blocks.

Setting Wait for Completion depends on whether your program can continue processing other blocks in parallel or whether you need to make sure the action has been completed before you continue. The Music Box program described in Chapter 5 can't play the next note while the first is still playing, so it defaults to Wait for Completion. The Reaction Timer can't Wait for Completion because it needs to Reset the Timer as quickly as possible after the sound starts.

Stop

Sometimes you reach a point in a program where there is nothing else to do but stop. Maybe you determine that your robot is hopelessly lost, has encountered too many errors, or simply has finished everything you wanted to do. The problem is, with all this parallel processing going on, it can be hard to stop it all at the same time. That is where the Stop block comes in (see Figure 9.24). Setting its input to True will stop your program just as though you had pushed the Stop button on the NXT. You'll find it in the Application Control palette, as shown in Figure 9.25.

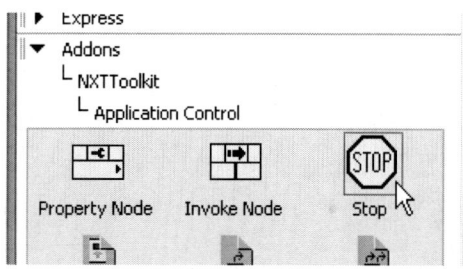

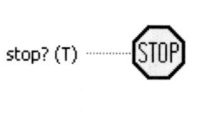

Figure 9.24
Stop Block

Figure 9.25
Stop Block in Application Control Palette

Reflections

Time was an important subject, but I suppose it's time to move on. Speaking of moving, we haven't done much with the motors lately. What fun is a robot clock that doesn't run into something every once and a while?

General Motors

10

It is possible to fly without motors, but not without knowledge and skill.—Wilbur Wright

We learned about the Sync Unlimited and Sync Stop blocks in Chapter 3. Unlike Sync type blocks that synchronously control pairs of motors for propulsion, Motor blocks control only one motor at a time. LabVIEW has four specialized Motor blocks; Unlimited, Distance, Time, and Stop, along with one all-purpose block simply called Motor.

Motor Unlimited

Motor Unlimited turns on a specified motor, and it will stay on until something else turns it off. The block shown in Figure 10.1 has inputs you would expect for Output Port, Power Level, and Direction. It also has the usual Sequence Flow input and output.

The Speed Regulation input tells the NXT that you want it to try to compensate for the amount of load on the motor. Without Speed Regulation, the greater the load on the motor, the lower the speed at which it will turn. That speed might be faster with higher Power, but it will still slow down with load. With Speed Regulation, the NXT watches the rotation rate of the motor and adjusts the Power level to try to hold the speed constant.

You might think Speed Regulation is such a cool feature that you should always enable it. However, you would be amazed by how much power can be commanded to a motor that wasn't keeping up because of the load. Mechanical assemblies can be torn apart and gears stripped with the torque exerted by a NXT motor at full power. Sometimes it is best to let the motor bog down and even stop rather than break apart your robot.

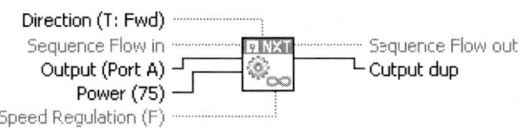

Figure 10.1
Motor Unlimited

Stop Motor

Stopping a motor that was started with the Motor Unlimited is the job of the Stop Motor block, shown in Figure 10.2. Actually it will stop the motor regardless of how it was started. The Output port input should be fed from the Output dup (short for duplication) from the Motor Unlimited, so changing the Port in one place automatically changes in the other.

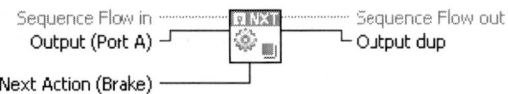

Figure 10.2
Stop Motor

Next Action can be set to either Brake or Coast. Brake means the NXT will apply the electronic equivalent of brakes to the motor. With Brake, the motor will stop rotating quickly and will actually resist further turning. Coast means the NXT will just remove the electrical power and the motor will slowly stop rotating well past the point where it first started to stop. Also, the motor shaft can be easily turned with Coast.

TriBot

Until now we have been using a slightly modified TriBot model called Elmer for the programming examples. Moving the Light Sensor to where the TriBot's Sound Sensor belonged made the example programs easier, but now it is time to reconfigure Elmer to be a true TriBot. You should refer to the plans in the NXT Robo Center to make the corrections. We are not going to use the Grabber part of the TriBot, and it would

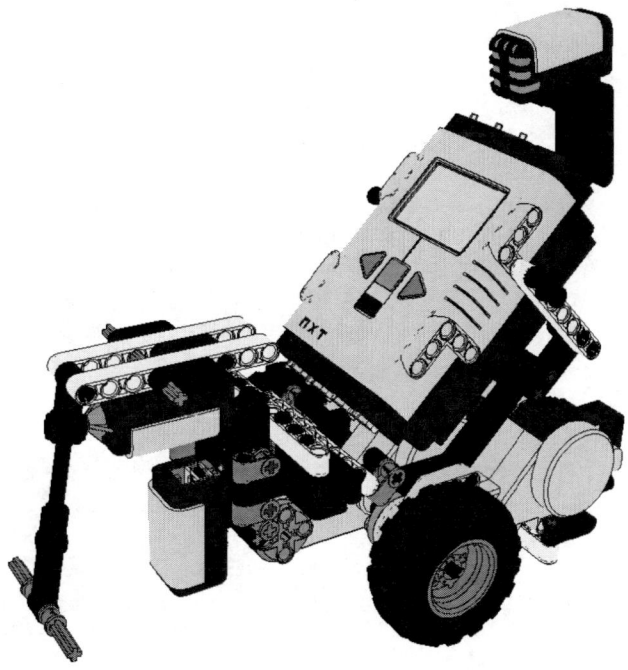

Figure 10.3
TriBot Without the Grabber

probably be simpler if you left that assembly off. The TriBot without the Grabber will look like Figure 10.3, except that the electrical cables have been left off to simplify the picture. The Sound Sensor cable connects to Input 2.

Line Following

Your NXT came with a large paper test pad with a thick black oval drawn on it. One of the programming challenges is to build a robot that will follow around the oval as though it were a train on a track. The idea may seem overwhelming until you realize you only need to follow the edge of the oval, not the line itself. The Light Sensor's built-in light will reflect a lot from the white part of the mat and much less from the black oval. The trick is to try to keep the Light Sensor Intensity value somewhere between the all-white and all-black levels. For my TriBot that value is 60, but it might be a little different for yours.

Bang-Bang Control

Figure 10.4 shows a program to alternately power the wheels of the TriBot depending on the Intensity of the Light Sensor. If the Intensity is greater than the Threshold, then the right-side motor is stopped and the left-side motor is started. That means the robot will turn to the right if it sees white under the sensor. Looking at Figure 10.5, you can see that the opposite thing happens when the Light Sensor is over black. This kind of control is called Bang-Bang, because it simply bangs back and forth between the two values.

The TriBot will trace around the outside of the track in the clockwise direction. Figure 10.6 shows the zigzag path the robot will follow. It will keep moving from

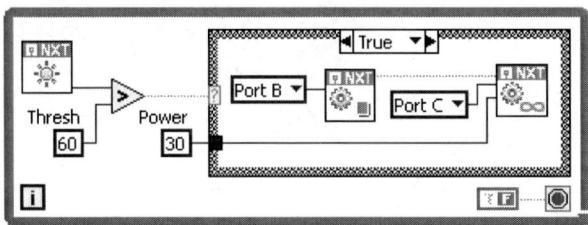

Figure 10.4
Bang-Bang Control

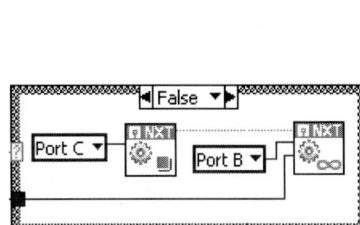

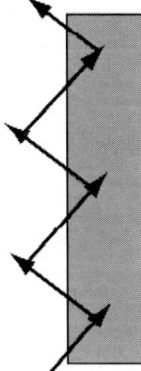

Figure 10.5
False Case

Figure 10.6
Bang-Bang Path

being too far left, then too far right, and then too far left again. You may have to adjust the Threshold and Power values to get your TriBot to work its best, but eventually something will trip up the process and the robot will wander off the track.

Proportional Control

The idea of Proportional Control is making adjustments in proportion to the size of the error, not just turning completely on or off. In other words, you leave the motors on all the time and adjust the power level to minimize the error. Figure 10.7 is a line follower that adjusts the power to the left and right motors in proportion to the Light Sensor Intensity. The subtraction of the Threshold creates a value that is zero when the Intensity indicates that the Light Sensor is directly over the edge. We add a Power value to give both motors a decent amount of power to move forward under that condition. To get opposing effects for the left and right sides, the Threshold is subtracted from the Intensity for one motor, but the Intensity is subtracted from the Threshold for the other.

There is one little catch to the math and the way the Power input to the Motor Unlimited works. The block treats negative Power values the same as positive ones. So, −30 is the same as +30, which is definitely not what we want. The Comparison and Selector blocks take care of making anything negative equal to zero. A plot of the Power to the two Motors versus Light Sensor Intensity is shown in Figure 10.8.

The robot will trace around the outside of the track in the clockwise direction as before, but the path will be much smoother. It will stay closer to the line and make much more gradual corrections, as illustrated in Figure 10.9. You may still need to adjust the Threshold and Power levels to get the best performance for your robot, but it should be less sensitive and more reliable than when the Bang-Bang control is used.

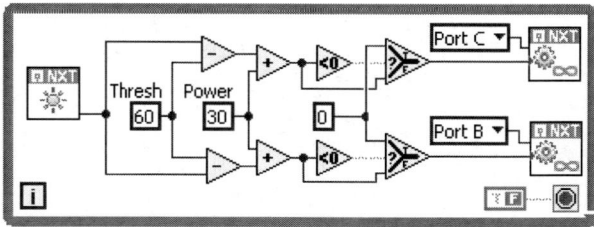

Figure 10.7
Proportional Control

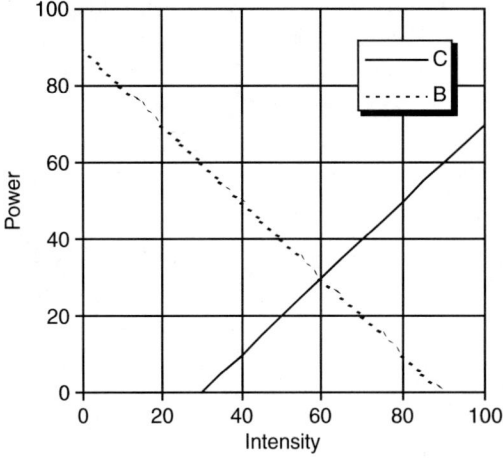

Figure 10.8
Power versus Intensity

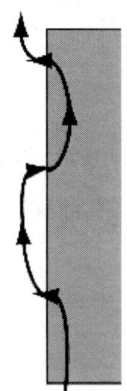

Figure 10.9
Proportional Path

Motor Distance

Motor Distance is a commonly used block with nine different inputs, as shown in Figure 10.10. Primarily, Motor Distance takes care of turning a motor a specified Distance in Degrees, but there are a number of ways it can do that. Output port, Power level, Direction, Speed Regulation, and Sequence Flow are the same as Motor Unlimited. The Next Action input is the same as the Stop Motor, but there is an unexpected interaction with another of the block's inputs; Wait for completion. You can get the Brake Next Action only if you also choose to Wait for completion. If you

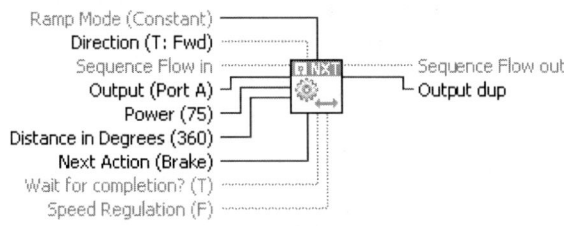

Figure 10.10
Motor Distance

don't Wait, you will always get Coast. Whereas Brake stops the motor very close to the target angle, Coast can continue a full rotation before the motor finally comes to rest.

Ramp Mode is normally set to Constant, and the NXT tries to rotate the motor to the desired Distance with a constant speed associated with the Power input. This can lead to a rapid acceleration at the start of the movement, which may cause the robot to jerk violently. You can lessen this effect by setting the Ramp Mode to Ramp Up. Ramp Up slowly accelerates the motor so it takes off more gradually. Be especially careful with Ramp Down, because it requires the motor to be already turning. The program will get stuck in the Motor Distance block forever if you set Ramp Down for a motor that had not been previously turning.

Sound Control Robot

A very simple wireless technique is to use sound to remotely control a robot. You have probably seen toys that did different things depending on how many times you clapped your hands. The Clap Control program in Figure 10.11 and Figure 10.12 counts loud sounds, and when there has been one second of silence, it controls a robot

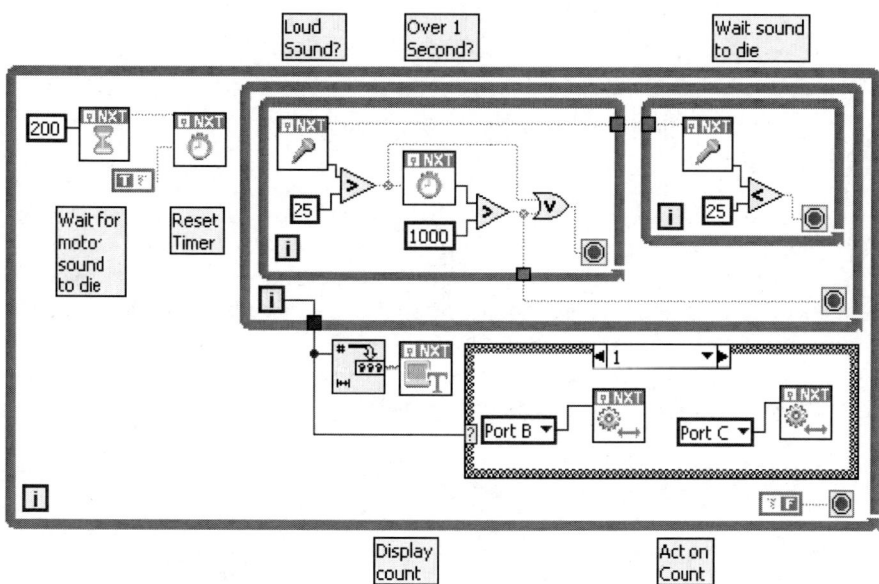

Figure 10.11
Clap Control

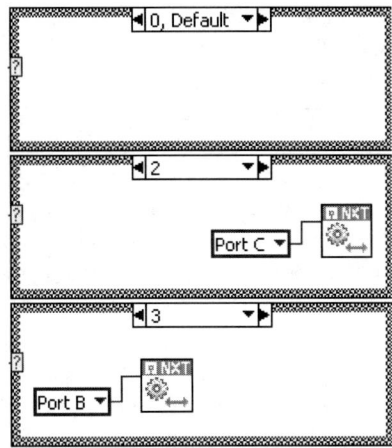

Figure 10.12
Other Cases

based on the count. One clap means go forward, two claps means turn right, and three claps means turn left. The count is also displayed on the screen for convenience and to help you get the hang of clapping the right way.

Sound Sensor

This is the first time we have used the Sound Sensor block, shown in Figure 10.13. The sensor reports the average Volume of the sound in the environment. That means it responds relatively slowly to sound level and is not rapidly picking up sound waves like a microphone. There is an input to select a frequency sensitivity to favor the range of hearing for humans called dBA.

The relatively slow response of the sensor means that even though a clap is a sound of short duration, the sensor will register an increased Volume for a longer period of

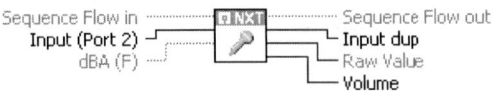

Figure 10.13
Sound Sensor Block

time. That is why the program first waits for the presence of the clap and then waits to make sure it has gone away. This also helps it to ignore any echoes that might sound like multiple claps. The Wait at the very start of the main While Loop is there to allow the sound of the robot motors to die down between movements.

Logic

The only new programming concept in Figure 10.11 is the logic Or gate that feeds the Loop Condition for the center While Loop. You find it and the three other logic functions—And, Exclusive Or (XOr), and Not (see Figure 10.14)—in the Boolean palette. The Or function is True if either or both of the inputs are True, as can be seen in Table 10.1 along with the outputs of the other functions. In this case, either the time exceeding one second "or" the loud sound terminates the loop.

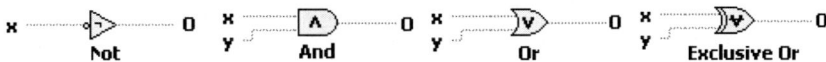

Figure 10.14
Logic Function Symbols

Table 10.1   *Logic Functions*

x	y	Not	And	Or	XOr
F	F	T	F	F	F
F	T	T	F	T	T
T	F	F	F	T	T
T	T	F	T	T	F

Motor Time

The remaining specialized motor block is Motor Time. Shown in Figure 10.15, it also has Output port, Power, Direction, Sequence Flow, Speed Regulation, and Next Action, such as Motor Distance. The amount of Time is specified in milliseconds (ms). Wait for Completion is missing, because Wait is not an option for the block. It always Waits.

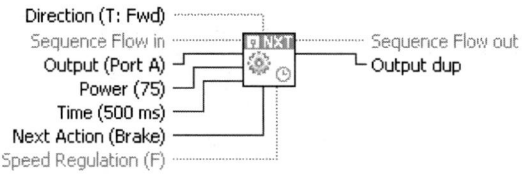

Figure 10.15
Motor Time

Motor

Motor (see Figure 10.16) is really designed to exactly duplicate the functionality of the Motor block in NXT-G. You configure the NXT-G block with the complex control panel shown in Figure 10.17, and the various menu options eventually become inputs to the Motor block. The Goal Type input allows you to program Motor to behave just like the Unlimited, Distance, Time or Stop blocks, but it doesn't do anything that they can't. For the most part, you will probably use only the specialized Motor blocks.

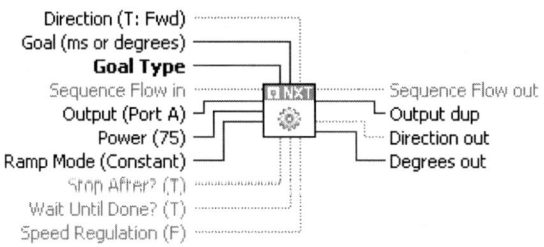

Figure 10.16
Motor Block

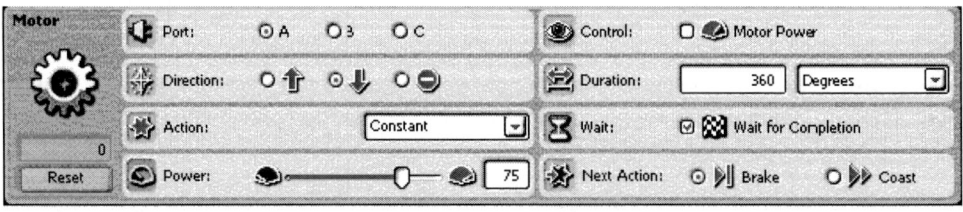

Figure 10.17
NXT-G Motor Configuration

Table 10.2   *Motor Block Options*

Motor Block Goal Type or Specialized Block Name	Ramp Mode	Next Action	Speed Regulation
Time with Wait		☺	☺
Distance with Wait	☺	☺	☺
Distance without Wait	☺		☺
Unlimited			☺
Stop		☺	

Table 10.2 summarizes the options available for the four specialized blocks and the versatile Motor block. Boxes that have a mark indicate that that option is available with that goal type. For example, neither the Motor Distance block nor the Motor block with the Distance Goal Type with Wait for Completion False can have a Next Action.

Sync Distance

Let's finish up the Sync type blocks as long as we are talking about motors. Sync Distance (see Figure 10.18) is similar to Motor Distance with an added input for Steering from the Sync Unlimited block. Steering, as you recall, varies from –100 to 100 with 0 for going straight. Notably missing is the Wait for Completion input, because the block always does a Wait.

The Distance is in degrees with 360 degrees or one revolution as the default. One interesting quality of the block is its ability to keep track of distance over a long sequence of moves. It is probably best to explain this with an illustration. Figure 10.19 shows a Sync Distance that will move a robot forward 1080 degrees, whereas Figure 10.20 shows the equivalent movement split up into three 360-degree moves.

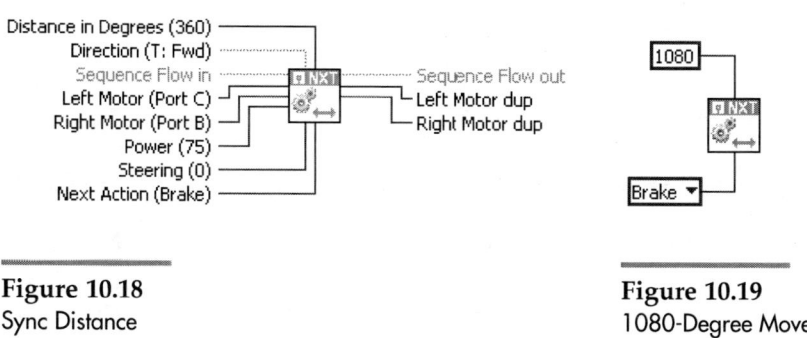

Figure 10.18
Sync Distance

Figure 10.19
1080-Degree Move

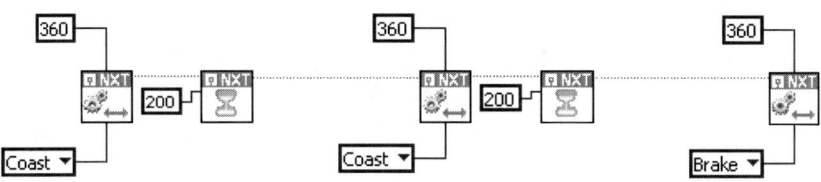

Figure 10.20
Equivalent 1080-Degree Move

Although there are Waits for 200 ms in the program, this could be any other processing that would consume time.

You should make a little mark on a tire and actually try these two programs to see what happens. The Figure 10.19 program does exactly what you would expect and rotates the tire exactly three times. However, Figure 10.20's first move coasts many degrees past 360 during the 200 ms Wait and even further during the second move. Because the third Sync Distance has the Brake option, the final move actually rotates only enough to take the tire to the same location as the single move, because Sync Distance corrects for the buildup of errors in the previous two moves. Another interesting experiment is to hold one of the tires while the NXT runs the Figure 10.19 program. Because the NXT is trying to synchronize both motors, the motor you are not holding will also stop rotating and will not turn until you release the tire.

Ultrasonic Distance Sensor

The Ultrasonic Distance Sensor measures the distance to the nearest object in front of it. It does this by sending out a pulse of ultrasonic sound and then timing how long it takes for the echo to return. Its block is shown in Figure 10.21. The Distance is measured in centimeters, but it can be converted to inches by setting the Convert input to True. The range is about 0 to 2.5 meters or 100 inches. Some problems occur when there are multiple Ultrasonic Sensors in the same room, because they can't tell the difference between another sensor's pulse and their own echo.

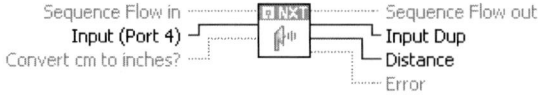

Figure 10.21
Distance Sensor Block

Measure Pi

Let's use the Ultrasonic Distance Sensor to measure a value for pi. The circumference of a circle is just pi (3.14) times the diameter. If we command the tires of a robot to rotate forward one full turn (360 degrees), the robot will move forward by the circumference of the tire. Attach the sensor to the TriBot or Elmer, as shown in Figure 10.22, and connect it to Input Port 4.

We will measure the distance to a wall, move forward an exact number of tire rotations, remeasure the distance, and then divide by the tire diameter to get pi. The Program in Figure 10.23 doesn't contain anything new except the Ultrasonic Distance Sensor block. About the only thing to be aware of is that the constant 0s feeding into the Shift Registers are I32 to accommodate the large accumulated value. It reads the sensor 100 times at both positions to both average the value and to scale it up so we get a more accurate value for pi. The tire diameter is 5.5 cm, so rather than move only one rotation, we will move two (720 degrees) and double the diameter to 11 cm. Start the robot with the Ultrasonic Sensor about 80 cm from a wall and then start the program. It will take several seconds to make the first reading, and then it will move forward. After a few more seconds 100 times the value of pi will be displayed on the NXT screen. Ideally you would get 314, but I have seen answers from 298 to 345.

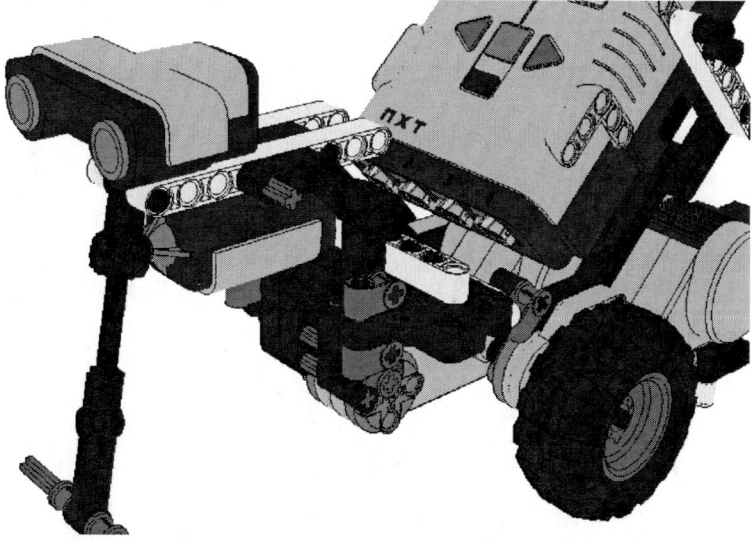

Figure 10.22
Mounted Ultrasonic Distance Sensor

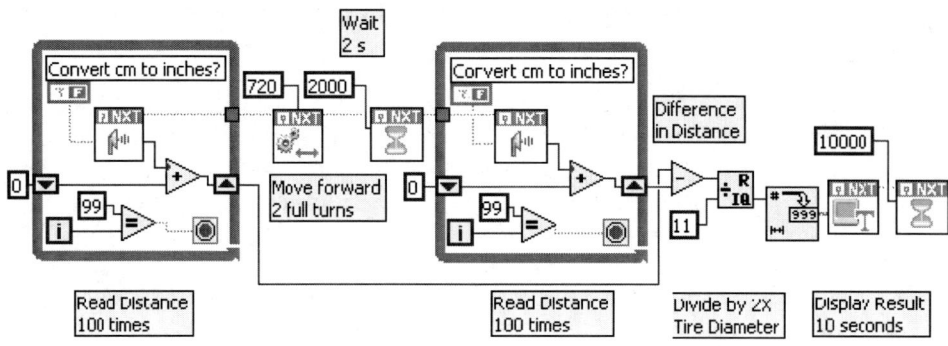

Figure 10.23
Calculate pi Program

Reset Motors

Sometimes you don't want the error correction feature of the Sync Distance block. In that case you throw a Reset Motors block (see Figure 10.24) in the sequence to reset the distance the Sync Distance block is using. You can pick which motors you want to Reset by setting their particular input to True. Figure 10.25 is a modified version of

Figure 10.24
Reset Motors Block

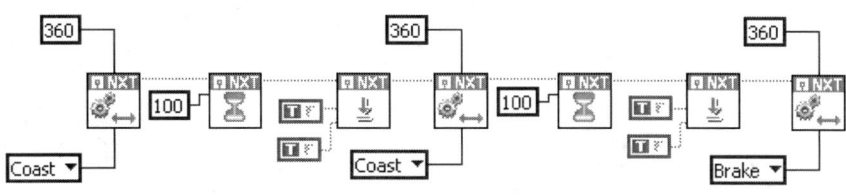

Figure 10.25
Sequence with Reset Motors

the program shown in Figure 10.20 to have the Reset Motors blocks before the second and third Sync Distance blocks. When you run it, the total rotation will be about 90 degrees past 1080, due to the additional distance covered during the coasts.

The distance between the TriBot's wheels happens to be very close to the circumference of one of its tires. That means that one full rotation of the tires in opposite directions will execute a near perfect 180-degree about face. You get this clockwise or counterclockwise rotation by setting the Steering to –100 or 100, respectively, and doing a Sync Distance of 360 degrees. The Patrol Program in Figure 10.26 makes the TriBot patrol back and forth almost perfectly in a line.

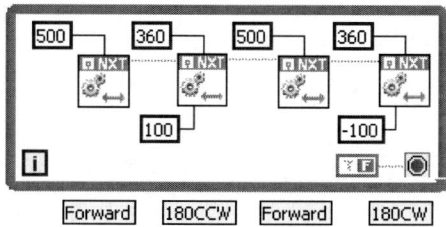

Figure 10.26
Patrol Program

Sync Time

Sync Time, illustrated in Figure 10.27, works much like Sync Distance, except that the move is defined by an amount of Time in milliseconds (ms). There are many factors, such as battery level and friction that make movement based only on time unreliable. The preferred way to get from one point to another is by defining the distances to travel, but occasionally you might want a robot to dance or shake in a particular way that is better defined by time; then you would need the Sync Time block.

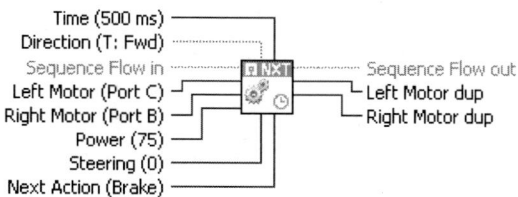

Figure 10.27
Sync Time

Reflections

We have covered all the NXT Output, File, Display, Sound, Time, and Record/Play blocks. There are just a few blocks left to cover; after that, we will be done with the NXT Toolkit part of the book. The blocks include some sensors from the original MINDSTORMS kits, Bluetooth communications, and more on Debugging.

Something Old, Something New

11

It is the loose ends with which men hang themselves.
—Zelda Fitzgerald wife of author F. Scott Fitzgerald

There are only a few function blocks left to discover. Most of them are related to devices that were used in the original LEGO MINDSTORMS RCX kit. They can be easily identified, because they have the word "Legacy" in their name. There is also a complex block called Calibrate, which allows you to customize the sensitivity of several sensors, including the Legacy Light.

Legacy Motor

The NXT has backward compatibility with the first-generation MINDSTORMS motors, shown in Figure 11.1. The original motor didn't have a built-in Rotation Sensor as does the NXT motor, and that limits the features of the Legacy Motor block (see Figure 11.2). The block does have the ability to Stop and apply a Brake just as the other Motor blocks did with the Next Action input, as shown in Figure 11.3. Oddly, the block doesn't have the ability to Stop and Coast, but you can use the Stop Motor block for that. The physical size and high-speed output still make these motors worthy of consideration in robot building. However, you will find their older-style construction method is a little hard to combine with the NXT elements. It also uses the older LEGO Electric Plate type connector that requires an adapter cable.

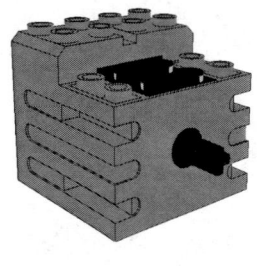

Figure 11.1
Legacy Motor

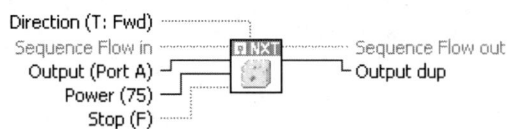

Figure 11.2
Legacy Motor Block

Figure 11.3
Equivalent Ways to Brake

Legacy Lamp

The Legacy Lamp block is the last block in the Output palette. The Lamp, pictured in Figure 11.4, uses the older LEGO Electric Plate–type connector. It is not just handy as a decoration; it also provides remote status and debugging information. Its block (see Figure 11.5) can be used to turn the Lamp on to a defined Intensity or turn the Lamp off by setting the Power input to False. You can also turn the Lamp off with a Stop Motor.

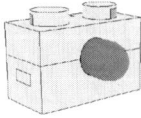

Figure 11.4
Lamp

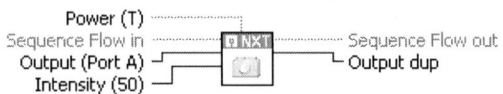

Figure 11.5
Legacy Lamp Block

Legacy Temperature

The Legacy Temperature sensor (see Figure 11.6) looks like a LEGO brick with a metal rod sticking out of its side. Its block is shown in Figure 11.7. The output is in Fahrenheit by default but can be set to Celsius by setting Units to True. The Temperature output is 10 times the actual temperature. For example, 68.3°F is read as a Temperature equal to 683, and that way you get 1/10 degree resolution with only an Integer value. The output range is from –20° to 70°C or –4° to 158°F. It uses the older LEGO Electric Plate–type connector.

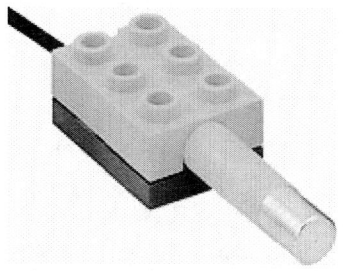

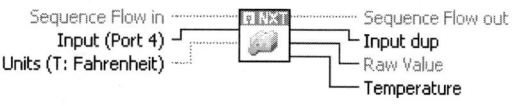

Figure 11.6
Legacy Temperature Sensor

Figure 11.7
Legacy Temperature Block

Legacy Light

The Legacy Light sensor (see Figure 11.8) works like the NXT Light Sensor, but it doesn't have the option of turning off the built-in red LED. In addition, like the NXT Light Sensor, it uses a silicon-based phototransistor, so it is mostly sensitive to near

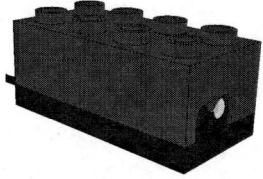

Figure 11.8
Legacy Light Sensor

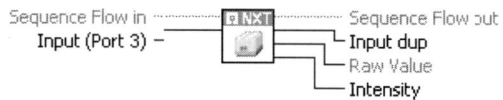

Figure 11.9
Legacy Light Block

infrared light. Its block is shown in Figure 11.9, and it also uses the LEGO Electric Plate–type connector.

Legacy Touch

Functionally, the Legacy Touch Sensor works the same as the NXT Touch Sensor. However, physically they are very different, as you can see from Figure 11.10. The Legacy Touch Sensor has a softer switch mechanism that doesn't require as much travel to activate as the one on the NXT. Like the other Legacy blocks, it uses the older Electric Plate–type connector. Its block (see Figure 11.11) is the same as the NXT Touch.

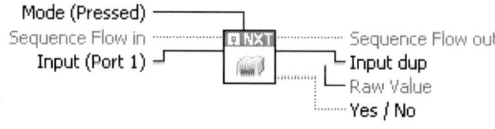

Figure 11.10
Legacy Touch Sensor

Figure 11.11
Legacy Touch Block

Legacy Rotation

The Legacy Rotation Sensor looks like a large brick with an axle hole toward one end, as shown in Figure 11.12. The great advantage to the Legacy Rotation Sensor is that it takes much less torque to rotate it. Unlike the NXT Rotation sensor with one-degree accuracy, the Legacy produces only 16 ticks per revolution. Don't confuse these ticks with the time-related ticks; they are basically 22.5-degree increments of rotation. The NXT will keep track of the ticks over time, and you can zero the count by setting

Figure 11.12
Legacy Rotation Sensor

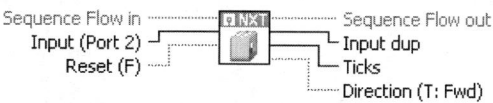

Figure 11.13
Legacy Rotation Block

the Reset input to True, as shown in its block in Figure 11.13. As with other Legacy Sensors, it uses the LEGO Electric Plate connector.

Calibrate

The Light and Sound Sensors neatly scale their readings into a range from 0 to 100. The scale is based on the operating range of the sensor itself, and not the widest range needed for a given application. This is probably best understood with an example. Figure 11.14 is a simple Light Meter program much like the ones we have used before. It puts the Light Sensor value in the corner of the NXT display. If you place the TriBot on the Test Pad mat and move it from the black line to the white background, as shown in Figure 11.15, you will find that the reading varies from around 40 to 80. It might be nice to have the reading actually go from 0 to 100, and that is where the Calibrate block comes in.

The block, shown in Figure 11.16, is so complex that it is better to use a utility program that comes with the NXT Toolkit rather than deal with it directly. I'm not going to dissect the program here, but it is well worth your time to dig down into it

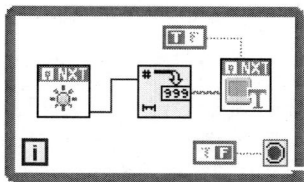

Figure 11.14
Light Meter Program

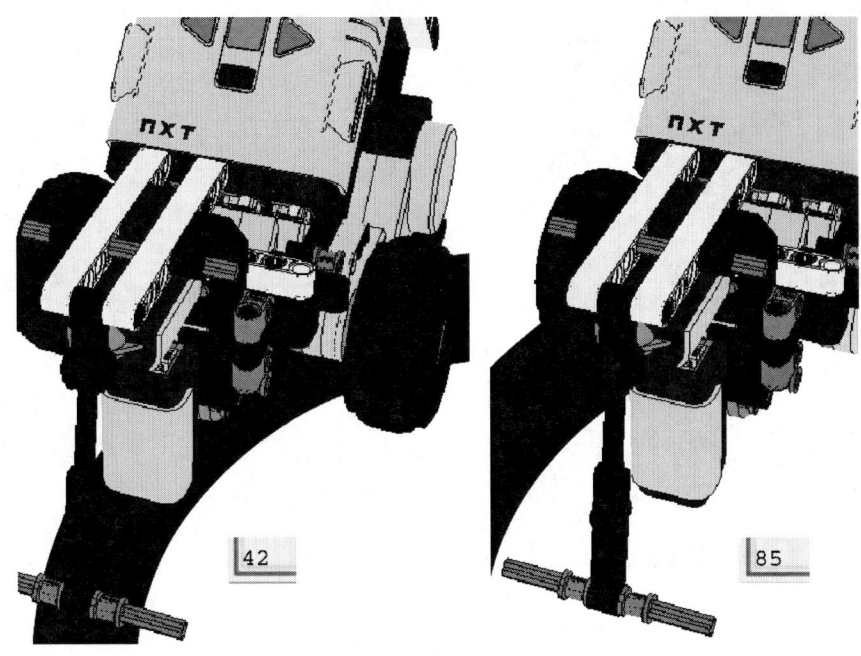

Figure 11.15
Initial Light Meter Readings

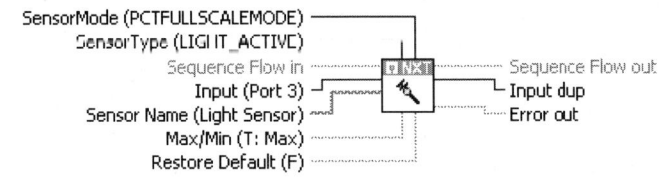

```
SensorMode (PCTFULLSCALEMODE) ──────────────
    SensorType (LIGHT_ACTIVE) ─────────────
            Sequence Flow in ·········           ········· Sequence Flow out
              Input (Port 3) ─┐                 └─ Input dup
     Sensor Name (Light Sensor) ~~               ····· Error out
              Max/Min (T: Max) ············
            Restore Default (F) ············
```

Figure 11.16
Calibrate Block

to see how it was written. You will find the program in the Program Files/National Instruments/LabVIEW x.x/examples/NXTToolkit/NXT Programs directory.

Open the file calibration.llb, as shown in Figure 11.17. This is actually a collection of VIs that includes the main Cal_Program and supporting VIs (see Figure 11.18). Select the main program and Compile, Download, and Run it with the NXT Terminal.

The first screen on the NXT will look like Figure 11.19. You are calibrating a sensor on Port 3, so use the right button on the NXT to advance the Port Number to 3 and then press the Enter button. If you go too far, you can back up with the left button.

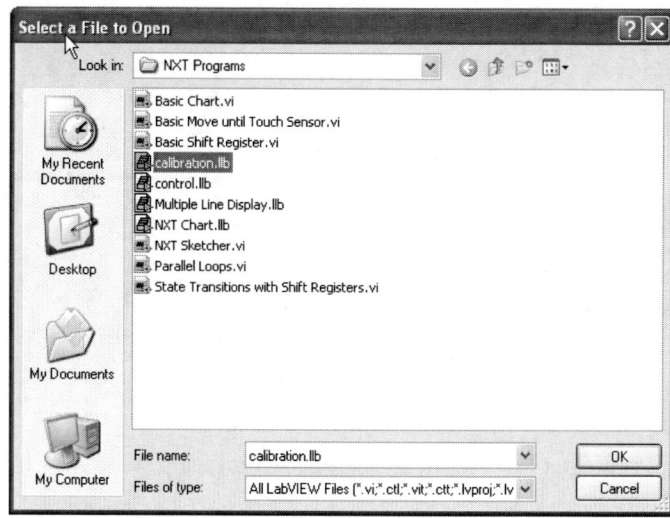

Figure 11.17
Calibration VI Library

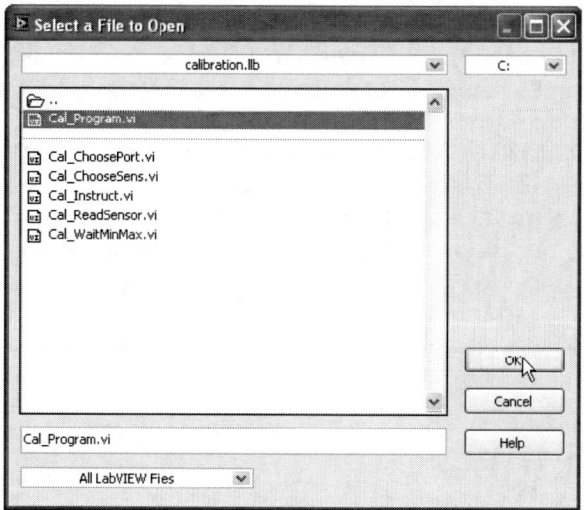

Figure 11.18
Main Cal_Program

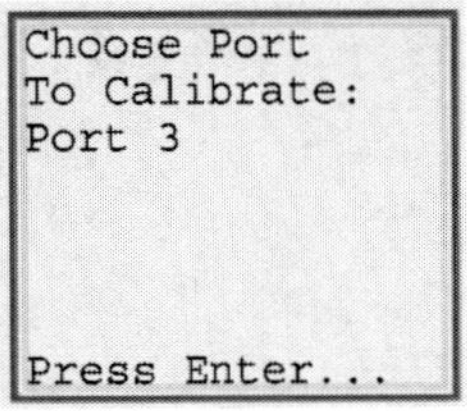

```
Choose Port
To Calibrate:
Port 3



Press Enter...
```

Figure 11.19
Choose Port Screen

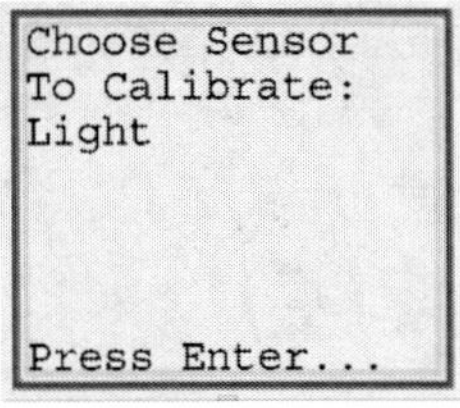

```
Choose Sensor
To Calibrate:
Light



Press Enter...
```

Figure 11.20
Choose Sensor Screen

The screen will change (see Figure 11.20) to allow you to select from the Light, Sound, or Legacy Light sensors. We are calibrating the NXT Light Sensor, so press the Enter button.

Now move the TriBot so the Light Sensor is directly over the black line on the mat. Pressing the Enter button will calibrate the NXT to accept this light level as the minimum, and it will become the new zero. Figure 11.21 shows the display when calibrating the minimum.

Finally, move the TriBot so the Light Sensor is over a white part of the mat. Pressing the Enter button will calibrate the NXT to accept this light level as the maximum, and it will become the new 100. Figure 11.22 shows the display when calibrating the maximum.

The Light Sensor has now been calibrated for the black and white levels of the mat. Rerun the Light Meter program to see that the black line will read near zero and the white background will be near 100, as shown in Figure 11.23. Calibration data is stored in a small file that carries the .cal extension. You can see with the NXT Terminal in Figure 11.24 that the file is called Light Sensor.cal. When you no longer need the calibration, just delete the .cal file. Leaving this file in place could lead to some very confusing results for programs that were expecting the usual sensor operating range.

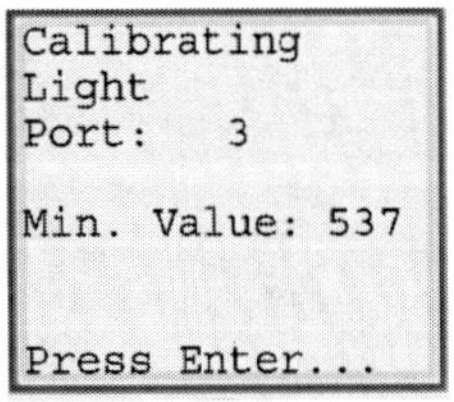

```
Calibrating
Light
Port:    3

Min. Value: 537

Press Enter...
```

Figure 11.21
Minimum Screen

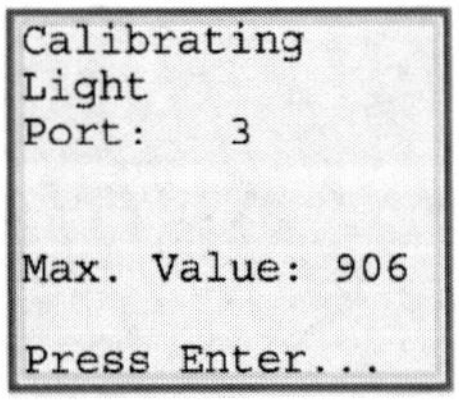

```
Calibrating
Light
Port:    3


Max. Value: 906

Press Enter...
```

Figure 11.22
Maximum Screen

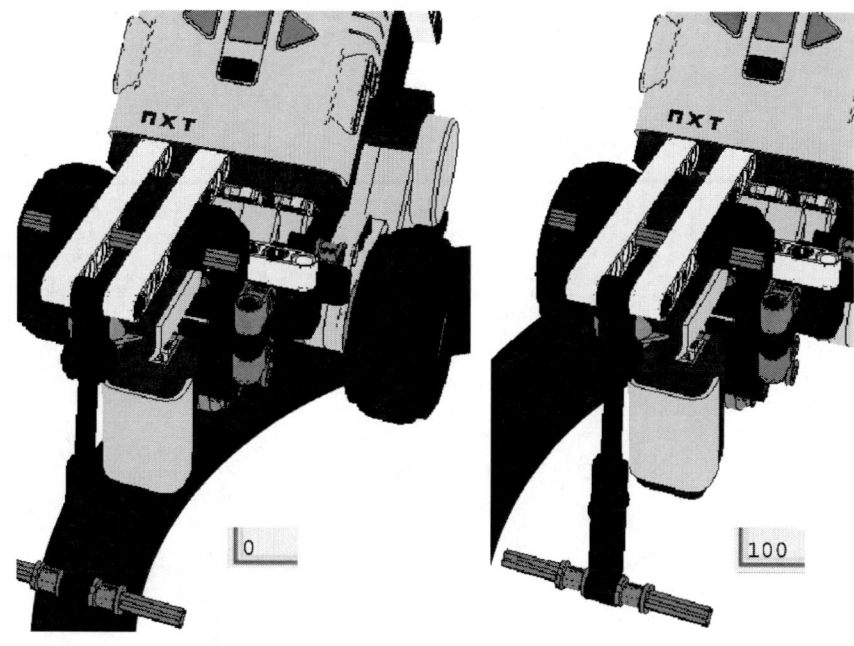

Figure 11.23
Calibrated Light Meter Readings

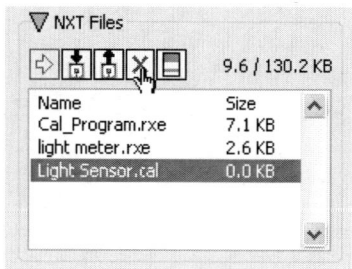

Figure 11.24
Delete Light Sensor.cal File

Reflections

The Legacy Temperature and Rotation Sensors have some unique qualities and will be covered again in Chapter 16. Remember, when ordering the older-style sensors and motor that they need an adapter cable to connect them to the NXT. You will need more than one NXT to make use of the Bluetooth blocks that are discussed in the following chapter. If you aren't fortunate enough to own two NXTs, maybe you can borrow one.

Something Blue

12

The wireless telegraph is not difficult to understand. The ordinary telegraph is like a very long cat. You pull the tail in New York, and it meows in Los Angeles. Wireless is the same, only without the cat.—Albert Einstein

The name "Bluetooth" is an English nickname for the 10th-century Danish King Harald Blatand, who was instrumental in uniting warring factions in parts of what are now called Norway, Sweden, and Denmark. In a similar way, the Bluetooth standard unites competing companies by providing a common way for their products to wirelessly communicate. NXTs use Bluetooth to communicate with each other and with the PC. The two Bluetooth blocks are for communication between NXTs; communication with the PC doesn't even require programming, as we will see later.

NXT to NXT

Before you can communicate with Bluetooth, you must first establish a Connection. This is accomplished from one NXT, which will be considered the Master, to the other NXT, which will be known as the Slave. However, once the link is established, messages are sent and received in either direction. The first step is to have both NXTs turned on and both of their Bluetooth functions also turned on. Once you turn Bluetooth on, it will automatically turn on every time you turn on the NXT. You do that using the menu shown in Figure 12.1 and then by checking the On/Off menu, as shown in Figure 12.2.

Although Bluetooth will automatically be on, you will still need to reestablish a connection every time you turn the power off. On the Master NXT, go to select Search, as shown in Figure 12.3. Some question marks will appear while the NXT is searching for Bluetooth devices. After a while it will show a list of devices, and you should select NXT only as shown in Figure 12.5. There may be other Bluetooth-enabled devices close enough, such as PCs and cell phones, to be on the list too.

Then you select between three Connection Numbers. That means you can have four NXTs networked, but just select one for now (see Figure 12.6). The NXT Bluetooth

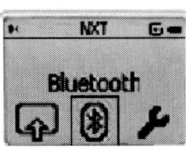

Figure 12.1
Bluetooth Menu

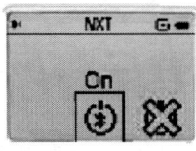

Figure 12.2
On/Off Menu

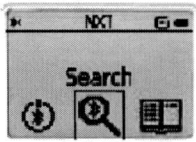

Figure 12.3
Search

Figure 12.4
Wait for List

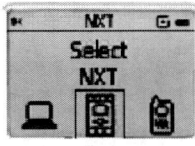

Figure 12.5
Select NXT

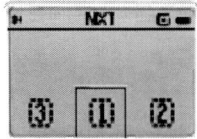

Figure 12.6
Select Connection 1

Connections screen will look like Figure 12.7. Because this NXT is the Master, it uses Connection Number 0. The Slave will use Connection 1.

The first time a pair of NXTs are networked they need to exchange a Passkey. As you try to make the connection, you will have to go to the Slave NXT and select a Passkey and confirm it with the Master, as shown in Figure 12.8. Usually the Passkey is just 1234. Fortunately, this needs to be done only once.

Figure 12.7
Icon Shows NXT on Connection 1

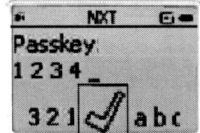

Figure 12.8
First Time Will Require Passkey Exchange

Write Message

Sending a message is simple with the Write Message block, shown in Figure 12.9. You specify the Connection number and then a Mailbox number. Each Connection can have 10 mailboxes, and the message is a Text String up to 58 characters long. The

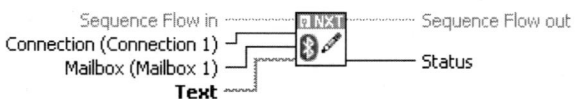

Figure 12.9
Write Message

multiple mailboxes make sending many values simple; just use a different mailbox for each variable you need to exchange. You will need to convert the value into a String or flatten it before you send it.

Read Message

Reading a message is even simpler with the Read Message block, shown in Figure 12.10. On the receiving end there is no need for a Connection number, because messages will be delivered only to the Connection number they were addressed to. You do need to specify which of the Mailbox numbers you want to look at. If there is a new message in that Mailbox, the Message Received output will be True and the Message will be in the Text out String. Depending on how you encoded it, you will then need to convert the String back or unflatten it into a value.

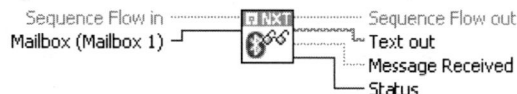

Figure 12.10
Read Message

Master/Slave Programs

Two nearly identical programs are shown in Figure 12.11 and Figure 12.12. The only difference is the Connection Number. Both are using Mailbox number one. The Master Writes messages to Connection 1, and the Slave Writes to Connection 0. The two programs keep exchanging their Loop Interation values just to show you the bidirectional nature of the link and the speed. You could just as easily exchange sensor values, status information, and output commands. If you wanted to use the value for something other than the display, you would need to convert it with the Decimal String to Number block.

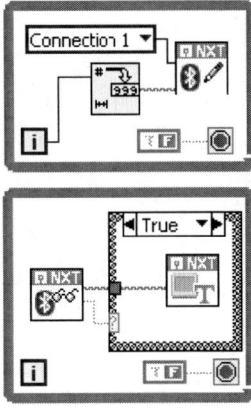

Figure 12.11
Master Program

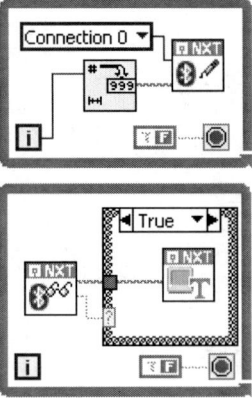

Figure 12.12
Slave Program

NXT to PC

Bluetooth communication between a NXT and a PC doesn't involve programming at all. It is just a choice of connecting to the NXT using a cable with USB or wirelessly with Bluetooth. USB is noticeably faster, more reliable, and easier to use. However, as we have seen with using mobile robots, it can be really inconvenient to get tangled up in a USB cable.

Much as with the NXT-to-NXT Bluetooth connection we have already discussed, we first need to make a connection; this can be done with the NXT Terminal. If you don't have a NXT connected with USB, when you open the NXT Terminal the Status will say Not Connected. Figure 12.13 shows how you select Find NXT, and Figure 12.14 shows how you select Scan to actually find the NXT. Then the window will show the "Scanning for NXT devices." message for a while, as shown in Figure 12.15. Make sure the NXT is turned on and its Bluetooth is also turned on.

The available NXTs will be in a list. Sometimes you may need to Scan more than once to find a NXT. Select the one you want and click Connect, as shown in Figure 12.16. The PC will pair with the NXT if necessary, which will bring up a window like the one in Figure 12.17. The NXT will show a display like Figure 12.18, and, when you select 1234 on the NXT, the PC will connect to the NXT. At first, it will gather such information as battery voltage and firmware version to show that the connection has been made (see Figure 12.19). After that, you use the NXT Terminal as though the NXT was connected to the PC with the USB cable. For example, if you want to Debug a program, just click the Debug button to Compile, Download, and Debug the selected program, as shown in Figure 12.20.

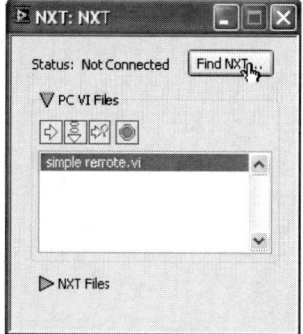

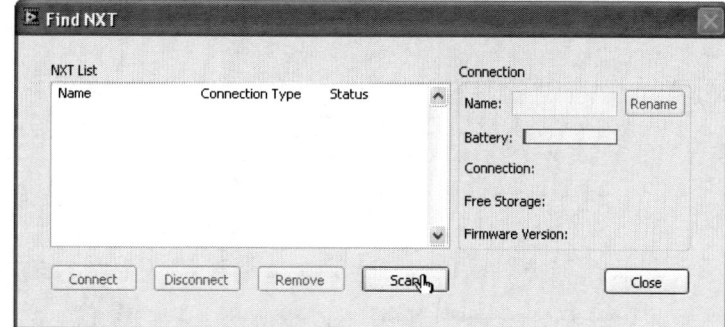

Figure 12.13
Finding the NXT

Figure 12.14
Scan for NXT

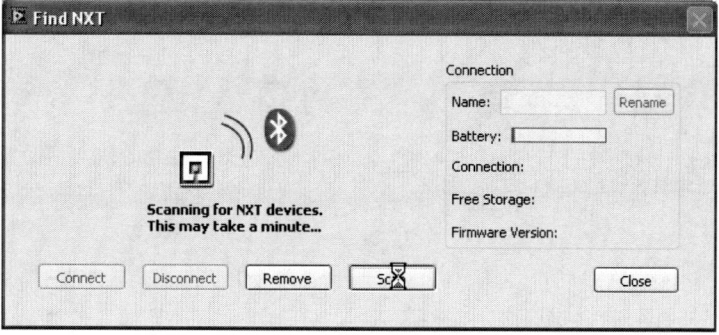

Figure 12.15
Scanning for NXTs

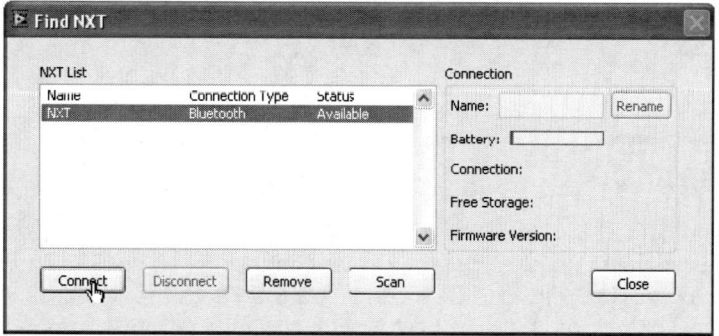

Figure 12.16
Connecting to NXT

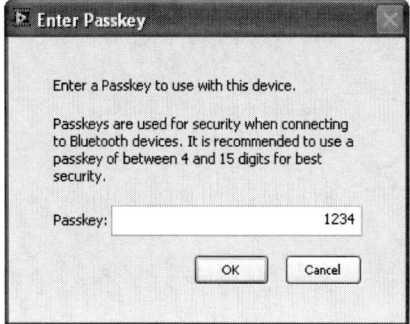

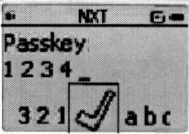

Figure 12.17
Request for Passkey

Figure 12.18
Accept Passkey on NXT

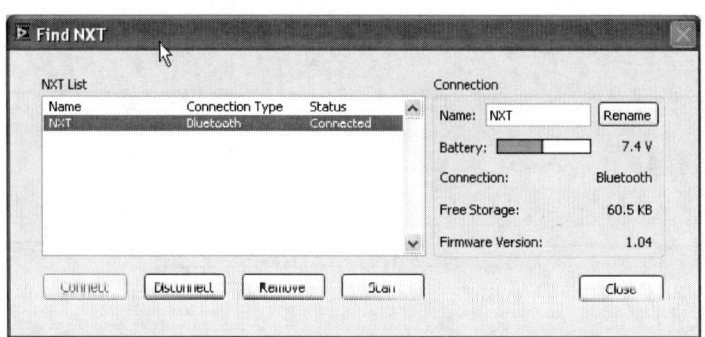

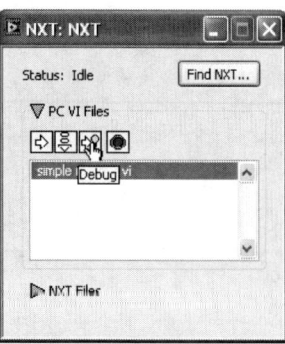

Figure 12.19
NXT Connected

Figure 12.20
Using the Connection to Debug

Reflections

Bluetooth allows for some really cool remote control robot experiments, but it can be frustrating to make and maintain the connections. If you are having trouble, you may need to delete all the known connections on both the NXT and the PC and start over to get things to work properly. We have touched on the debugging features of the NXT Toolkit before; now let's really get to know how to use it to create cool remote control displays.

Deeper Debugging

13

Debugging is twice as hard as writing the code in the first place. Therefore, if you write the code as cleverly as possible, you are, by definition, not smart enough to debug it.
—*Brian W. Kernighan*

Ordinarily, debugging is used only for figuring out why a program isn't working correctly and fixing it. We started using the debugging capability of LabVIEW in Chapter 2 and a couple times since—not so much for debugging, but as a convenient way of seeing values inside a NXT program. The LabVIEW Front Panel is not usually used for NXT programs, but it is an essential part of debugging. In this chapter we will get to know the Front Panel better.

Controls Palette

The Front Panel is populated with Controls. When a program's Front Panel window is active, you can view the Controls palette, as shown in Figure 13.1. It consists of a variety of specific palettes, but only a few are of interest to us. In particular the Numeric, Boolean, and Graph palettes are the most useful.

Numeric Controls

Strictly speaking, a Control is an input device, whereas the output devices are Indicators. The Numeric Controls palette (see Figure 13.2) has a few unexciting text-oriented and many interesting graphic-type controls. The method for placement of Controls on a Front Panel is the same as placement of Blocks on the Function Block Diagram.

Place a Knob, a Vertical Pointer, a Meter, and a Tank Control on a blank program's Front Panel in a row, as shown in Figure 13.3. They can be moved around and resized, but for now just line them up and leave their size alone.

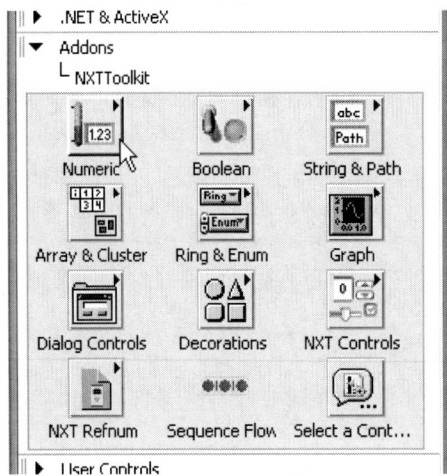

Figure 13.1
NXT Toolkit

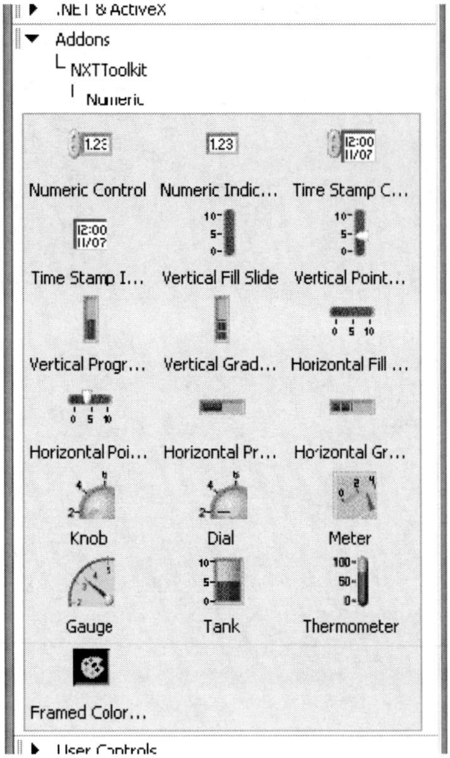

Figure 13.2
Numeric Controls palette

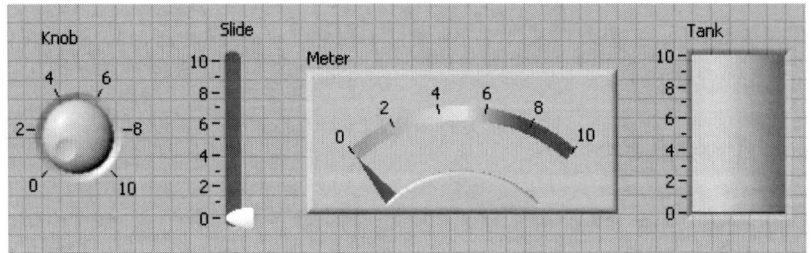

Figure 13.3
Initial Front Panel Placement

Changing Scale Range

Right clicking with the cursor over a Control will bring up a menu, as shown in Figure 13.4. Select Properties to change the characteristics of the Control. For the Knob, we need to change the range of operation from the default 0-to-10 range to a wider –100-to-100 range. To do that, select the Scale tab of the Knob Properties window (see Figure 13.5) and then type new minimum and maximum values.

Repeat these steps to make the Vertical Slide scale also go from –100 to 100 and the Meter and Tank to go from 0 to 100. You should also change each of the Control's labels to Steering, Power, Sound Level, and Light Level. When you are done, the Front Panel should look like Figure 13.6.

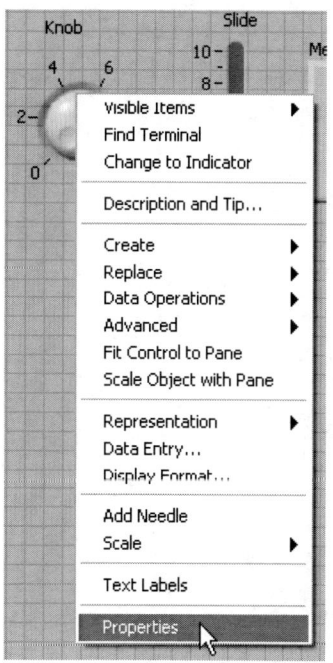

Figure 13.4
Changing Knob Properties

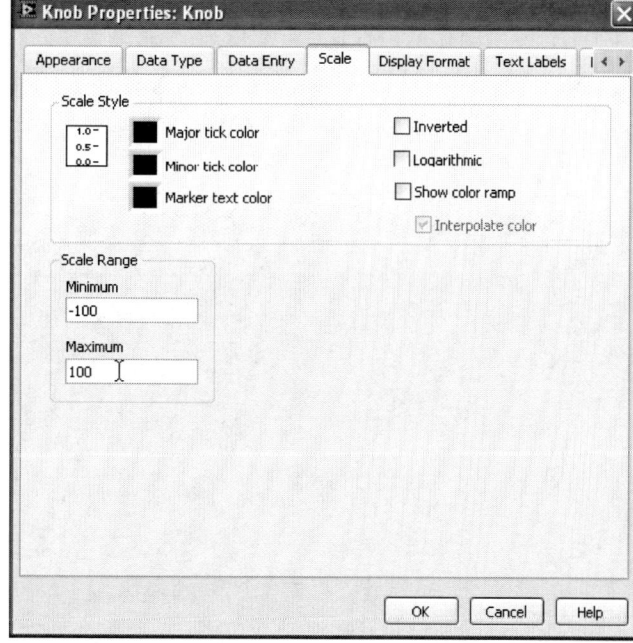

Figure 13.5
Changing Maximum and Minimum

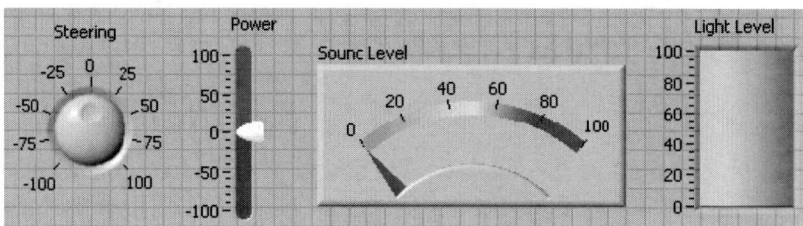

Figure 13.6
Front Panel with proper ranges

Boolean

As you might expect, the Boolean Controls deal with Boolean variables. The palette is shown in Figure 13.7. These Controls graphically represent a variety of different types of switches, pushbuttons, and lights that work with True or False values. Place an OK Button Control on the Front Panel near the Knob control (see Figure 13.8).

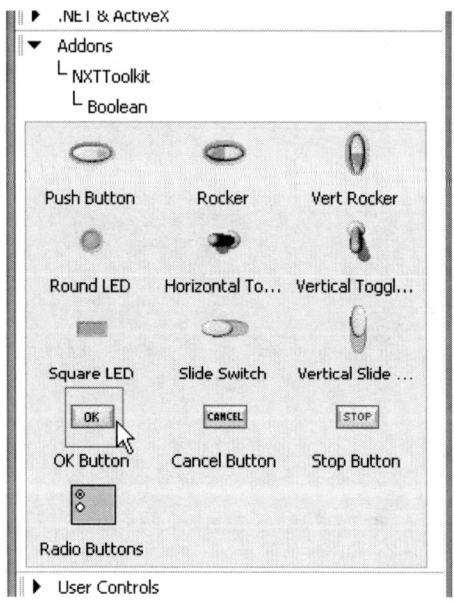

Figure 13.7
Boolean Controls palette

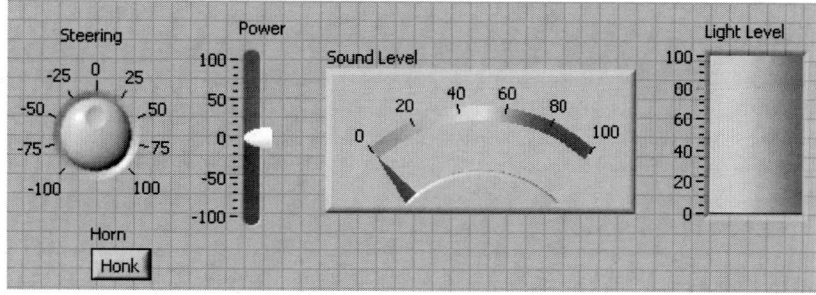

Figure 13.8
Finished Front Panel

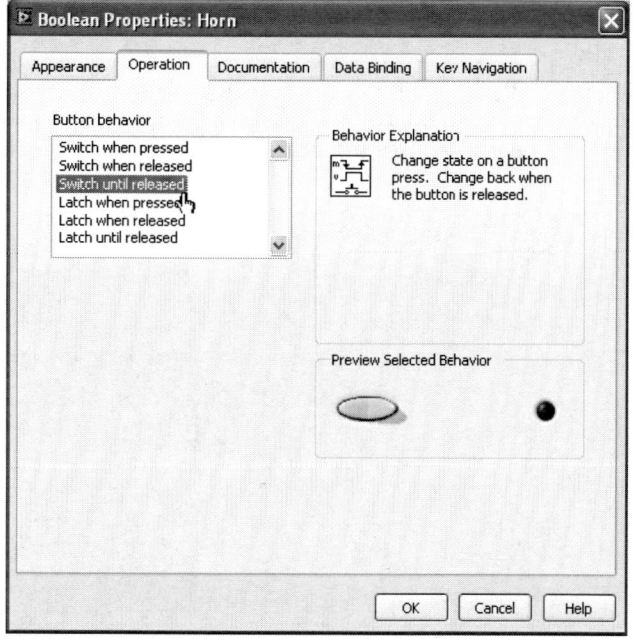

Figure 13.9
Changing Button behavior

We want a button that will output only True while we are holding the left mouse button down with the cursor over the button—much like the Pressed option for the Touch Sensor. By default, the OK Button latches to the True state and stays True until you click it a second time. To change the Operation, go to the OK Buttons Property window and then the Operation tab. Select the "Switch until released" option. You should also change Label to Horn and the Caption to Honk.

Block Diagram

Now look at the Block Diagram. It will already have five blocks, as shown in Figure 13.10. Each block relates to the corresponding Control on the Front Panel. In fact, if you double-click on a block, it will automatically take you to the Control on the Front Panel. Notice that the input Controls have small triangles on their right side, whereas the output Indicators have triangles on the left.

Arrange the blocks and add the other elements shown in Figure 13.11. The program will take the Power and Steering Controls and feed them to a Sync Unlimited block. It will also use the Horn value to select between 400 Hz and 0 Hz for the frequency of a Play Tone. Finally the Light Sensor and Sound Sensor levels will be displayed graphically.

Run the program with the NXT Terminal using the Debug option with either the Tribot or the Elmer mobile robot. While the program is compiling, you will get a few warnings messages, because the default for the Controls is Floating Point but all the

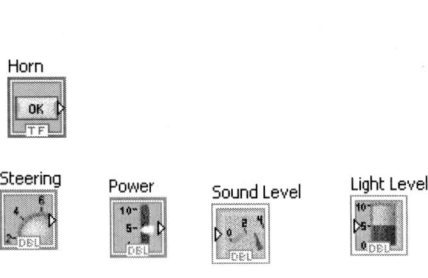

Figure 13.10
Initial Block Diagram

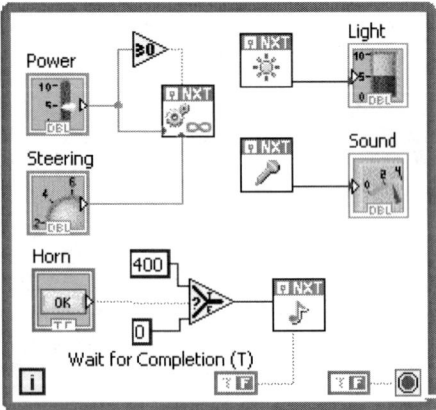

Figure 13.11
Simple Remote

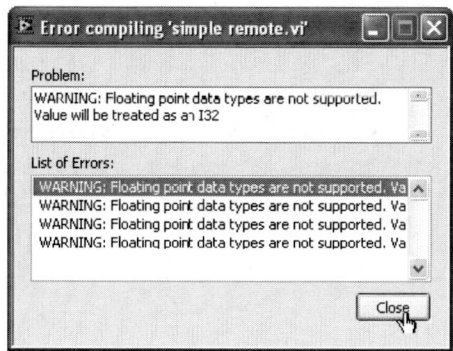

Figure 13.12
Floating Point warning

NXT function blocks are Integer. Just ignore the warnings, because LabVIEW will make the necessary conversions for you.

Eventually the Front Panel will spring to life. If you tap on the Sound Sensor, the meter arrow will move to the red zone. If you wave your fingers in front of the Light Sensor, the blue tank level will move up and down. Now gently push the Power slider up with the mouse to about 25. The robot will slowly start moving forward. Use the Steering knob to drive the robot to the right or left. If you apply negative power, the robot will even move backwards. Running the program with a Bluetooth connection is possible, but the performance will be a littler choppier.

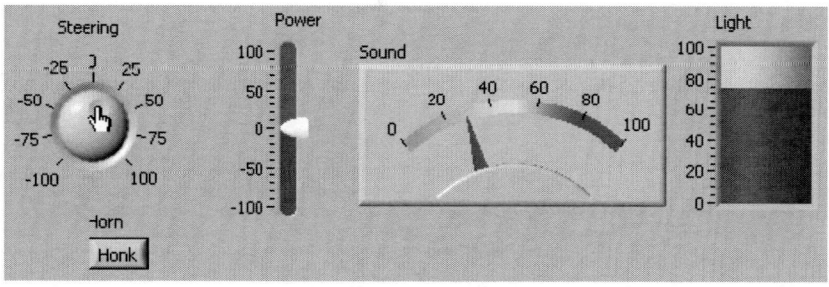

Figure 13.13
Running Simple Remote

Reflections

Debugging can involve a lot more than fixing programs. Programs like the previous one don't even make sense to run in the conventional way. However, the program is still primarily running in the NXT itself and is still limited to small subset of LabVIEW. In the next part of the book I will be showing you how to write LabVIEW programs that run on the PC but still control the NXT using blocks called Direct Commands.

Making a Connection

14

Creativity is the power to connect the seemingly unconnected.
—William Plomer, South African Author

With Direct Commands, the whole world of LabVIEW is available to you, and in the next few chapters I can only touch on its full capability. For the most part I will introduce you to all the NXT Direct Commands and give you enough LabVIEW knowledge to get by. There are many available resources for learning LabVIEW more thoroughly, and many of them are listed in Chapter 21.

NXT Direct Commands

The NXT Direct Commands are also in the Addons section of the Functions palette, as shown in Figure 14.1. Unlike the NXT Toolkit, the general programming blocks for Direct Commands are spread out in the Programming palette of LabVIEW. You will find the familiar structures and functions from the toolkit, along with many new ones.

The Direct Command palette is broken down into groups similar to those in the NXT Toolkit, as can be seen in Figure 14.2. These blocks let you control the NXT hardware for getting input values from sensors or setting output values to turn motors. They also let you control the operating system of the NXT, much as you do with the NXT Terminal.

Connections Palette

The Connections palette is shown in Figure 14.3. There are commands that are common to NXTs that are connected by either USB or Bluetooth, and a few commands that are specific to Bluetooth. The good news is that you probably need only the Create and Destroy blocks for most programs.

Many of the Direct Command blocks do minimal things by themselves, so it makes sense to introduce a pile of them in a single example. Figure 14.4 uses nine different

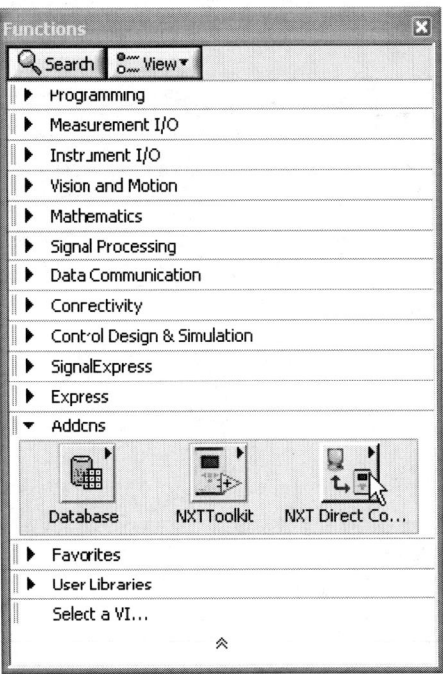

Figure 14.1
Addons Palette

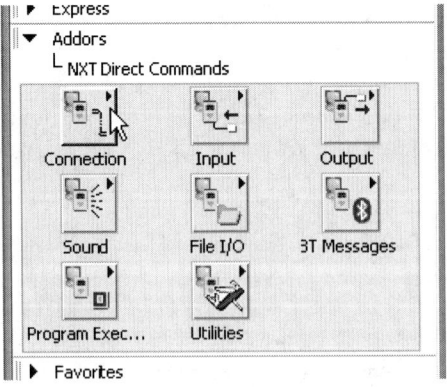

Figure 14.2
NXT Direct Command Palette

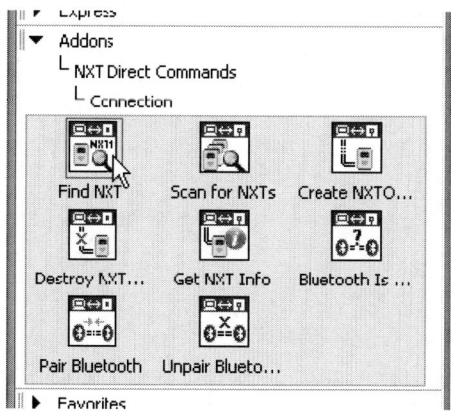

Figure 14.3
Connection Palette

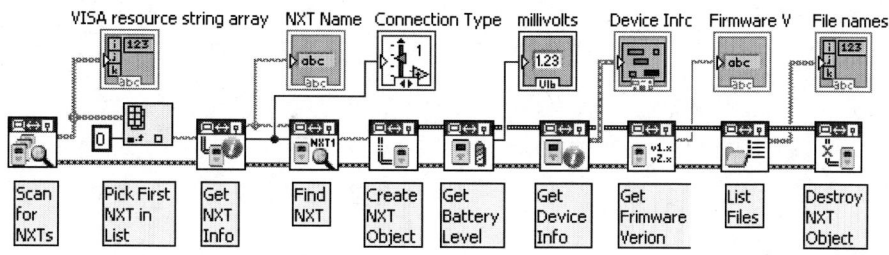

Figure 14.4
Connecting Program Block Diagram

blocks to demonstrate connecting, getting information, and then disconnecting. The blocks are from several of the Direct Command palettes, and the Indicators were produced by simply right-clicking on the appropriate block output and selecting the Create Indicator. The only non-NXT block is the Array Index block that comes from the Array palette. Also notice the daisy-chained yellow wire along the bottom of the blocks that is used to pass along any error status.

The program scans through both the USB and Bluetooth ports for possible NXTs to connect and stores them in an Array of Strings. Then it takes the first NXT in the list (element 0) and gets its Name and Connection Type using the Get NXT Info block. Using that, it actually makes the connection using the Find NXT and Create NXT Object. The NXT Object contains all the information needed for the remaining blocks to perform and will be passed along to them using a daisy chain of wires. There are blocks that get Battery Level, internal Device Information, Firmware Version, and a Listing of Files in the NXT. Finally, the NXT Object is deleted when it is no longer needed, using the Destroy NXT Object.

Scan for NXT

The key ingredient to making a connection to a NXT is getting its VISA resource string. That string is unique to every NXT in the universe, and if you actually wrote a program with a constant VISA resource, it would work only with that one NXT. To get around that, Scan for NXT (see Figure 14.5) will tell you all of the possible NXT VISA resource strings that the PC can see on USB and Bluetooth. It makes sense to set Search Bluetooth to False in situations where there are a lot of NXTs and you want to connect only by USB.

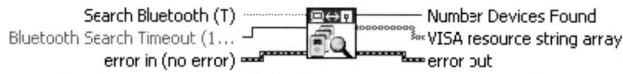

Figure 14.5
Scan for NXT

Get NXT Info

Generally you don't need to acquire the NXT information from the VISA resource string. The Find NXT block that follows does that for you. However, should you need the NXT Name or other connection details; the Get NXT Info block shown in Figure 14.6 can do that.

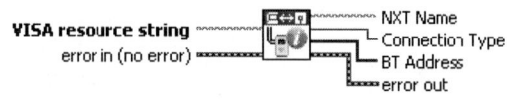

Figure 14.6
Get NXT Info

Find NXT

You should know the Name of your NXT if you changed it, or it will be NXT by default. The Find NXT block (see Figure 14.7) does a Scan for NXT and then looks for an NXT in the Array of resource strings that has the right name with the right connection type. You will need to use this block if you have more than one NXT. Otherwise the Create NXT Object can do all the work.

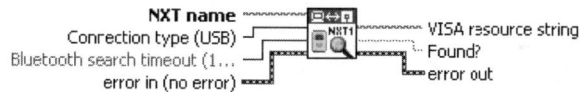

Figure 14.7
Find NXT

Create NXT Object

Usually Create NXT Object will be the first block in your Direct Command program., This block, shown in Figure 14.8, takes the VISA resource string and actually makes the connection to the NXT. The default string causes it to connect to the first NXT it finds on USB. After that, all of the blocks will use the NXT Object to specify which NXT they want to work with.

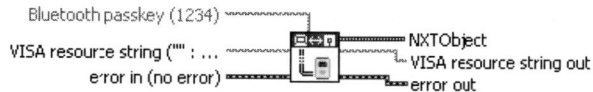

Figure 14.8
Create NXT Object

Get Battery Level

Get Battery Level, found in the Utilities palette, is a simple block, shown in Figure 14.9, that comes in handy just to make sure the link is working. Also, you might not want to run a long-term program if you see that the NXT's batteries are nearly dead. The voltage is in millivolts, so 1V is read as 1000.

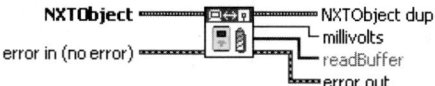

Figure 14.9
Get Battery Level

Get Device Info

As with Get NXT Info, you probably will not need to use Get Device Info (see Figure 14.10), which is also found in the Utilities palette. About the only really useful piece of information the block gives is the amount of available flash memory the NXT has. If you were going to download a large file, you might check to see whether it will fit. The Device Info is a cluster, and you use the Unbundle from the Cluster palette to get to the individual elements.

Figure 14.10
Get Device Info

Get Firmware Version

If, for some reason, you know your program depends on a later version of firmware to work, you can use Get Firmware Version to check the level of the version required. This is probably another block you will never use, but if you need it, it is in the Utilities palette.

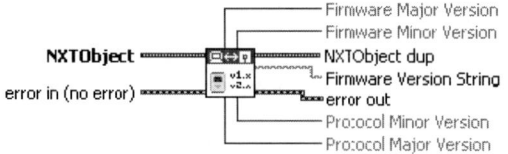

Figure 14.11
Get Firmware Version

List Files

Getting a directory of the files stored in a NXT can be very useful. For example, you might want to check that a data file has been created or a sound file downloaded. List Files (see Figure 14.12) creates an Array of Strings with the names of the files in the NXT. Using the wildcard (*) you can limit the search to all files with a specific extension or to all files with a specific name. Not surprisingly, List Files is in the File I/O palette.

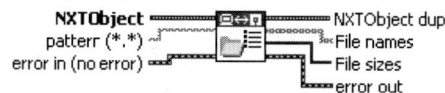

Figure 14.12
List Files

Destroy NXT Object

Destroy NXT Object is shown in Figure 14.13, and it is usually the last block in your Direct Command program. Destroy NXT Object disconnects the NXT and frees up the connection's resources. I haven't noticed anything particularly bad happening if a program doesn't successfully get to a Destroy NXT Object, but it is a good idea to make sure the program flow eventually gets to one.

Figure 14.13
Destroy NXT Object

Front Panel

Figure 14.14 shows how I arranged the various Indicators on the Front Panel. For the first time you will be running a program using the Run button on the LabVIEW toolbar. Remember, these programs run entirely on the PC, and they don't need to be downloaded to the NXT. Scanning Bluetooth is a rather slow process and it will take several seconds for the program to complete. Figure 14.15 shows the output of the program where the same NXT is available on both USB and Bluetooth.

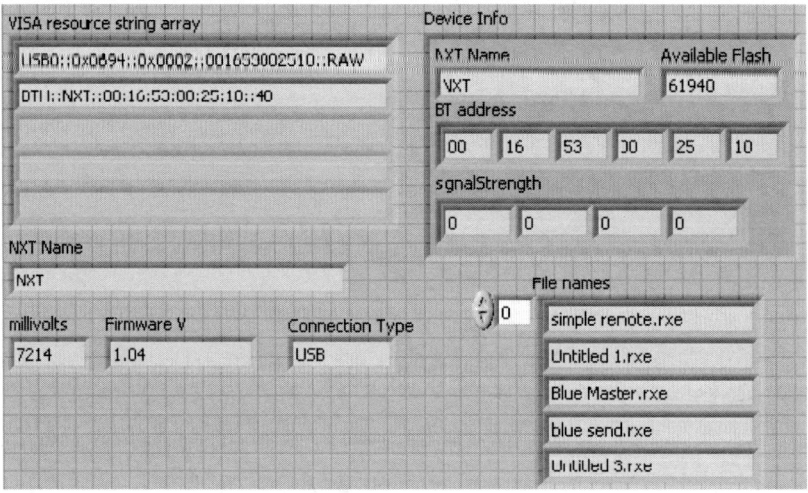

Figure 14.14
Connecting Program Front Panel

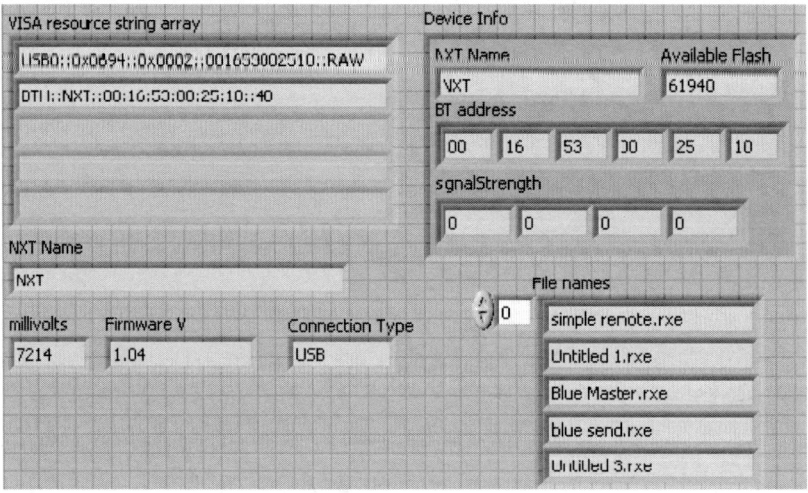

Figure 14.15
Connecting Program Output

Bluetooth Connection Blocks

Bluetooth connections require only a couple of steps. Figure 14.16 shows a program that uses all three Bluetooth Connection blocks to illustrate how they work together. It assumes that the NXT has Bluetooth turned on but was not previously paired or was already unpaired at the start. It never actually Creates a NXT Object, but that is what would follow if you really wanted to do something. Only the True Case is shown, because the False Case just passes the NXT Object and Error through unchanged.

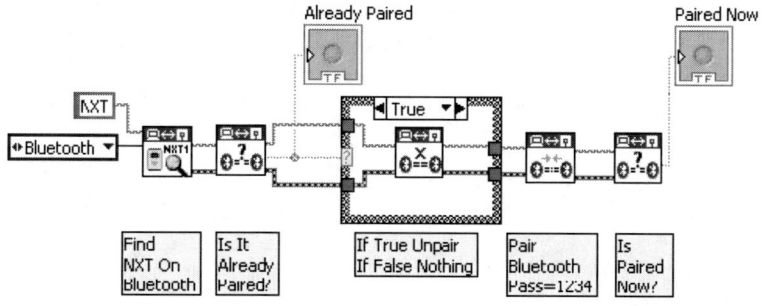

Figure 14.16
Pair Bluetooth Program

Is Paired

Is Paired (see Figure 14.17) tells you whether a NXT is already paired. It simply outputs a Boolean that will be True if the NXT and PC are paired. Unpair Bluetooth (see Figure 14.18) will break any pairing that exists. Finally, Pair Bluetooth, shown in Figure 14.19, will pair a NXT using a passkey that is provided as a String.

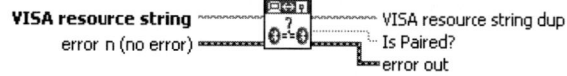

Figure 14.17
Is Paired

When you run the program for the first time, the NXT should not be paired and the Pair Bluetooth will attempt to pair it. The NXT will show the display in Figure 14.20, and you should quickly press the Enter button on the NXT to accept the pairing. The

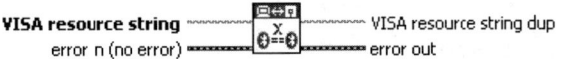

Figure 14.18
Unpair Bluetooth

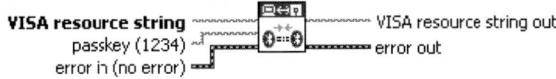

Figure 14.19
Pair Bluetooth

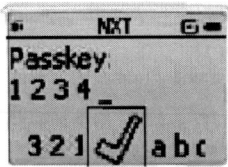

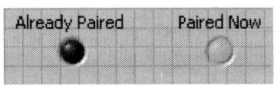

Figure 14.20
Passkey Exchange

Figure 14.21
First Run with Unpaired NXT

status lights on the Front Panel will look like Figure 14.21 when the program has finished.

When you run the program a second time, the Front Panel will look like Figure 14.22, because the NXT is already paired at the start. The NXT will be unpaired and then paired again, so you will need to press the Enter button on the NXT again.

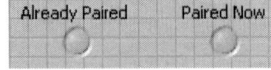

Figure 14.22
Second Run with Pairing

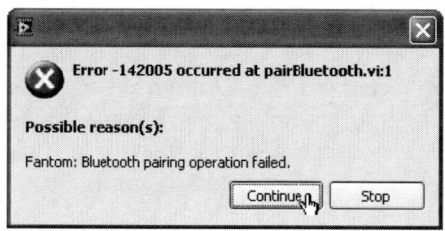

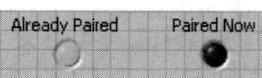

Figure 14.23
Error with Timeout

Figure 14.24
Second Run without Pairing

Now run the program a third time, but this time, *do not* press the Enter button on the NXT. After a while, the process will time out and you will get the error message shown in Figure 14.23. This error means the pairing failed; therefore, the NXT will remain unpaired, as shown in Figure 14.24.

Rename NXT

Rename NXT, shown in Figure 14.25, is a mostly self-explanatory block from the Utility palette. A NXT can have a name of up to 15 characters long. The name change is permanent till you change it again with another Rename NXT or a tool such as the NXT Terminal (see Figure 14.26). Generally, unless you have more than one NXT and you need to distinguish between them, it is better to stick with the default NXT.

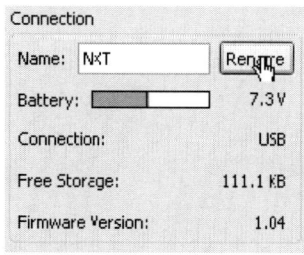

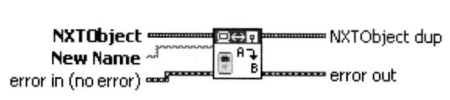

Figure 14.25
Rename NXT

Figure 14.26
Rename in NXT Terminal

Reflections

If all you have is one NXT and it is connected with USB, you need only Create NXT Object and Destroy NXT Object. The other blocks allow you to manage multiple NXTs and use wireless connections. Now, let's look at the cool stuff we can stick between these two blocks to make the NXT do what we want by remote control.

Up, Down, and All Around

15

The computer is no better than its program.
—*Elting Elmore Morison, author Men, Machines, and Modern Times*

Among other things, a computer's operating system keeps track of files and executes programs. The NXT has a rather simple operating system, and there are Direct Command blocks that allow you to remotely control it. You have already seen how to get a directory of files on a NXT in the previous chapter. Everything you have been doing with the NXT Terminal can be done automatically from a program on the PC using the following blocks.

Controlled Data Logging

Remember the little Data Logging program from Chapter 5? In case you don't, it was the program shown in Figure 15.1. It stores 10 samples of the Light Sensor value into a text file called Data.txt. Because there is a one-second interval between samples, it takes 10 seconds to run.

Figure 15.2 is a Direct Command program that downloads the Datalog program itself, tells the NXT to run it, waits until it is done, uploads the data file, and then displays its contents on the Front Panel. It does all that with only four new Direct Command blocks. In fact, it does all that with only eight blocks total.

Before you can run the program, you need to get the Datalog.rxe file into the root directory of your PC's hard drive. You accomplish that by doing a Compile and Download of the Datalog program and then Uploading the Datalog.rxe file from the NXT to the PC, all using the NXT Terminal. Then you can Delete the .rxe file from the NXT if you want, because the Control Datalog program will download a copy to it anyway.

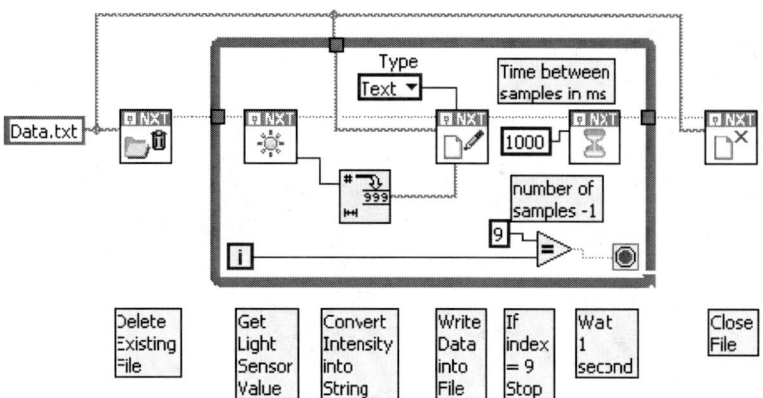

Figure 15.1
Data Logging Program

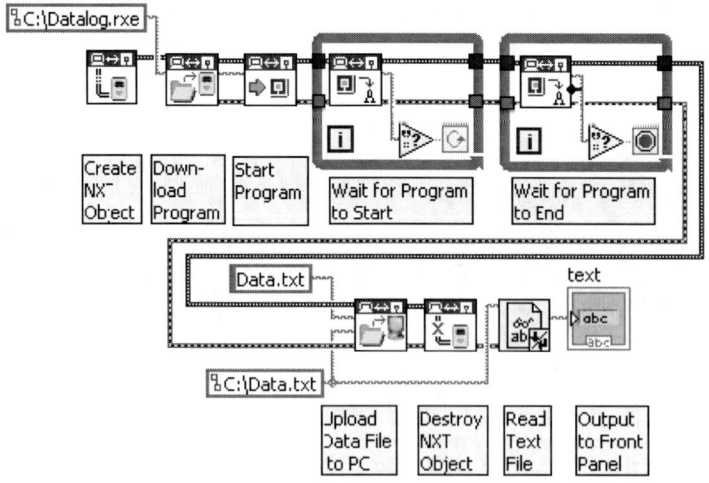

Figure 15.2
Control Datalog Program Block Diagram

Download File

The first new block in the Control Datalog program is Download File, shown in Figure 15.3, from the File IO palette. The only tricky part of using the block is creating the File Path for the file to be downloaded. LabVIEW has a pile of Function Blocks that deal with creating file paths in the File I/O palette, but the easiest way is just to create a File Path Constant. You right-click on the File Path Constant and select "Browse for Path…:" from the menu that pops up, as shown in Figure 15.4. Just select the Datalog.rxe file out of the root directory. This would all work if the file had been in a subdirectory of the PC as well, but doing it this way keeps the path simple.

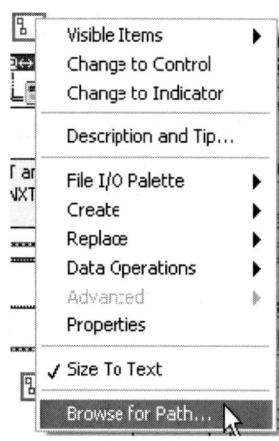

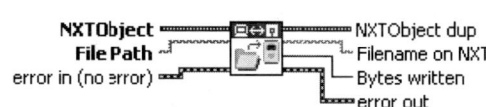

Figure 15.3
Download File

Figure 15.4
Creating File Path

Start Program

Download File conveniently tells you the name of the file it just downloaded as it appears on the NXT. Basically, it is what you would expect, with all the path junk from the PC stripped off. This String can be fed directly to the Start Program (see Figure 15.5) to tell the NXT to run it. The Start Program is found in the Program Execution palette.

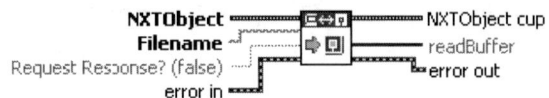

Figure 15.5
Start Program

Get Current Program Name

It might take some time for the NXT to get around to running the program, and then it will take about 10 seconds for it to complete. Get Current Program, shown in Figure 15.6 and also available from the Program Execution palette, tells you the Program Name of the current program in a String. If no program is running, the string will be Empty. First, Control Datalog waits till the Program Name String is not Empty, meaning that the program has started. Then it waits till the String becomes Empty, signifying that the program has finished. The Empty String block (see Figure 15.7) is found in the Comparison palette.

Figure 15.6
Get Current Program Name

Figure 15.7
Empty String

Upload File

A file named Data.txt should have been created for us to upload with the Upload File block, shown in Figure 15.8. Just as with the downloaded File Path, we need to specify where on the PC to store the Uploaded file. You might think you only needed to supply the path, but you will also need to specify the whole filename the file will have on the PC as well. That way you can easily change the name of the file. As before, you create a Constant Destination File Path and right-click on it to select "Browse for Path...".

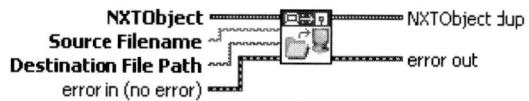

Figure 15.8
Upload File

Read Text File

You could do just about anything with the file at this point, but I thought it would be nice to display the text contents on the Front Panel without using a separate program such as Notepad. Read Text File (see Figure 15.9) can be found in the Programming File I/O palette. It is a simple matter of providing the exact same filename that we provided to the Upload File to read the file into a text String. You can see the contents of my Data.txt in Figure 15.10.

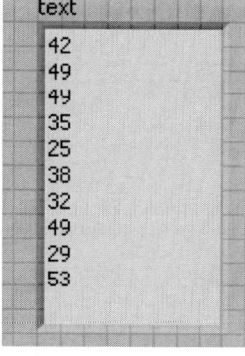

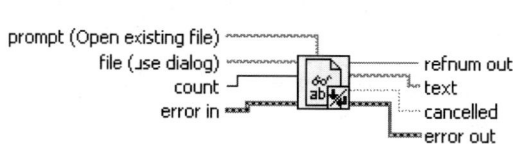

Figure 15.9
Read Text File

Figure 15.10
Control Datalog Program Front Panel

Stop, Delete, and Defrag

Stop Program, Delete File, and Defrag Files are blocks that don't really need examples to understand. Stop Program, shown in Figure 15.11, is just like pressing the Stop button on the NXT. Whatever program is running on the NXT it will be stopped.

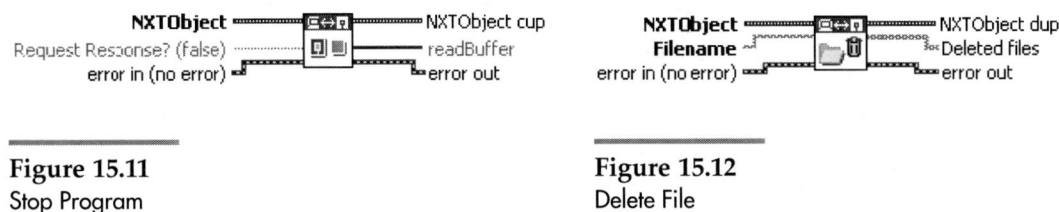

Figure 15.11
Stop Program

Figure 15.12
Delete File

Delete File, shown in Figure 15.12, deletes the specified file on the NXT. The specified file can contain the wildcard (*) for either the name or the extension, so more than one file can be deleted at a time.

Defrag Files (see Figure 15.13) deserves a little explanation. The file system in the NXT stores files in continuous blocks of memory. As you make and delete files on the NXT, it creates holes in the memory. The NXT tries to fit new files into the holes if the holes are big enough. However, after a long time, there can be a lot of free memory, but it is spread out over a lot of little holes. Defrag Files moves the files around to create a single big hole.

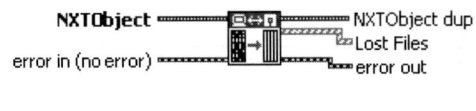

Figure 15.13
Defrag Files

Reflections

Believe it or not, we have covered all of the File- and Program-related Direct Command blocks. At this point you could probably write your own version of the NXT Terminal if you really wanted. However, I'll bet you really want to look at sensors and control motors from the PC instead.

Making Sense

16

The only way to make sense out of change is to plunge into it, move with it, and join the dance.—Alan Watts

NXT sensors can be broken down into two categories: those read with an analog-to-digital converter and those that exchange data with a Low-Speed (LS) Communications bus. The bus is actually an I²C bus which stands for Inter-Integrated Circuit. If you stick with the Touch, Sound, Light, and Distance sensors that came with the NXT, you don't need to worry about the distinction. However, if you want to work with Legacy or after-market sensors, you will need to know the details. The NXT Rotation sensor is in a whole category by itself. Because it is so integrated with the motor, it is actually read with an Output block.

Charting Program

Charting is a basic Direct Command demonstration program to display NXT sensor levels over time. The sensor shown in Figure 16.1 happens to be the Light Sensor, but it could be any of the NXT Sensors. The Chart Indicator itself is from the Express Graph palette, and it keeps track of 100 data points by itself. As written, the program will get sensor values as fast as possible, but you could introduce a delay by adding a Wait block from the Timing palette into the While Loop.

The Front Panel of Chart looks like Figure 16.2 when it is running. By default, the amplitude or *y*-axis will automatically scale itself. This is convenient, but it can also lead to a rather difficult display to watch. You can fix the range by going to the Scales tab in the Chart's Properties menu, unchecking Autoscale, and entering minimum and maximum values of 0 and 100. The program works with a Bluetooth, but you really need a USB connection for it to perform well.

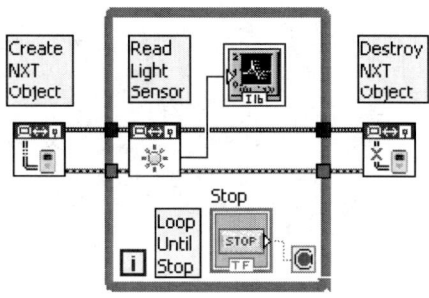

Figure 16.1
Charting Block Diagram

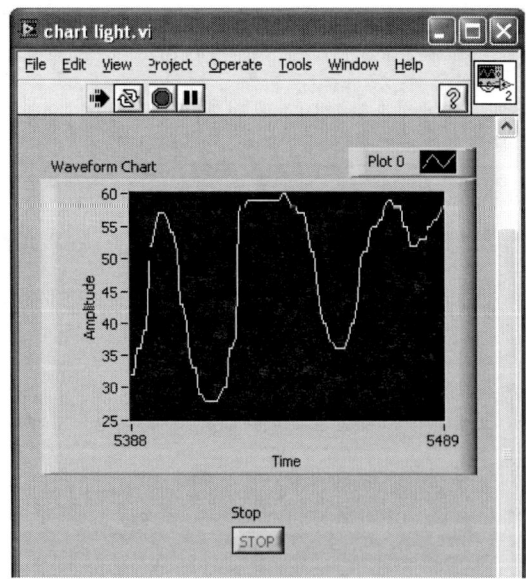

Figure 16.2
Charting Light Front Panel

Read NXT Sensors

The four main Read NXT Sensor blocks are illustrated in Figure 16.3 to Figure 16.6. There is no particular difference between these blocks, and I'll assume you would know how to substitute any of these for the sensor in the Chart Program. About the only thing you would need to change is the scale of the chart, since the sensors have different ranges of operation.

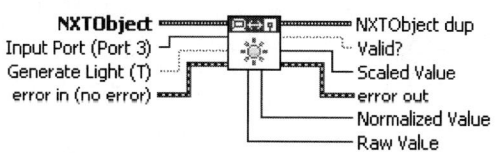

Figure 16.3
Read Light Sensor

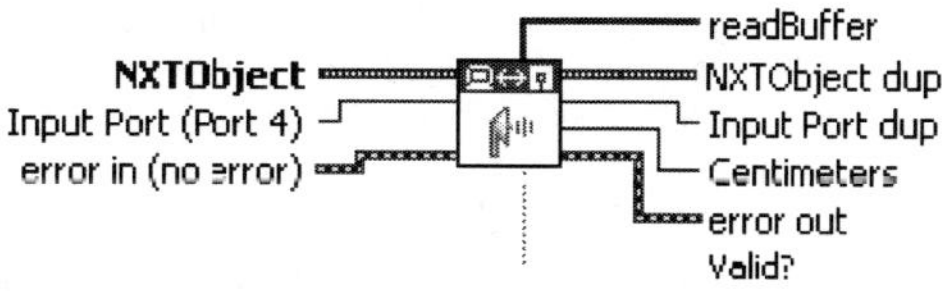

Figure 16.4
Read Distance Sensor

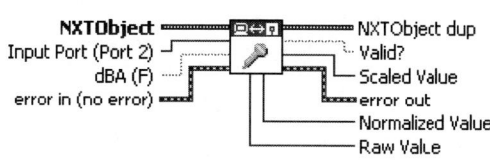

Figure 16.5
Read Sound Sensor

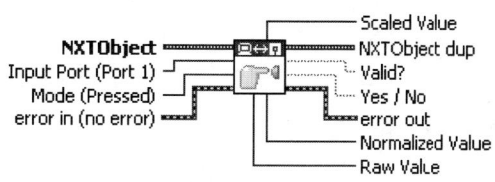

Figure 16.6
Read Touch Sensor

Other Inputs

You might have noticed the lack of Legacy Sensor blocks in the Input palette, but you can still read these sensors with Direct Commands. All the Legacy Sensors use the analog-to-digital converter for input. I'll assume you don't actually have a Legacy Sensor, so I'll demonstrate using the NXT Light Sensor, which also uses the analog-to-digital-converter. The Three Ways program, shown in Figure 16.7, reads the Light Sensor using the Read Sensor, the Get Input, and the Read Light Sensor blocks.

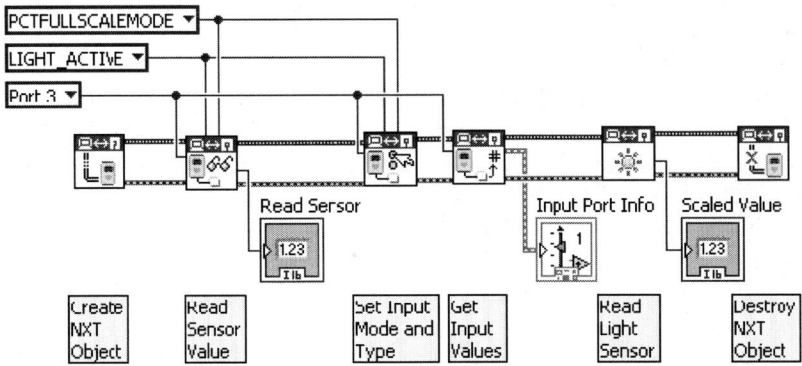

Figure 16.7
Three Ways to Read

Read Sensor

Read Sensor (see Figure 16.8) is the single-block way to read a sensor. The Sensor Type and Mode define the way the sensor should be read, and Table 16.1 shows the values for three of the NXT Sensors and the four Legacy Sensors. Just create constants for these inputs and select the appropriate values.

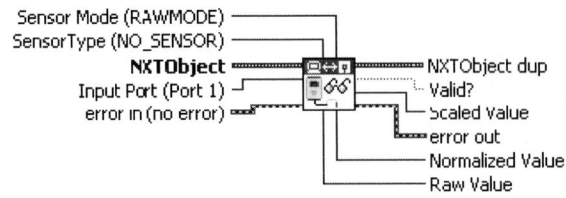

Figure 16.8
Read Sensor

Table 16.1 *Sensor Information*

Sensor	Mode	Type
NXT Touch	BOOLEANMODE	SWITCH
NXT Sound	PCTFULLSCALEMODE	SOUND_DB or SOUND_DBA
NXT Light	PCTFULLSCALEMODE	LIGHT_ACTIVE or LIGHT_INACTIVE
Legacy Touch	BOOLEANMODE	SWITCH
Legacy Light	PCTFULLSCALEMODE	REFLECTION
Legacy Angle	ANGLESTEPMODE	ANGLE
Legacy Temperature	CELSIUSMODE or FAHRENHEITMODE	TEMPERATURE

Set Input Mode

An alternative to the single-block Read Sensor is the Set Input Mode (see Figure 16.9) in conjunction with Get Input Values. This method is a little more efficient because once the NXT knows the Sensor Type and Mode on an Input Port, it really doesn't need to be retold over and over again. The other methods redundantly keep checking the Type and Mode to make sure they haven't changed. This block is particularly important for using the Low-Speed Communications port, as we will see subsequently.

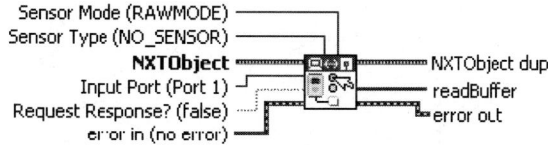

Figure 16.9
Set Input Mode

Get Input Values

Once you have configured the Input Port, you can get the current reading with Get Input Values, as shown in Figure 16.10. You actually get a lot more than just the value, as shown in Figure 16.11. Unbundle the Input Port Info and pick off whatever value you need. For example, to get the Scaled value, add the Unbundle by Name block from the Cluster, Class & Variant palette and then select the Scaled element.

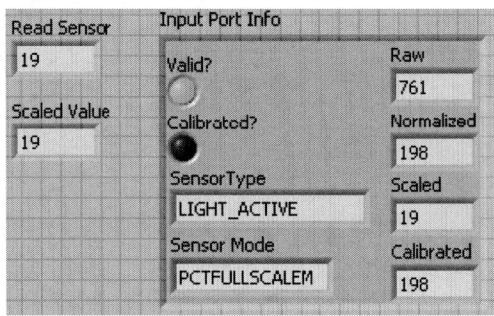

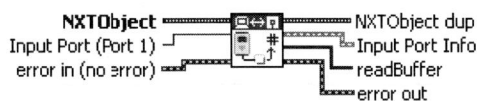

Figure 16.10
Get Input Values

Figure 16.11
Three Ways Front Panel

Counting Modes

By using the Type and Mode inputs you can create an interesting new sensor. Either the NXT or Legacy Touch Sensors can be configured to tell you the number of times they have been bumped instead of just the fact that they had been bumped. You set the Type to SWITCH and the Mode to either PERIODCOUNTERMODE or TRANSI-TIONCNTMODE, as illustrated by the little demo program shown in Figure 16.12. In period counting, every time you press and release the Touch Switch the Scaled Value will count up by one. In transition counting, just pressing or releasing will count up. The only reason the count starts with zero is the effect of the Clear Input Value block at the beginning of the program.

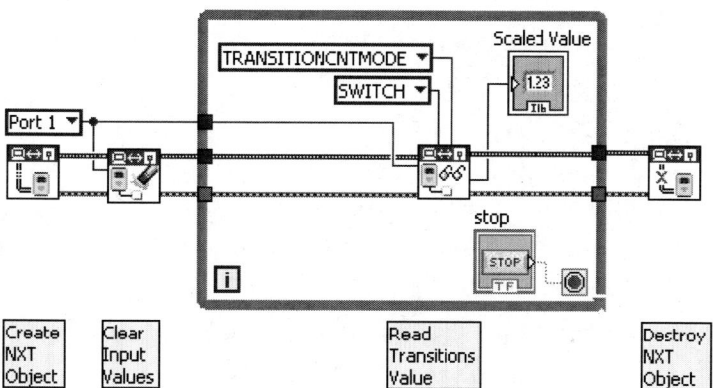

Figure 16.12
Counting Program

Clear Input Value

The counting and angle modes retain values between calls, so they give you the accumulated amount. You might want to reset the counts while a program is running. The Clear Input Value block shown in Figure 16.13, sets the value to zero.

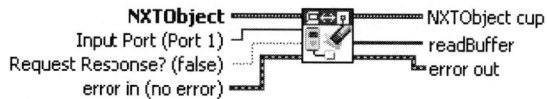

Figure 16.13
Clear Input Value

Low-Speed Communications

Sophisticated sensors, such as the Ultrasonic Distance Sensor, actually have their own microprocessors inside and use a Low-Speed (LS) Communications bus to talk to the NXT. The LSComm program, shown in Figure 16.14, reads the Product ID bytes from the Ultrasonic Distance Sensor as an example. There are two Types of LS sensors—those that require a 9V power supply (e.g., the Ultrasonic) and those that don't. Multiple sensors could be connected to the same input port if they used only LS Communications. All sensors have a unique address to tell them apart, and the

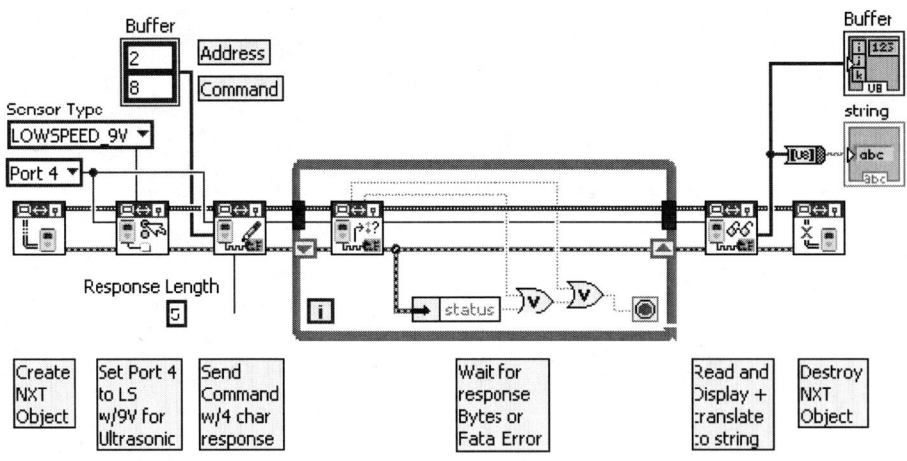

Figure 16.14
LSComm

Ultrasonic Sensor has the address 2. Unfortunately, the physical connector scheme on the NXT doesn't allow you to connect more than one sensor to a port at a time.

LS Write

The sensor address (2) for the Ultrasonic and the command value (8) that requests the Product ID are elements in an array sent to the sensor using the LS Write block (see Figure 16.15). Notice that the LS Write block also has an input for Response Length. This is the length in bytes that will be automatically read from the LS immediately after the write. It is very common in LS communication for a write to be followed with a read—for example, a command to take a new reading and a one-byte reply to get the value.

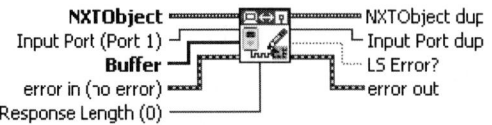

Figure 16.15
LS Write

LS Get Status

The While Loop causes the program to wait for the LS communications to finish or fail, whichever comes first. LS Get Status (see Figure 16.16) has a variety of status outputs, but if everything goes right, the Status element of the Status bundle will become True when the response bytes are ready to be read.

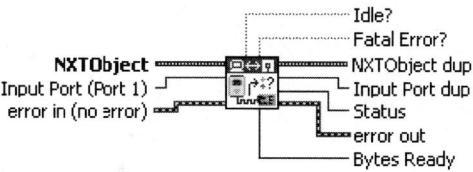

Figure 16.16
LS Get Status

LS Read

LS Read (see Figure 16.17) will read the bytes that have been received on the LS Communications bus. In this case there will be five bytes; one each for the letters L, E, G, O, and one with a value of zero. Figure 16.18 shows the Front Panel after the program has run.

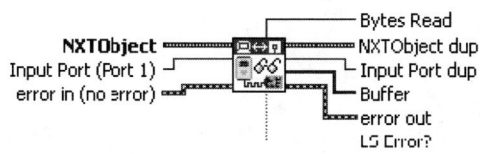

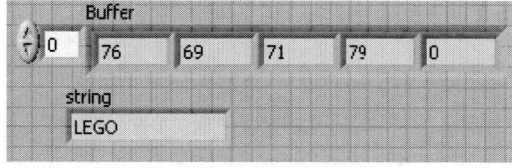

Figure 16.17
LS Read

Figure 16.18
LSComm Front Panel

NXT Rotation Sensor

The NXT Rotation Sensor is actually in the Output palette, because it is so integrated into the NXT Motor. The Read Rotation program in Figure 16.19 clears the angle with a Reset Motor block and then repeatedly reads the angle with the Get Output Values block. There are actually nine different values (see Figure 16.20) returned by

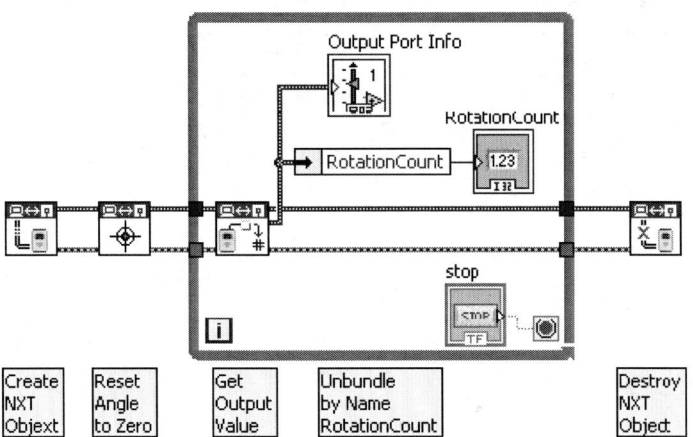

Figure 16.19
Read Rotation

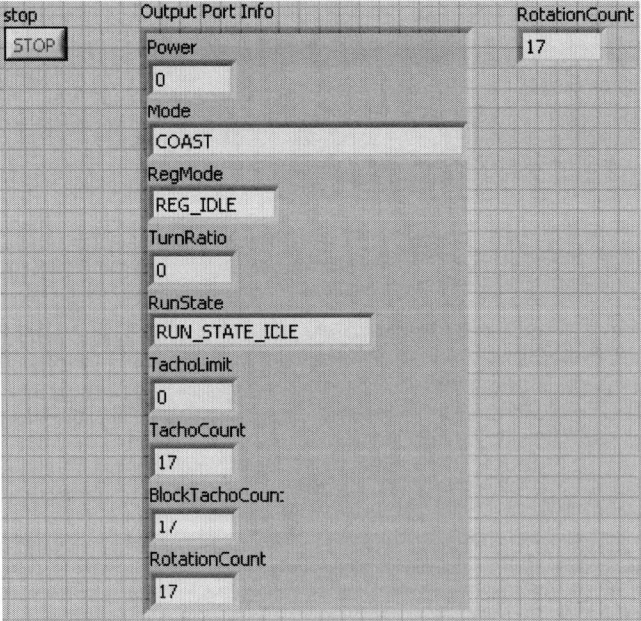

Figure 16.20
Read Rotation Front Panel

the block, but only the RotationCount behaves like the rotation value we are familiar with. In case you haven't unbundled before, Figure 16.21 shows how to select the RotationCount element from the Unbundle by Name block output.

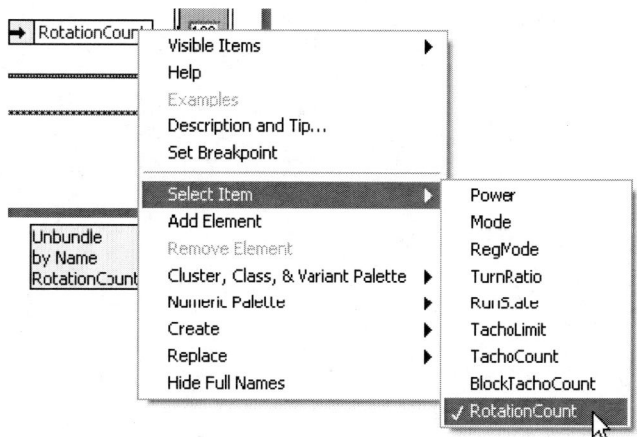

Figure 16.21
Unbundle RotationCount

Reset Motor

Reset Motor (see Figure 16.22) just sets the RotationCount value to zero for the specified Output Port.

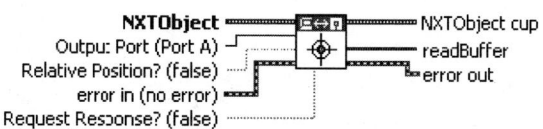

Figure 16.22
Reset Motor

Get Output Values

Get Output Values, shown in Figure 16.23, returns a variety of status information about the specified Output Port in a bundle named Output Port Info. We will get to the meanings of some of these values in more detail in the following chapter. There are three count values in the bundle, as can be seen in Figure 16.20, but the RotationCount value behaves like the Rotation value used in the NXT Blocks.

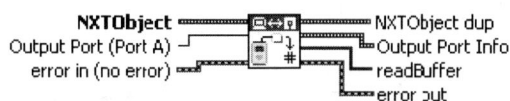

Figure 16.23
Get Output Values

Cage Monitor

I've got a little pet mouse named Mini Fig. I hooked her cage up to record a day's worth of activity using the NXT to measure her cage temperature, light level, sound level, and the angle of the running wheel. The four readings are displayed with 100 samples per hour resolution.

The Legacy Rotation sensor is used to monitor the running wheel, because the NXT Rotation Sensor has too much friction for the job. I replaced the spindle of the wheel with a LEGO axle and extended it outside the cage to the Rotation Sensor, along with the other three sensors and the NXT. The Legacy Temperature Sensor was used to measure the ambient temperature just outside the cage. The NXT has the rechargeable battery pack and is plugged into the wall at all times. Otherwise, it would not have enough power to stay on for such a long time.

The program in Figure 16.24 looks a lot more complicated than it actually is. Let's focus on a few parts to make it easier to understand. First of all, I want to record enough data to accurately measure the activity, so I decided to record 100 samples per hour. The index for the data arrays is generated from the time of day using the blocks shown in Figure 16.25. I'll spare you the detailed arithmetic, but every 36 seconds the index goes up by one. The result is an index that counts from 0 to 2399 over a day, and that way the index value is easily related to the time of day in 24-hour military time. For example, 1250 is half past noon. Within the 36 second interval, the value is updated many times just to give the display a more real-time effect.

I've isolated just the Light Sensor's flow in Figure 16.26. The values are displayed using a Graph Indicator which, unlike the Chart Indicator we have been using up to this point, requires an external data storage array. The 2400-element array is initialized

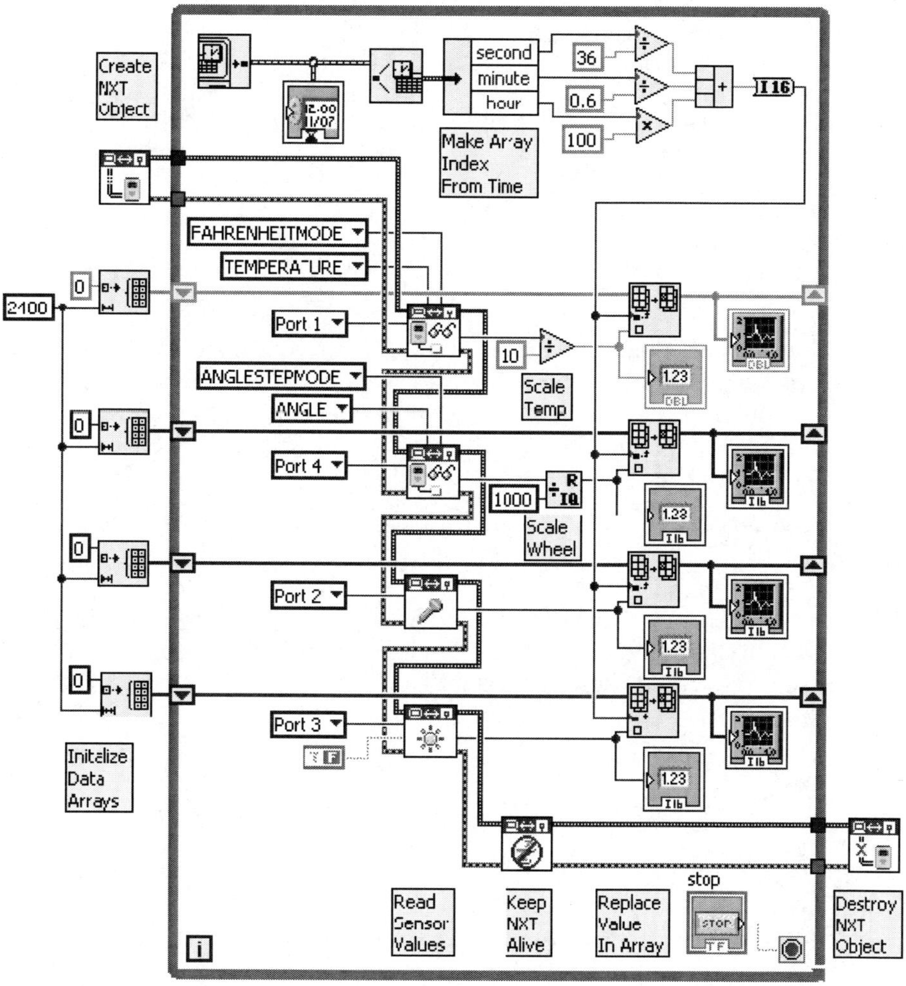

Figure 16.24
Cage Monitor

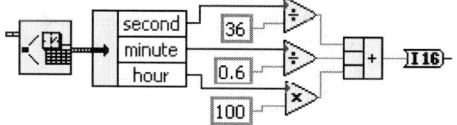

Figure 16.25
Making Time Index

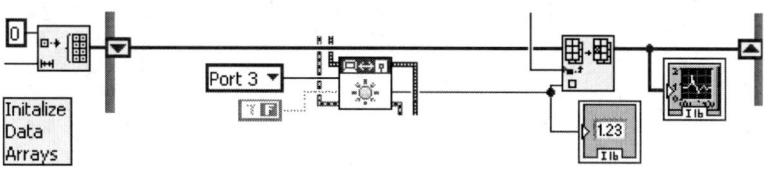

Figure 16.26
Light Sensor's Flow

to zero at the beginning of the program. The current measurement value is numerically displayed and is also replaced in the data array with every cycle of the While Loop. That occurs as often as the PC can execute the loop, so the values will be changing on the Front Panel much more often than they are actually recorded.

Keep Alive

There is one new Direct Command block in the program as well. The Keep Alive shown in Figure 16.27 keeps the NXT from going into Sleep Mode. The program is designed to be left running for days at a time, and we don't want the NXT to sleep on the job.

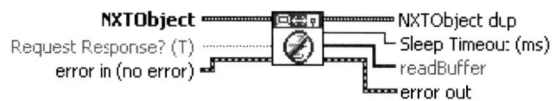

Figure 16.27
Keep Alive

Analysis

The Front Panel of the program after running for a whole day is shown in Figure 16.28. There are several things worth noting in the data. If you look closely at the temperature you can see some little spikes that I've isolated in Figure 16.29 and marked A and B. These are caused by the heating system of my house turning on for about 10 minutes to maintain the room temperature. The wheel's angle is divided by 1000 and I plot the remainder, because I'm only interested in when Mini runs and not how far. Inactivity will look like points A and B in Figure 16.30, where the wheel's value didn't change for long periods of time. Sound level picks up not only Mini's activity, but also the

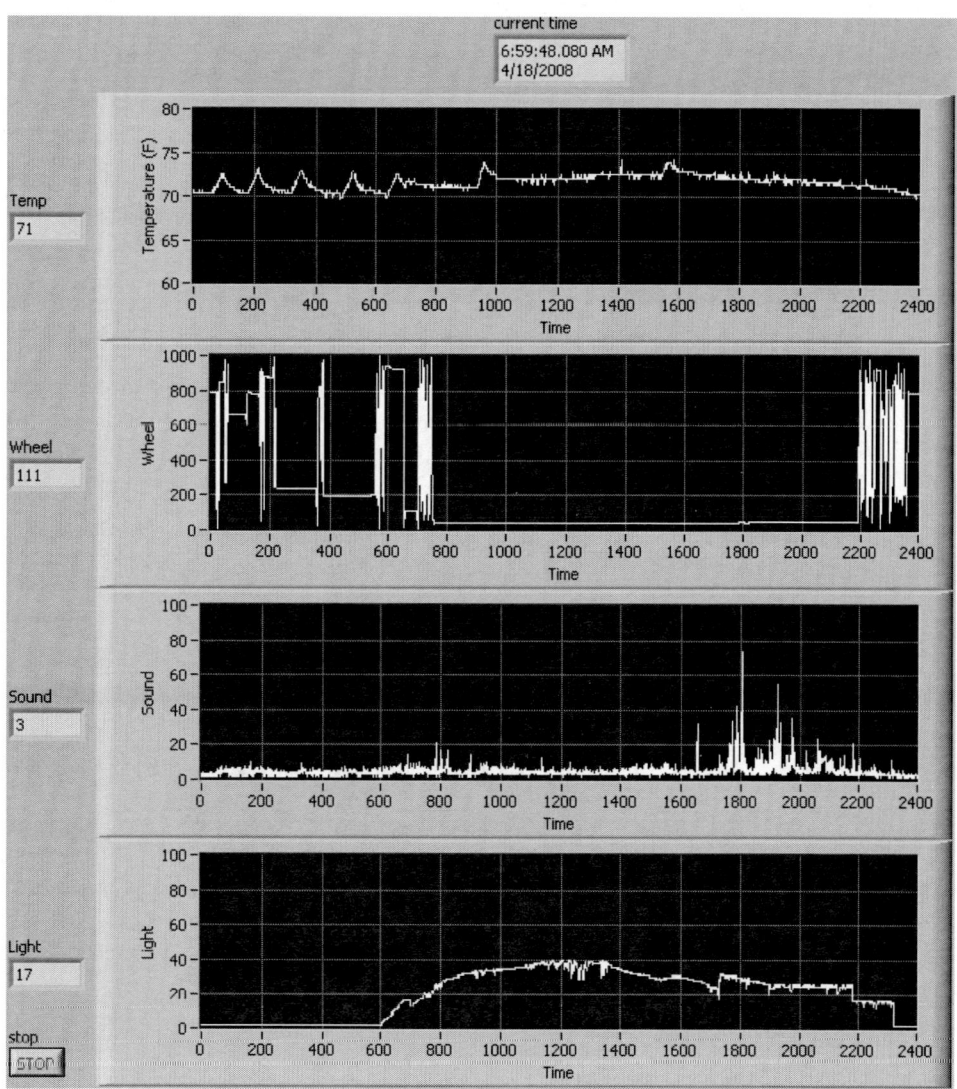

Figure 16.28
One Day

sound of my family, as can be seen in Figure 16.31, where the noise reaches a peak
around dinner time at 1800 or 6:00 PM. Finally, the light level shows the sunrise at A,
some clouds passing over at B past noon, and the switching on of the room lights at
C in Figure 16.32.

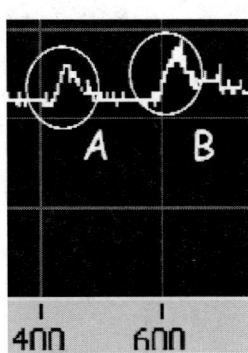

Figure 16.29
Heating System Affecting Temperature

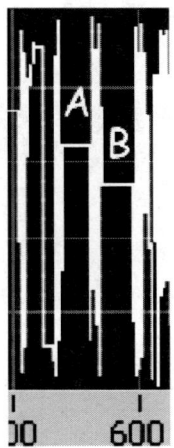

Figure 16.30
Periods of Inactivity

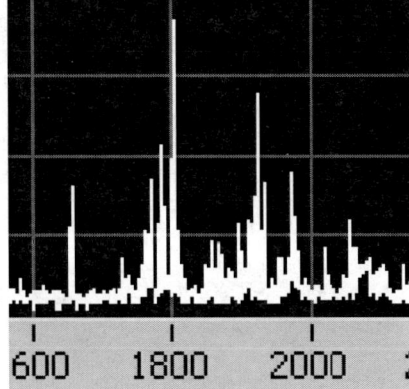

Figure 16.31
Family Noise from Outside Cage

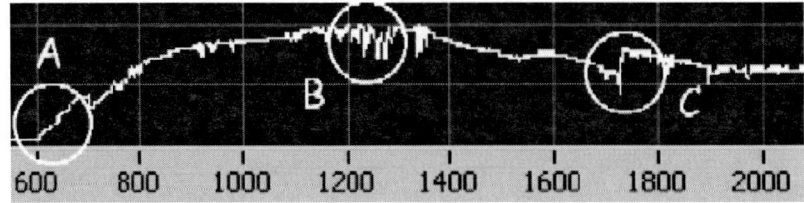

Figure 16.32
Daylight Level in Cage

Exporting Graphs

If you right-click on a graph, a menu like the one in Figure 16.33 will pop up. From this menu you can pick to Export the Image so that it can be included in a written report. With your word processor program running, Figure 16.34 shows the Export Simplified Image window that allows you to Export the graph as a bitmap, and Figure 16.35 shows the result of pasting it in a document.

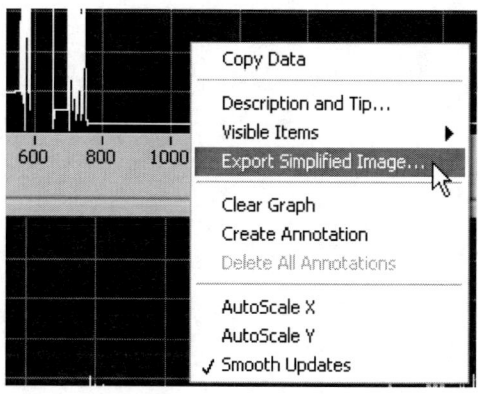

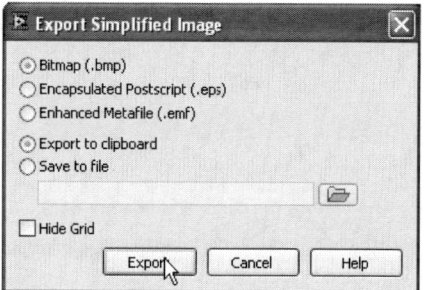

Figure 16.33
Right Clicking on a Graph While the Program is Running

Figure 16.34
Exporting the Graph

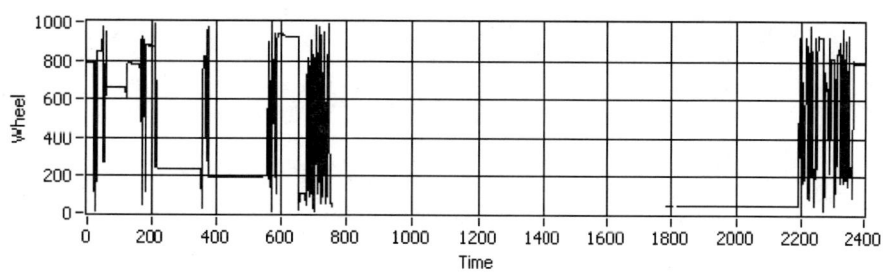

Figure 16.35
Pasted Graph in Document

Reflections

You now know how to read all the sensors using Direct Commands. I've shown you how to use it to record useful data from an experiment. Now let's turn to the output end of the NXT and control the motors and make some sounds.

Sound Out

17

Turn on, tune in and drop out.—Timothy Leary

There are only two ways to create output with Direct Commands—you can either turn on motors or make sounds. A much wider range of motor controls are available from NXT programs than are obtainable with Direct Commands. On the other hand, the Sound palette consists of pretty much the same three blocks.

Motors

We have already learned about Reset Motor and Get Output State from the previous chapter. They really have more to do with the Rotation Sensor than the motor. The Direct Commands are limited to control of one motor at a time. The Motor Control program shown in Figure 17.1 and Figure 17.2 shows the basic control of a NXT output using Direct Commands.

Motor Unlimited

Motor Unlimited (see Figure 17.3) is the workhorse of the Output palette. The same block is used to control Lamps and Legacy Motors. Although it has a Direction input, making the Power input negative will also reverse the motor. The block turns the Output Port on until a Stop Motor turns it off. With Direct Commands, that really means turned on, because you have to turn the NXT completely off to turn off an output if you don't send it a Stop Motor.

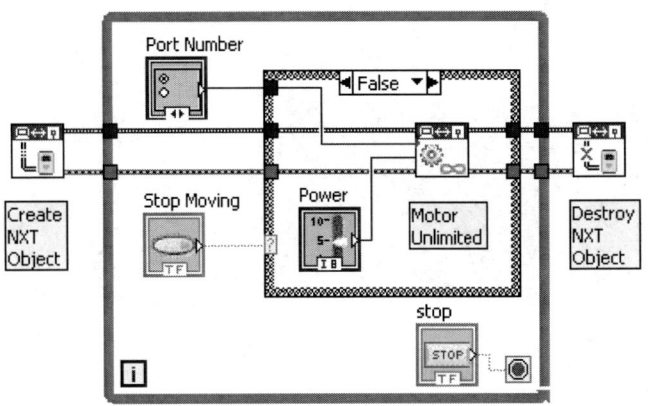

Figure 17.1
Motor Control (False Case)

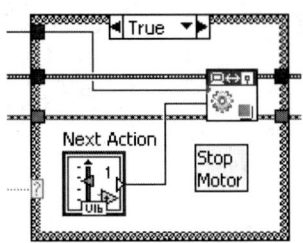

Figure 17.2
Motor Control (True Case)

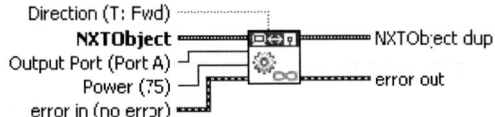

Figure 17.3
Motor Unlimited

Stop Motor

Stop Motor turns off the Output Port with the option of either braking or coasting. Braking causes the motor to stop abruptly and the motor will resist further turning. Coasting simply removes the power so the motor will slowly coast to a stop.

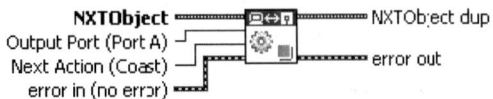

Figure 17.4
Stop Motor

Radio Buttons

The program uses Radio Buttons to select the Port Number. The control is in the Modern Boolean Controls palette, as shown in Figure 17.5. When you first place it on the Front Panel, it will have only two buttons. You add another button by simply right-clicking and selecting Add Radio Button, as shown in Figure 17.6. Change the Label to read Port Number and arrange it with the other controls to look like Figure 17.7. The output of the control is zero if the first button is selected, one for next, and so on. These values map perfectly to the port numbers that also start with zero for Port A. You could also change the labels on the individual buttons to read A, Port B, and Port C to make the buttons look more official.

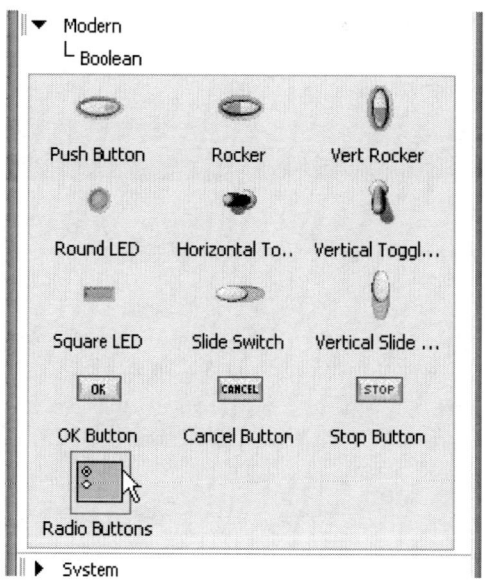

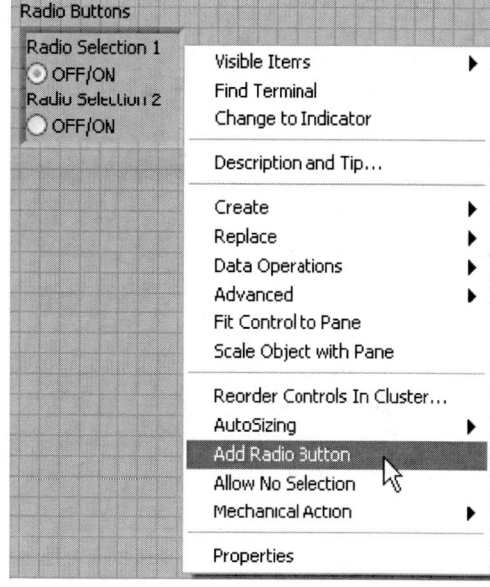

Figure 17.5
Boolean Controls Palette

Figure 17.6
Adding a Radio Button

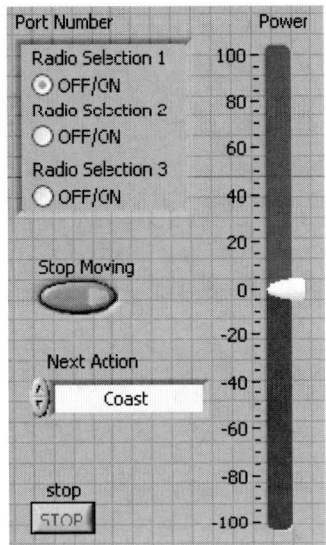

Figure 17.7
Motor Control Front Panel

Set Output State

Both Motor Unlimited and Stop Motor are really Set Output State blocks (see Figure 17.8) in disguise. For example, the Motor Unlimited Function Block Diagram, shown in Figure 17.9, basically feeds a Set Output State block with conditioned values. The Output Port Info is a bundle with six different variables that define the state of the output.

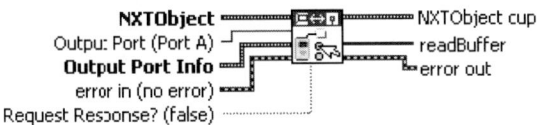

Figure 17.8
Set Output State

Despite the hundreds of potential combinations of these variables, I can figure out only one that isn't covered by the Unlimited and Stop blocks that actually does anything useful with Direct Commands. That would be a Speed Regulated output.

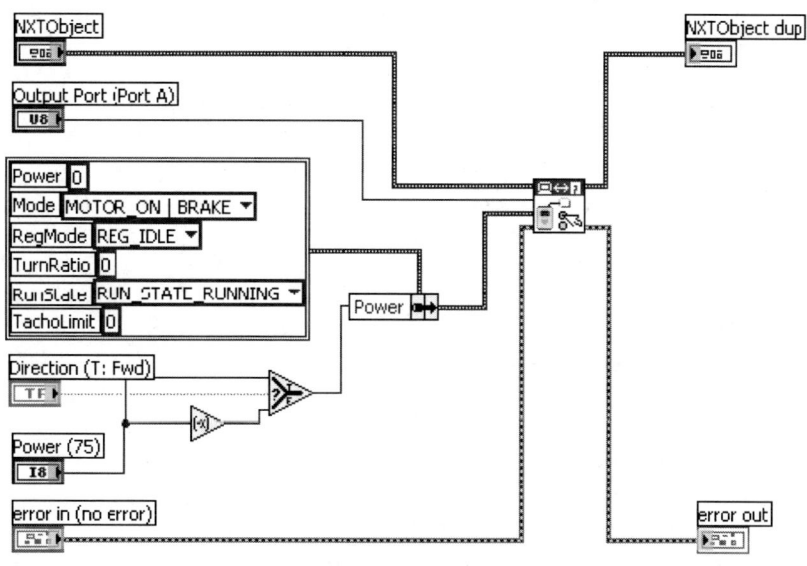

Figure 17.9
Function Block of Motor Unlimited

It would tell the NXT to adjust the power to compensate for load so that the speed would be more constant. Table 17.1 shows the settings for Power, Mode, RegMode, and RunState for the different output states. Notice that the new Speed Regulated state is really the Stop with Brake where the Power is something other than zero.

Table 17.1 *Variables for Set Output State*

Value	Motor Unlimited	Speed Regulated	Stop Motor Brake	Stop Motor Coast
Power	0–100	0–100	0	0
Mode	MOTOR_ON | BRAKE	MOTOR_ON | BRAKE | REGULATED	MOTOR_ON | BRAKE | REGULATED	COAST
RegMode	REG_IDLE	REG_SPEED	REG_SPEED	REG_IDLE
RunState	RUN_STATE_ RUNNING	RUN_STATE_ RUNNING	RUN_STATE_ RUNNING	RUN_STATE_ IDLE

Forward One Second

The Forward One Second program moves a two-wheeled vehicle such as the TriBot forward for one second. The program shown in Figure 17.10 turns on both the Port B and Port C motors with the same power and with regulated speed. This is not quite as good as the synchronized motion we could achieve with a program that actually ran on the NXT itself. It also turns off both motors with the Brake option. The new elements in the program are the Flat Sequence Structure and the LabVIEW Wait block.

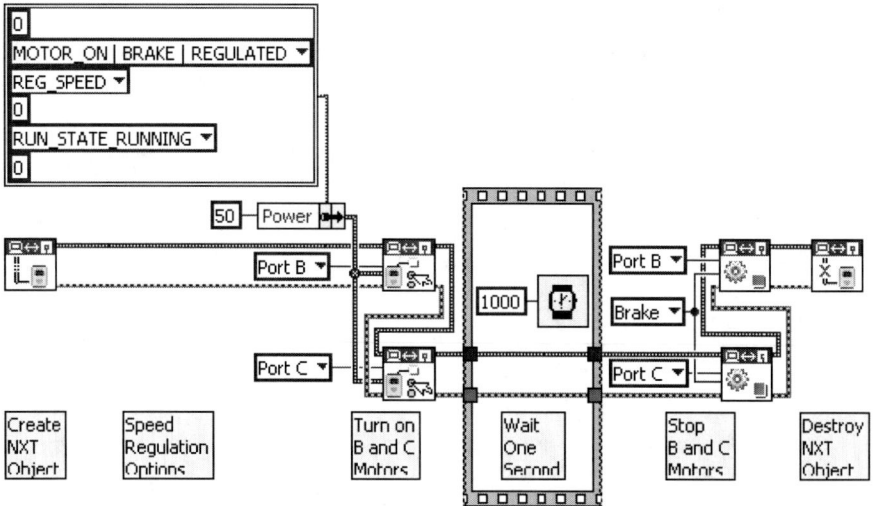

Figure 17.10
Move Forward One Second

Flat Sequence Structure

Block execution sequence is normally easy to control because the NXT blocks are daisy-chained with NXT or Error Objects, and that forces their order. However, the LabVIEW Wait block doesn't have any way to directly control its operation. That is where the Flat Sequence Structure comes in. Everything inside a frame of a Flat Sequence Structure must be done before the execution can continue. You find it in the Structures palette, along with the While Loop we already know about. The NXT Object and Error wires must pass into and then out of the frame to force the execution sequence.

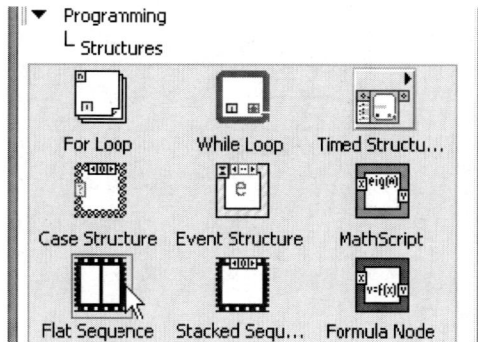

Figure 17.11
Structures Palette

Bundled by Name

The easiest way to provide the Output Port Info is to first create a Constant for the input by right-clicking, as shown in Figure 17.12. You can change the constants as needed, and if you need to change a value while the program is running, you add a Bundle by Name block, as shown in Figure 17.13. Delete the existing wire, rewire the constant block with the Bundle by Name, and then to the Set Output State, as shown in Figure 17.14. Now the Power level could be changed on the fly.

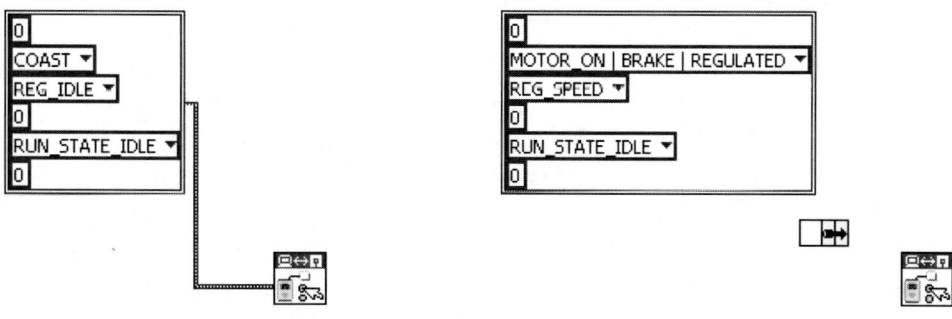

Figure 17.12
Output Port Info Constant

Figure 17.13
Delete Existing Wire and Add Bundle by Name

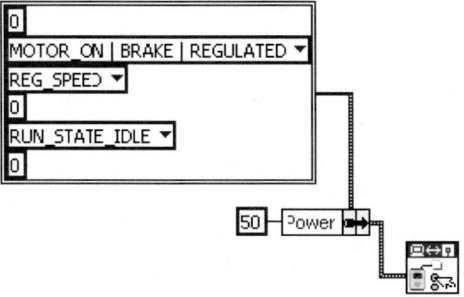

Figure 17.14
Rewire Blocks

Sounds

You can generate tones and play sound files with Direct Commands in much the same way as you did using NXT programs. The Stop Sound block also immediately turns off whatever sound the NXT is producing. These sounds could be mixed with any remote control or data acquisition program to provide audio feedback.

Play Tone

The Play Tone block, shown in Figure 17.15, plays a note with frequency Tone and for Duration in length. It does not have the option to Wait for Completion, as do NXT blocks. You will need to pace sending tones from the Direct Command program, or the next tone you send will replace the one already playing even if there is time left for it to play. It also doesn't have the option to Repeat.

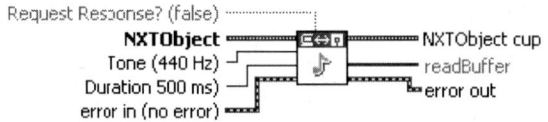

Figure 17.15
Play Tone

Play Scale (see Figure 17.16) can be used to demonstrate the necessary time pacing. Running the program as shown will produce tones that will be 500 ms long with a 100 ms space between them. If you make the time on the Wait less than 500 ms, then

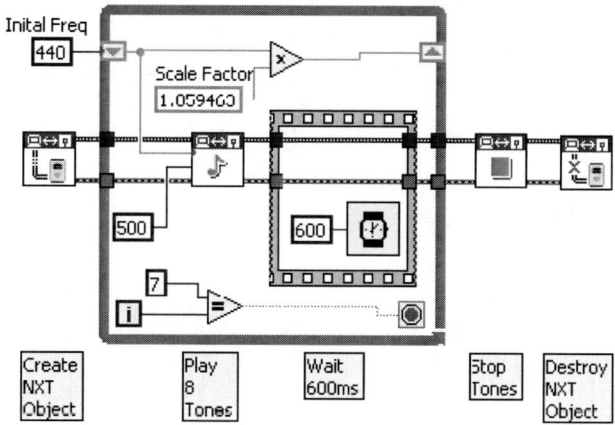

Figure 17.16
Play Scale Program

the tone duration will be limited by that time and there won't be any space between the notes.

Stop Sound

Stop Sound (see Figure 17.17) tells the NXT to turn off immediately whatever sound it happens to be making.

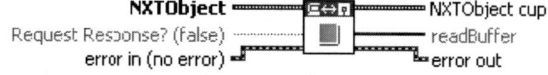

Figure 17.17
Stop Sound

Play Sound File

Play Sound File plays a NXT sound file. Naturally, the file must be previously downloaded to the NXT to work. You could use this to tell a laboratory assistant to make an adjustment or to give other instructions. The block shown in Figure 17.18 also has the option to Repeat playing the file.

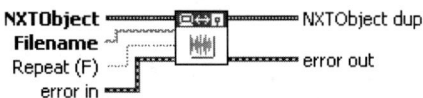

Figure 17.18
Play Sound File

The MINSTORMS kit comes with a wide variety of sound files. They can be found in the C:\Program Files\LEGO Software\LEGO MINDSTORMS NXT\engine\Sounds directory. Copy the file Yes.rso to the C:\ root directory before running the program shown in Figure 17.19. The program will download the Yes.rso file to the NXT and then tell the NXT to play it.

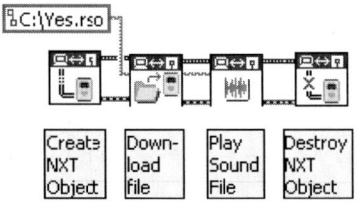

Figure 17.19
Play Sound File Program

Reflections

Turning motors doesn't always mean moving a vehicle around. For example, I could automate the mouse cage so that on command a motor would turn that would deliver some food to Mini. In a laboratory you could also use the motors to turn knobs or flip switches on other equipment. The possibilities are endless. You could even use the NXT as a part of a mouse-training experiment, where an audio instruction could be produced and then a food reward given for the desired response.

Read, Write, and Bluetooth

18

I feel red, white and blue all over.
—*Edward White,* first American astronaut to walk in space

The IOMap blocks are rather unusual. They work at a primitive level inside the NXT operating system, and you probably won't ever write a program that would use them. On the other hand, the Bluetooth blocks are about sending and receiving information between programs running in the PC and those running in the NXT. They don't actually require Bluetooth and are frequently used to fill in gaps in Direct Command functionality.

IOMap

The IOMap functions are really important only to people developing NXT firmware or interfaces to it. The IOMap is a block of memory inside the NXT that is used by different parts of its software to communicate with each other. Just to give you a taste of what goes on in the IOMap, here is a little program (see Figure 18.1) that will get the NXT battery voltage with the Read Battery Voltage block and also get it directly from the IOMap. I hope you can appreciate the complexity of the IOMap Read method for getting this simple value. The voltage is spread over two bytes in the IOMap, and they have to be combined to make a single 16-bit number. The Front Panel (see Figure 18.2) shows that the battery value is the same read either way.

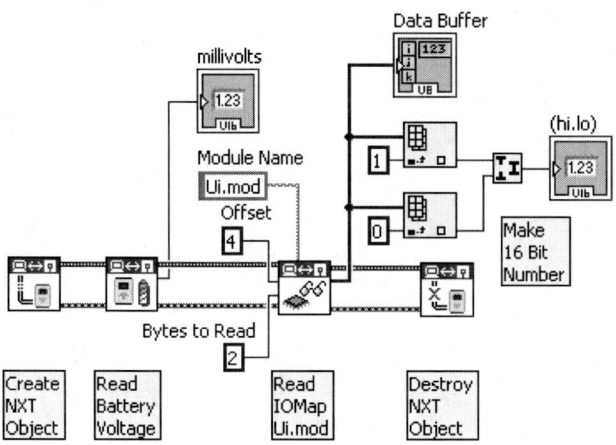

Figure 18.1
Read Battery Voltage

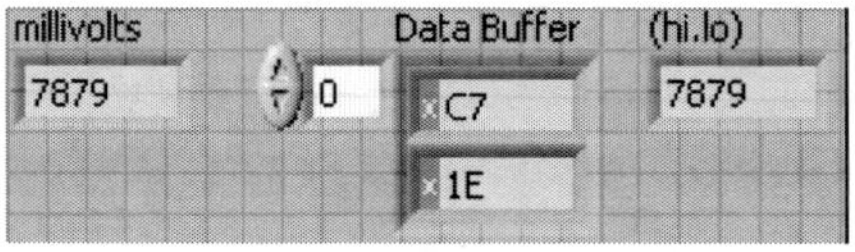

Figure 18.2
Battery Voltage Front Panel

Read IOMap

The IOMap is broken up into modules that are identified by a Module Name that looks like a filename with a .mod extension. Within a module, the values are retrieved at an Offset number of bytes and for a length of Bytes to Read. For example, the battery voltage is in module Ui.mod at an Offset of 4 for a length of 2 bytes.

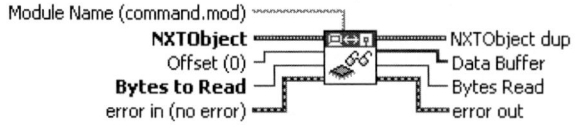

Figure 18.3
Read IOMap

Write IOMap

The obligatory warning is "Don't try this at home!" Writing the wrong thing to the IOMap can have devastating consequences than can only be remedied by reloading the firmware. Just like reading the IOMap, there is really nothing you can do that isn't probably done by some higher-level function block. However, there is one thing that you might find interesting. The PC can turn off the NXT by writing a couple of bytes to the IOCtrl.mod module. The program in Figure 18.4 does just that.

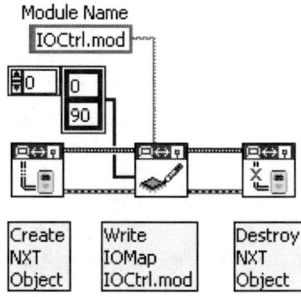

Figure 18.4
Turn NXT Off

Write IOMap

Write IOMap (see Figure 18.5) works just like the IOMap Read only in reverse. The Data Buffer is an array of bytes, and the block will write the full-dimensioned size of the array; be careful not to write too much.

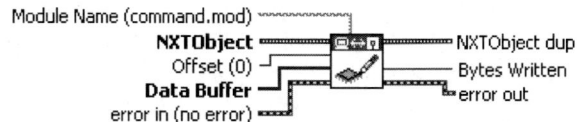

Figure 18.5
Write IOMap

Bluetooth

The Direct Command Bluetooth functions are really about mailboxes and messages more than they are about Bluetooth. They either simulate the reception of a Bluetooth message by inserting one in a Mailbox, or they let you see the contents of a Mailbox. The most important use of the blocks is to provide ways for a program running on the PC to exchange information with a program running on the NXT.

Message Write

A NXT has 10 mailboxes. When connected NXTs send messages to each other, they specify which mailbox to put their message in. Message Write, shown in Figure 18.6, puts a Message into any Mailbox without actually using a Bluetooth connection. The NXT will see the new message and retrieve it just as it would for a message coming from another NXT.

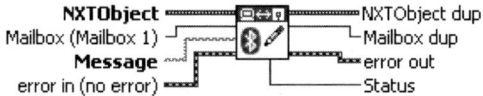

Figure 18.6
Message Write

Message Remote

The Direct Command Output blocks lack many of the best features available in Output blocks running on the NXT itself. The Direct Control program in Figure 18.7 illustrates a method of using messages to indirectly control the outputs on the NXT. It sends Power and Steering values in separate Mailboxes that are picked up and provided to a Sync Unlimited block by a program running on the NXT.

The Front Panel has a Knob type control for Steering and a Slider for Power, as shown in Figure 18.8. You can drive a mobile robot such as the TriBot or Elmer with it. The Knob's scale was increased, and its size was also increased to make fine adjustments easier. The Power scale was also increased, along with its height.

It is possible to connect the Power or Steering values to the Message Writes without the logic and Case Structures, but the block would be constantly sending the same message over and over again. This wouldn't be a huge burden for a USB-connected NXT, but if you are using Bluetooth to connect the PC to the NXT, it could have a big impact. The logic checks to see whether the value has changed before actually bothering to send.

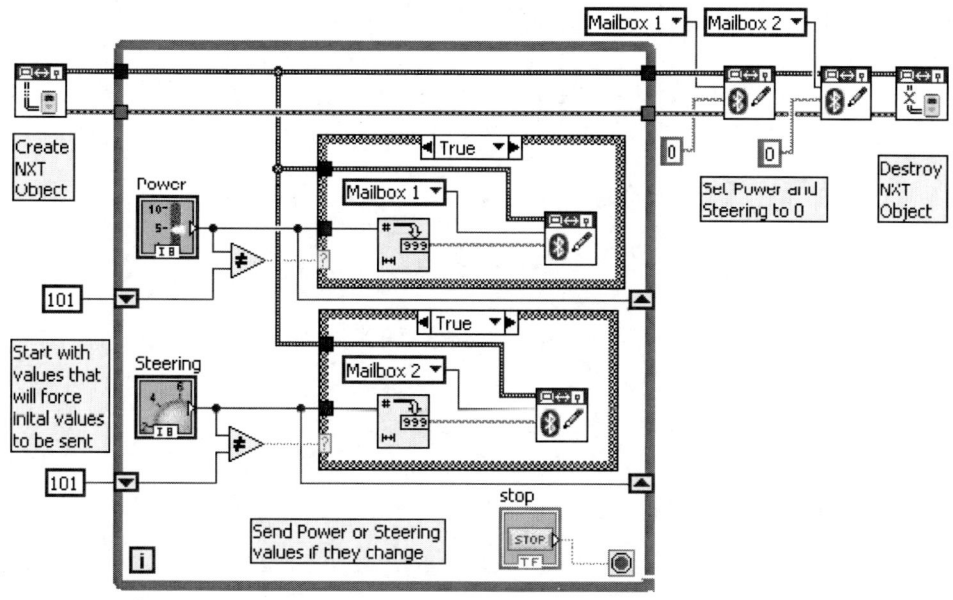

Figure 18.7
Message Remote

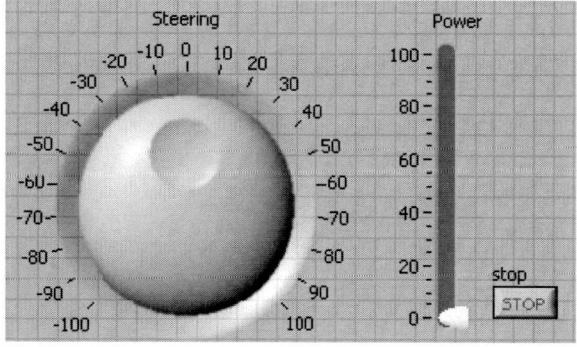

Figure 18.8
Message Remote Front Panel

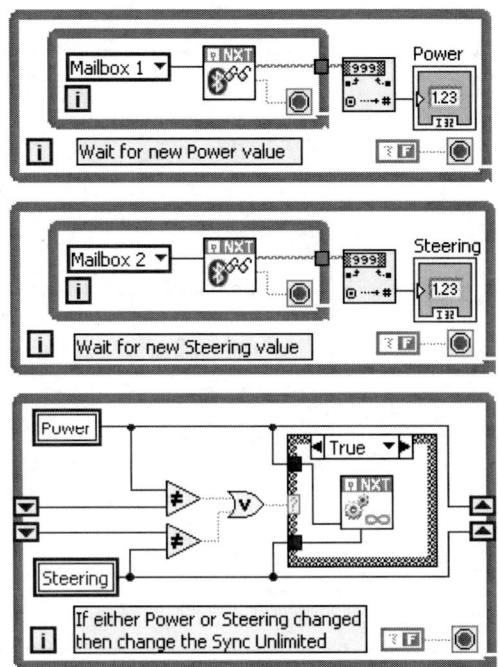

Figure 18.9
Mailbox Sync

Figure 18.9 is the program that runs on the NXT itself. It is called Mailbox Sync, because it receives the Power and Steering values from Mailboxes and feeds them to a Sync Unlimited block. The three loops work independently to check the mailboxes for new values and update the Sync Unlimited block. Notice the use of Local Variables to communicate between loops. Motor synchronization is disturbed every time the Sync Unlimited block is called, even if none of the input values has changed. The logic and Case Structure in the lower loop prevents the block from being redundantly called with the exact same input values.

Message Read

Message Read lets you see a Message in a NXT's Mailbox. You can choose to Remove the Message or leave it for the NXT to discover itself. You can examine the incoming mailboxes of the NXT or the outgoing boxes intended for transmission. The easiest way to use the block is to leave Read Masters inbox as True and arrange for the NXT to Write Messages to Connection 0.

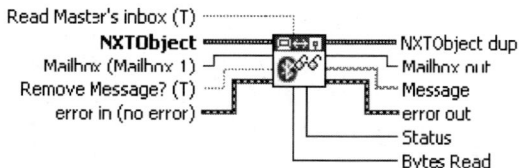

Figure 18.10
Message Read

Send Button

Another missing function in the Direct Command palette is an input for the NXT Buttons. As a substitute, the NXT can send a Message with a value for the button being pressed. The Send Button program, shown in Figure 18.11, looks at each button in a sequence to see whether it is being pressed. We don't need to worry about multiple buttons, because the NXT reports only that one of them is pressed at a given time. The program encodes the button into a numerical value with 1 to 3 for buttons and 0 for none. To save the conversion time, the constants are already strings ready for the Send Message to use.

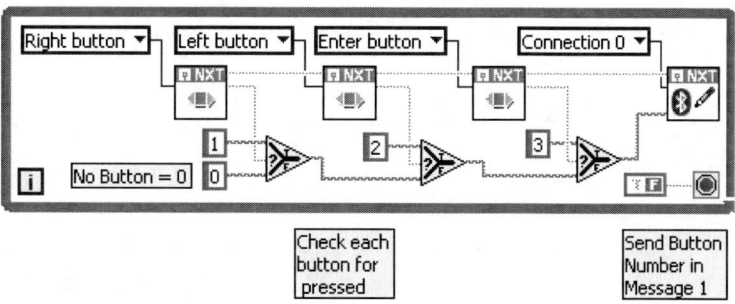

Figure 18.11
Send Button Program

The button value is read as Master Mailbox 1, as shown in Figure 18.12. The value is converted from string to number and displayed with an NXT Button indicator. The indicator was made by copying one of the Button Constant blocks from the Send Button program into the Read Button Program and then selecting to Change to Indicator, using a right mouse click. The indicator doesn't have a value for 0 or none, so it displays <0>, as shown in Figure 18.13. When you push a button on the NXT, the display will show the name of the button, as shown in Figure 18.14.

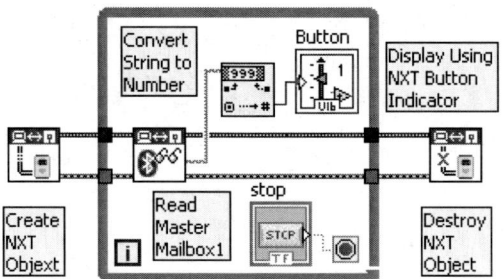

Figure 18.12
Read Button Program

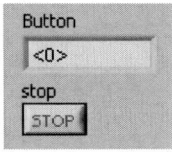

Figure 18.13
No Buttons Pressed

Figure 18.14
Right Button Pressed

Reflections

We have now covered all the basic LabVIEW for MINDSTORMS software. The next chapters are truly for black belts and the obsessed. I'll lift the veil and let you see the underbelly of the NXT software. Finally, I'll show you how to turn a Front Panel into a web page.

NXT Block Internals

19

All things must change to something new, to something strange.
—Henry Wadsworth Longfellow

In this chapter we will learn about the internal mechanisms of LabVIEW NXT Blocks. These are the blocks that actually run on the NXT itself that were covered in the first part of the book. You will probably need to write programs at this low level only if you are designing new MINDSTORMS products or using the NXT in ways unforeseen by its developers. Nevertheless, there is a lot of good information about creating SubVIs in this chapter that make it worth going through.

NXT Block Internals

I'm going to show you something I'll bet you didn't notice before. Create a blank VI and put a single Draw Circle on the Block Diagram. Now double-click on the icon, as shown in Figure 19.1. What you see is the Draw Circle VI's Front Panel. as shown in Figure 19.2. The surprise is that you can also look at the block's Block Diagram and see what LabVIEW is actually doing. Go to the toolbar, select Window, and then select Show Block Diagram.

The Draw Circle Function Block diagram is shown in Figure 19.3. It primarily consists of a single block called an Invoke Node that calls something named NXTSystemCall. Rather than a large number of specialized subroutines, the NXT operating system has just one generic subroutine with a parameter, NXTDrawCircle in this case, that tells it what function you want it to perform. Draw Circle needs three other variables for Center, Radius, and Options to work. I picked Draw Circle only because it is one of the simplest blocks. All NXT blocks can be opened up this way, but *never* save NXT blocks you have opened.

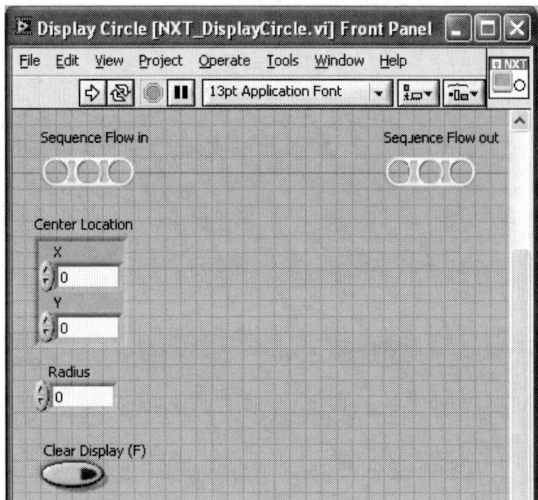

Figure 19.1
Draw Circle Block

Figure 19.2
Draw Circle Front Panel

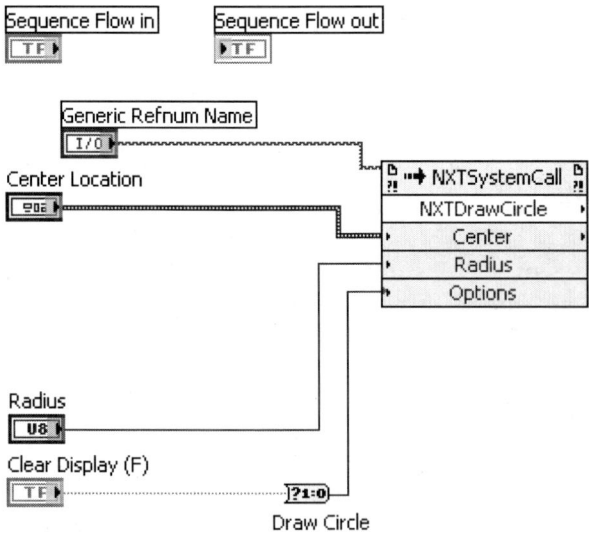

Figure 19.3
Draw Circle Block Diagram

Draw Rectangle

The best way to understand what is going on here is to build a little NXT block of our own from scratch. Let's start with a blank VI and paste a single Invoke Node on its Block Diagram. The Invoke node is in the NXT Toolkit under Application Control, as shown in Figure 19.4.

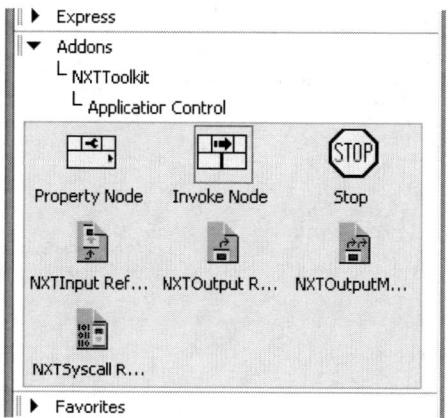

Figure 19.4
The Invoke Node

First you need to specify the name or Class of function you want the Invoke Node to invoke. Right-click on the top part of the Invoke Icon over the word App, and a menu that looks like the one in Figure 19.5 will appear. Follow Select Class off to the right to NXTInputOutput and then NXTSystemCall as shown.

With the cursor over the word Method, right-click, and a menu like the one in Figure 19.6 will appear. Study the list carefully, because you should be able to recognize many of the functions that have similarly named NXT Blocks. For example, NXTDrawCircle is Draw Circle. There is one method in the list that didn't get a NXT block of its own, and that is the NXTDrawRect. It draws a rectangle at a location with a given height and width.

With Class and Method selections made, the Invoke Node should now look like Figure 19.7. The required Location and Size along with an Options input automatically appear. There really isn't any output from the block other than the rectangle that will be drawn on the display.

The Invoke node needs a special type of input called a Refnum. Just take my word that you need it, and get it from the Application Control palette, as shown in Figure 19.8. Place and wire it to the top-left connector on the Invoke Node. Now

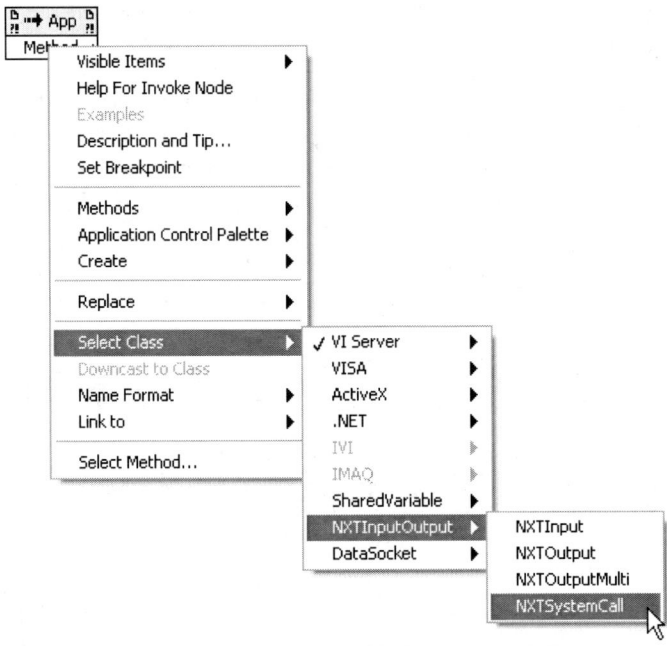

Figure 19.5
Selecting NXTSystemCall

right-click and select to Create Controls for the Location and Size inputs. The Function Block Diagram will look like Figure 19.9 when you're done.

Something all good NXT blocks have in common is a Sequence Flow input and output. These are important for forcing execution order. Go to the Front Panel and look in the Controls palette in the NXTToolkit for the Sequence Flow, as shown in Figure 19.10. Add two of the Sequence Flows and a Boolean pushbutton while you are at it. When you are done arranging and fixing up the labels, the Front Panel will look like Figure 19.11.

Back on the Block Diagram, right-click on the Control labeled Sequence Flow Out and select Change to Indicator (see Figure 19.12). That will turn that Sequence Flow into an output. Leave the other one as an input. Also connect the Pushbutton Control through a Boolean to (0,1) block to the Options input of the Invoke Node, as shown in Figure 19.13.

Draw Rectangle.vi is going to become a SubVI that will be used by other programs. When we made SubVIs before, the connection points to the block were made for us and we lived with their default placements. Now I'm going to show you how it is really done. Right-click on the block icon in the upper-right corner of the Front Panel Window, and a pop-up menu like the one shown in Figure 19.14 will appear. Select Show Connector.

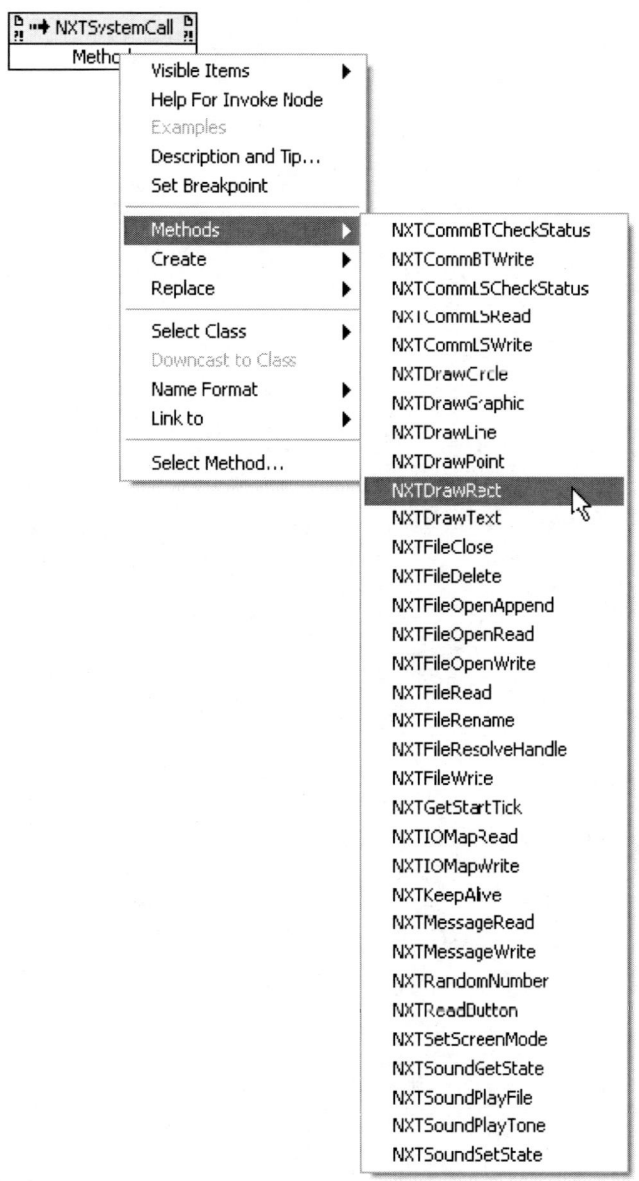

Figure 19.6
Selecting NXTDrawRect Method

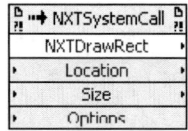

Figure 19.7
Invoke Node after Selections

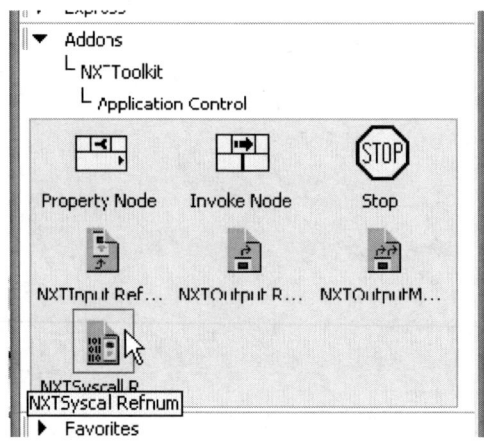

Figure 19.8
Getting NXTSyscall Refnum

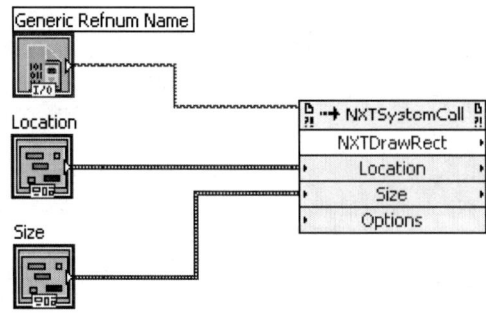

Figure 19.9
Making Controls for Other Inputs

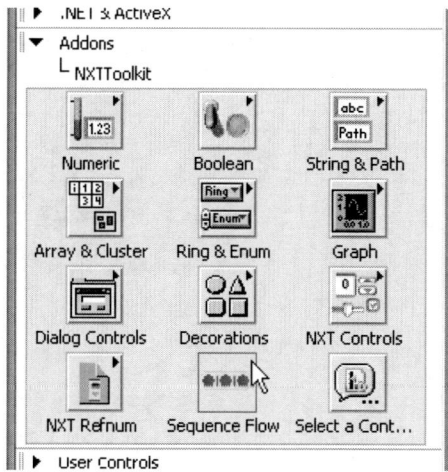

Figure 19.10
Adding Sequence Flow Controls

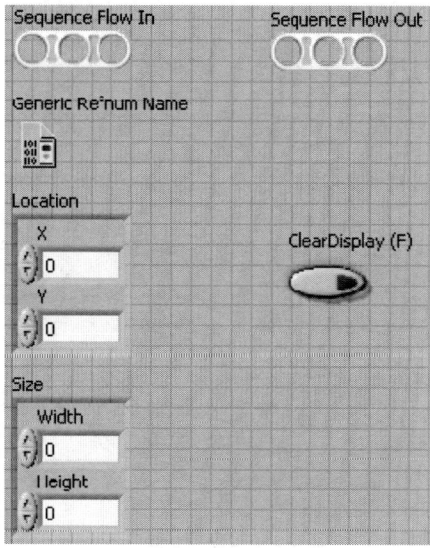

Figure 19.11
Arranged Front Panel

Sequence Flow Out

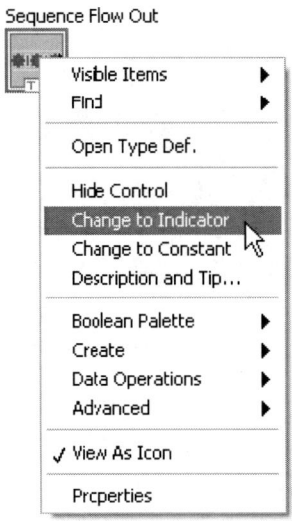

Figure 19.12
Changing Sequence Flow Out to Indicator

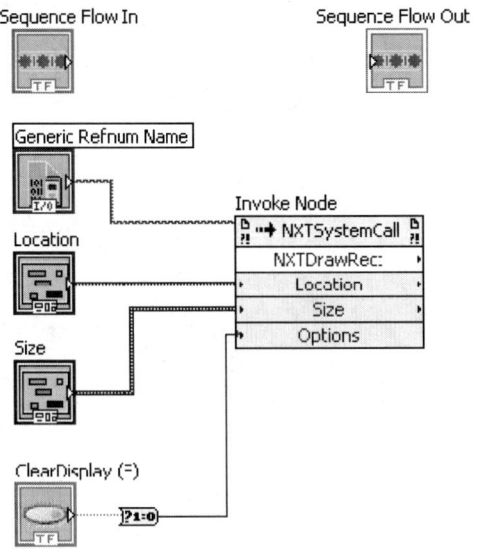

Figure 19.13
Draw Rectangle Block Diagram

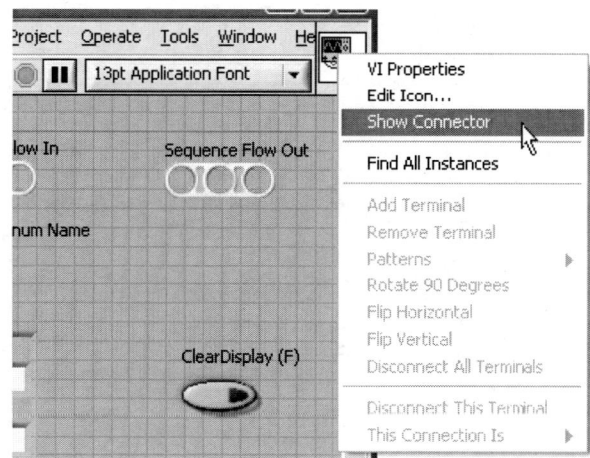

Figure 19.14
Showing the Connector Pane

The Connector Pane looks like Figure 19.15, and if you move the cursor over the little boxes, the Connect Wire tool will show up. Each of the boxes marks a location where a connector will appear on the finished VI's icon. Pick the top-left corner with a left mouse click; then move the cursor over to the Sequence Flow In icon (see Figure 19.16) on the left side of the Front Panel and click again. Now the Sequence Flow In's connection will be made to the top-left corner of the block, just as with other NXT Blocks.

Figure 19.15
Starting a Connection

Figure 19.16
Ending a Connection

Repeat the wiring process for the Location, Size, Sequence Flow Out, and Clear Display. The Clear Display Connector Pane box is taller than the others, but it will behave exactly the same. Figure 19.17 shows the mapping from the Connector Pane to the various Controls and Indicators. Generic Refnum Name doesn't get connected to anything.

Switch the Connector Pane back to Icon and select Edit Icon using another right click. An edit window like the one in Figure 19.18 will appear. I cut and pasted the icon from the Draw Circle block, erased the circle, and added a rectangle to make a very official-looking block icon.

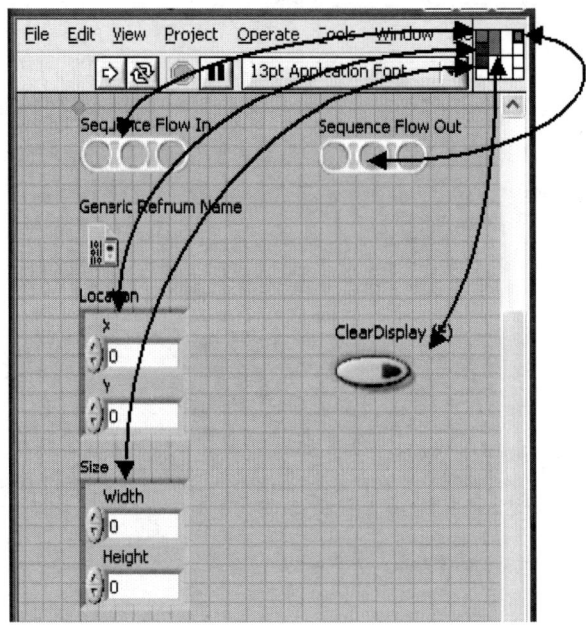

Figure 19.17
Connector Mapping

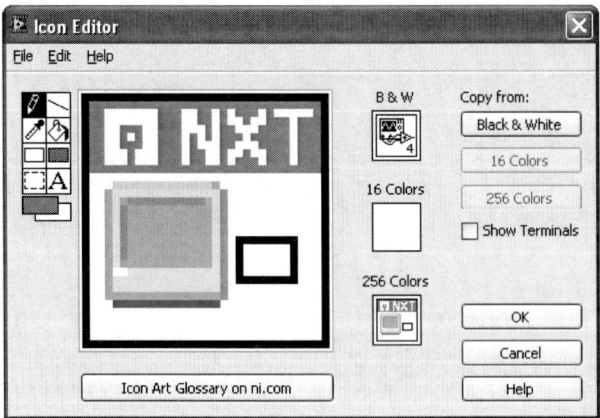

Figure 19.18
Draw Rectangle Icon

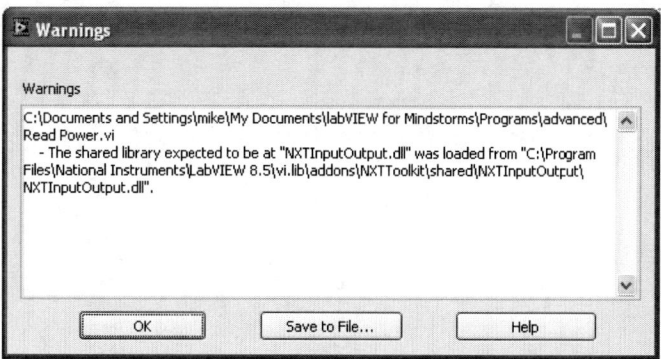

Figure 19.19
Sample Warning

When you save a VI that contains these low-level blocks, you may get a warning like the one in Figure 19.19. Just click OK. LabVIEW is warning you about some internal housekeeping that won't affect your program.

To use the new Draw Rectangle block, start a new blank VI and in the Function Block palette, pick Select a VI... as shown in Figure 19.20. Navigate to where you

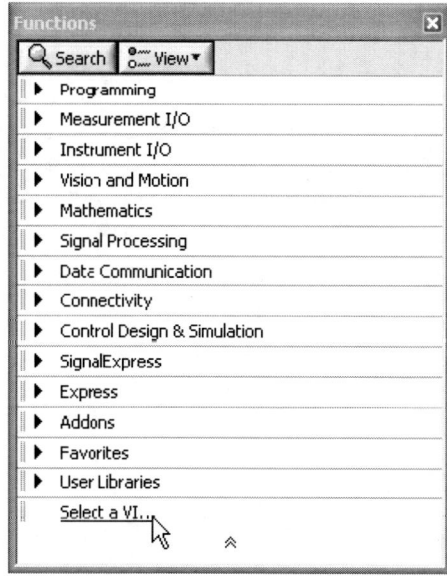

Figure 19.20
Getting Draw Rectangle Block

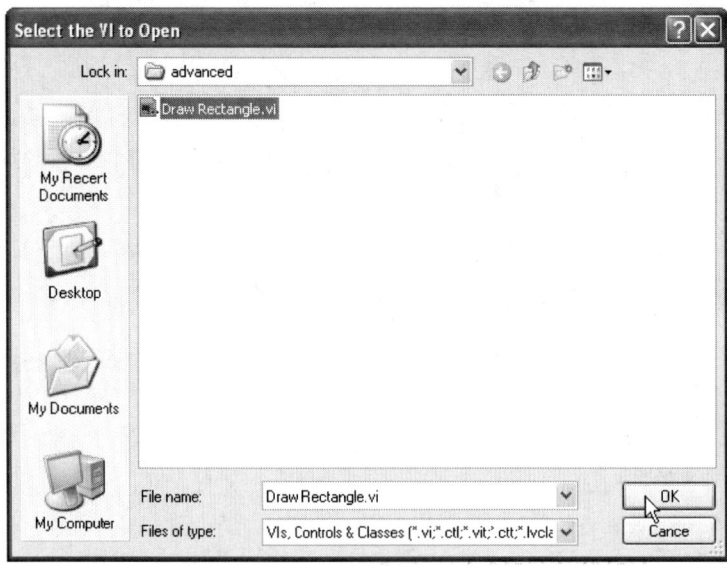

Figure 19.21
Selecting Draw Rectangle

saved the Draw Rectangle block and select it (see Figure 19.21). You can now place it on the Block Diagram.

Add the constants shown in Figure 19.22 and a Wait node to make the Test Draw Rectangle program. The program will draw a single large rectangle and display it for five seconds before terminating. The display should look like Figure 19.23.

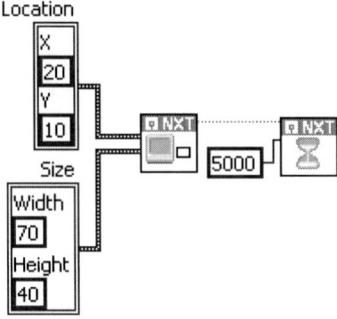

Figure 19.22
Test Draw Rectangle

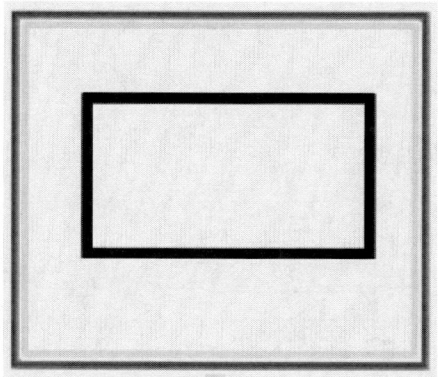

Figure 19.23
Rectangle Display

Read Power

NXT operating system control of inputs and outputs uses a different interface called a Property Node. The Property Node looks exactly the same as the Invoke Node, but the underlying mechanism is different. As we learned in the preceding chapter, different parts of the NXT software communicate through a region of shared memory called the IOMap. Putting new values into the IOMap is a little tricky, but getting values out of the IOMap is fairly simple, as shown in the following example.

When an Output Port has the Speed Regulation option True, it constantly adjusts the power going to the motor to try to compensate for the load. The value of the actual power at any instant is available in the IOMap, and it can be read with the Property Node, as shown in Figure 19.24. Oddly, the value is called ActualSpeed, but it really is a measure of output power. You need to specify only the Output Port whose value you're interested in. There is also a Boolean that will become True if the required power ever hits 100, meaning the output had become Overloaded at some time.

Creating the Block Diagram should be pretty straightforward by now. All of the controls and indicators are made with the familiar right-click Create menu pick we have been using all along. The Refnum is also from the Application Control palette, but this one is specific for the NXTOutput. I developed an Icon, shown in Figure 19.25, from one of the other Motor blocks that has a graphical power meter and alarm signal. The connections are also straightforward, as can be seen in Figure 19.26.

Testing the block is more complicated than the block itself. Figure 19.27 shows a program that first turns on Port B with a power level of 50 and, most importantly, sets the Speed Regulation input to True. The While Loop keeps displaying the current value of the Power in the lower-left corner. If the output ever becomes Overloaded, the

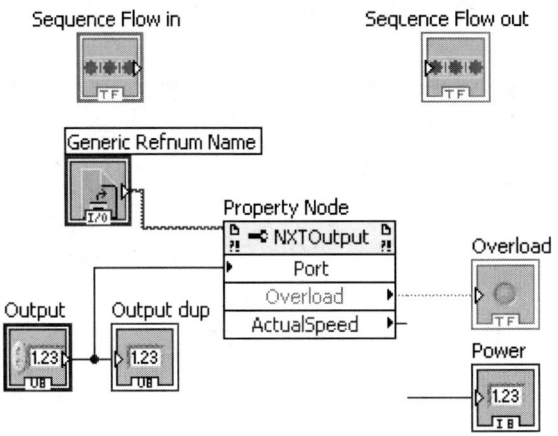

Figure 19.24
Read Power Block Diagram

Figure 19.25
Read Power Icon

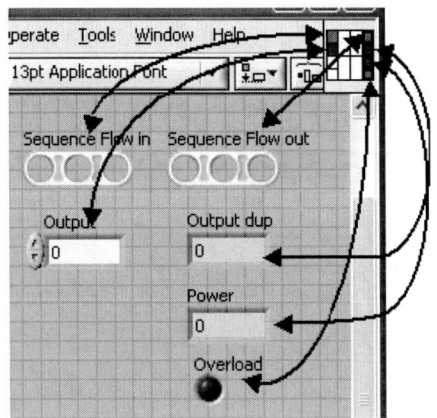

Figure 19.26
Connector Mapping

motor is Stopped and Braked. A tone is also played just so you know that something just happened.

Figure 19.28 shows the Power value display for four different conditions. At first the value will be close to the set point of 50. If you drag your fingers on the tire, the power level will rise and eventually hit 100, which turns on the Overload. Immediately the

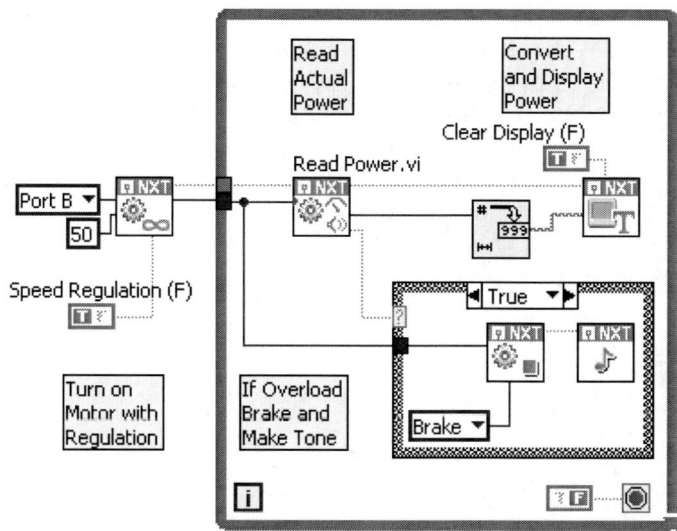

Figure 19.27
Test Read Power

Figure 19.28
Lightly Loaded, Loaded, Overloaded, and Braking

commanded power will be changed to zero in an effort to brake the motor. Now you will find that as you try to rotate the tire, the power will vary from positive to negative depending on the direction and amount you try to turn it.

Period Count Sensor

For efficiency, the NXT doesn't reconfigure an Input Port every time it is read. The only way it knows you want to change the Type or Mode is by setting a Boolean variable called InvalidData to True. When it sees the True value, it reconfigures the port and sets the InvalidData variable back to False. It is important for your program to wait until this handshake is complete.

In the preceding chapter I showed you how to create a Period Counter–type sensor with Direct Commands. The Figure 19.29 VI sets up an Input Port to also do the Period Count input. It uses a Refnum called NXTInputRefnum from the Application Controls palette. The first Property Node reads the existing Type and Mode to see whether the port has already been configured. If so, the False case does nothing, and the flow follows to the last Property Node that retrieves the current value of the count. If the Type or Mode needs to be changed, the True case first writes the correct values and then waits for the software to acknowledge that it made the change by watching the InvalidData value.

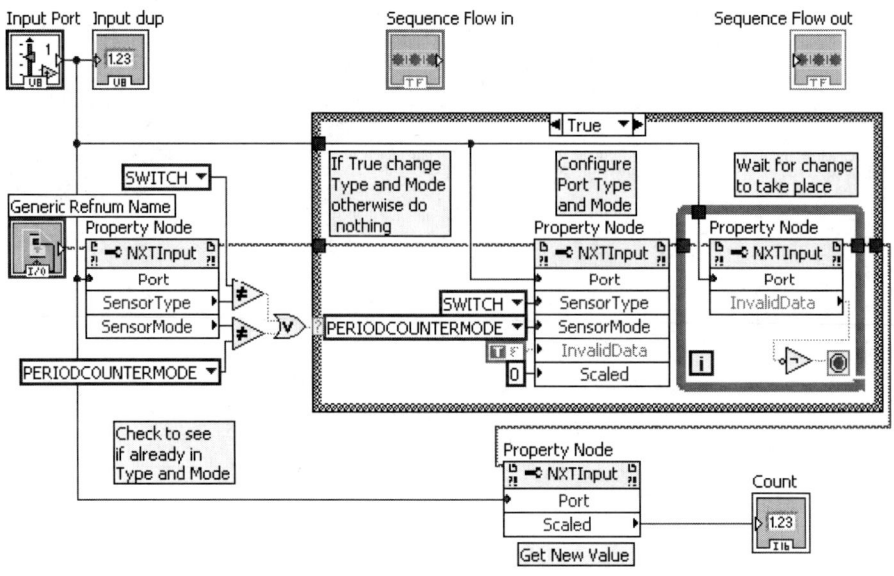

Figure 19.29
Period Count Sensor Block Diagram

There are a couple of new programming features in Figure 19.29 worth noting. The Input Port uses a control that will let you select only from a list of valid Port Numbers. This Control is not in a palette, but can be found by going to Select a Control... from the Controls palette and navigating to C:/Program Files/National Instruments/LabVIEW x.x/vi.lib/addons/NXTToolkit/Library VIs/Block Support, as shown in Figure 19.30. Where the x.x refers to the particular version, you have, for example, 8.5.

Also in the directory are some useful controls such as HWPage SensorMode.ctl and HWPage.SensorType.ctl. Paste one of each of these and Change them to Constants, as illustrated in Figure 19.31. They can now be used as the inputs for Type and Mode

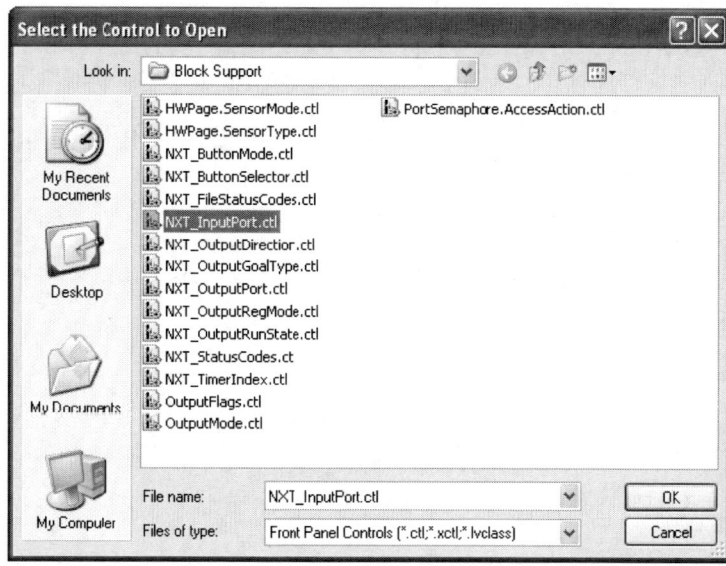

Figure 19.30
Getting Input Control

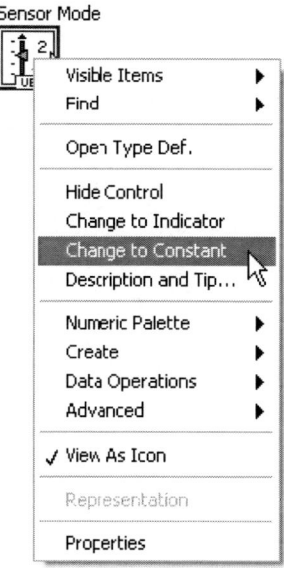

Figure 19.31
Turning a Control into a Constant

inputs to the Property Nodes. Your program will have descriptive words such as Switch instead of the actual value of the Type, which happens to be one.

When you are done, the Period Counter Front Panel will look something like Figure 19.32. I copied the NXT Touch Sensor icon and pasted it to make the Period Counter icon. I also drew the numbers 1234 to help distinguish it from the regular Touch Sensor (see Figure 19.33).

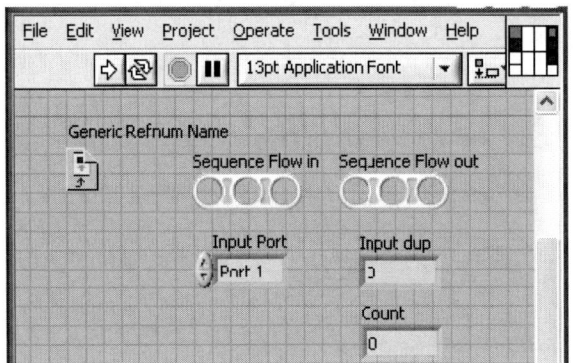

Figure 19.32
Period Counter Front Panel

Figure 19.33
Icon

Testing the block is easy. The count value is converted to Text and displayed in a While Loop, as shown in Figure 19.34. Every time you push and release the Touch Switch, the count will increase by one. The NXT display will look like Figure 19.35 after a dozen bumps.

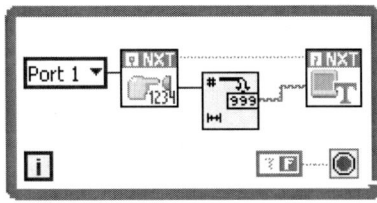

Figure 19.34
Test Period Counter

Figure 19.35
Period Counter Display

Reflections

The System Call, Input, and Output methods are the primary low-level way LabVIEW controls the NXT hardware. There is one more method called NXTOutputMulti that is essentially the same as the NXTOutput, except that it is designed to work with multiple motors for synchronous operation. This method is best understood by looking inside the existing NXT Sync Motor blocks and seeing how they were programmed. In fact, any further curiosity you may have about Property and Invoke nodes should be satisfied this way.

Web Publishing

20

A page of history is worth a pound of logic.—Oliver Wendell Holmes

A program known as a Web Server is built into LabVIEW; it allows other networked computers to see and control your Front Panel remotely. It is remarkably easy to set up, and it expands access of your NXT to the whole world. There is nothing specific about the server to the LEGO MINDSTORMS NXT, so any LabVIEW program can be networked this way. I'll explain how to create a web application with a little example.

Mini Fig's World

Imagine how cool it would be to check up on my mouse Mini Fig from anywhere. In Chapter 16 I developed a mouse cage monitor using Direct Commands to plot the activity of Mini over the course of a day. With some obvious reformatting of the graphs and the addition of a live picture, Figure 20.1 is the Front Panel from that program. I eliminated the time display and the *x*-axis from some of the plots to simplify things.

The live image is actually updated with an external program called Fwink, but I'll get to that in a minute. Figure 20.2 shows the very bottom of the While Loop in the Cage Monitor's Function Blocks Diagram. I've added only a few new blocks to display the picture from the Graphics & Sound palette. The first block reads a jpg file format image called webcampix. The second converts the raw image data into a bitmap picture that can be displayed with the Picture Indicator Control. A Wait for one second was also added just to slow the process down so it isn't needlessly redisplaying the same picture over and over.

Fwink

Fwink is a great freeware program from Chris Lundie that periodically captures an image from a webcam attached to your computer and stores it in a file. The program can be downloaded from: http://lundie.ca/fwink/. We are using only a small part

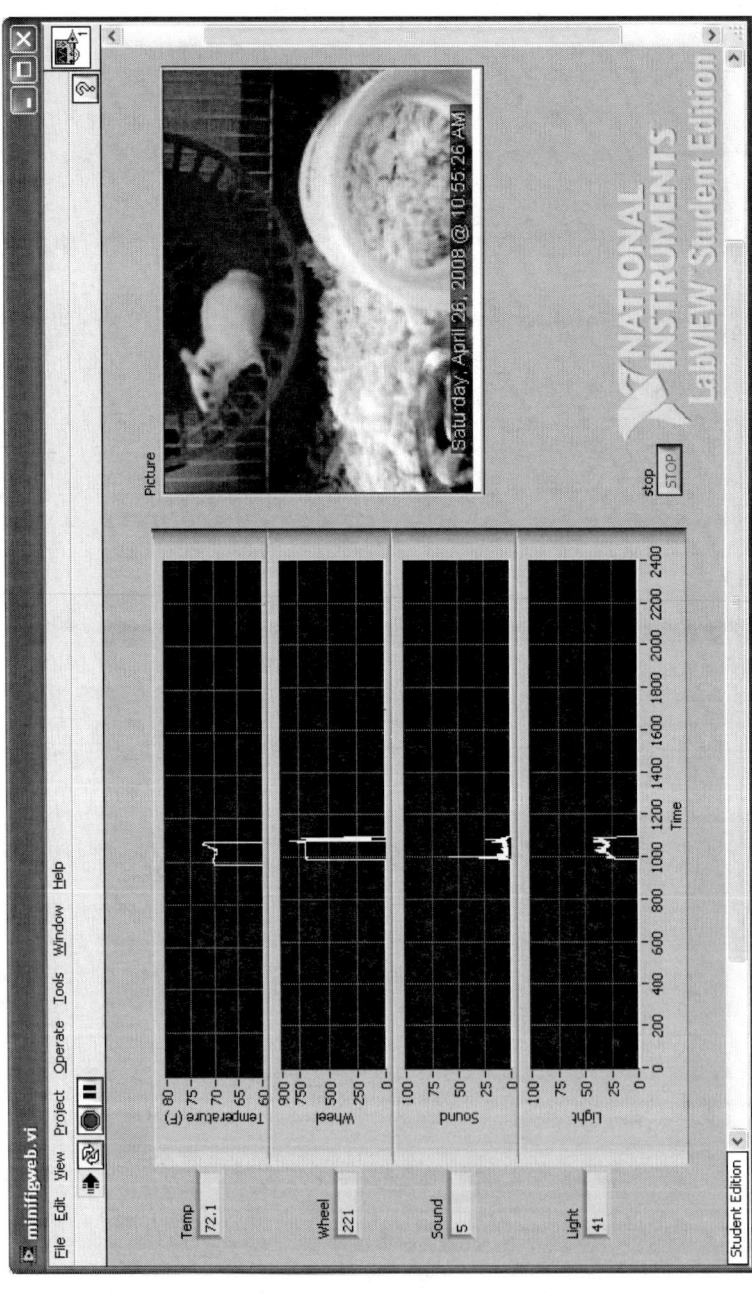

Figure 20.1
MiniFigWeb Program

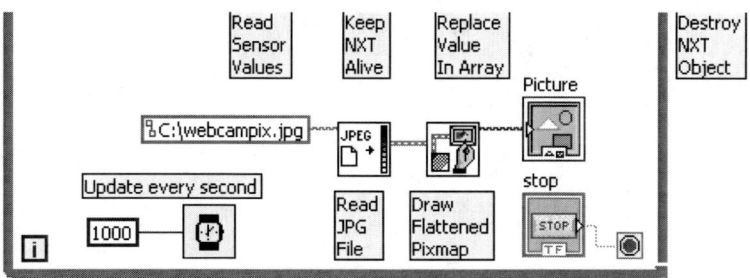

Figure 20.2
Additional Blocks to Display Image

of what Fwink can do, and Chris supplies documentation about how to use Fwink in general. When you run Fwink for the first time, you will see the Figure 20.3 window. Select Settings to control the input device and how often it takes pictures.

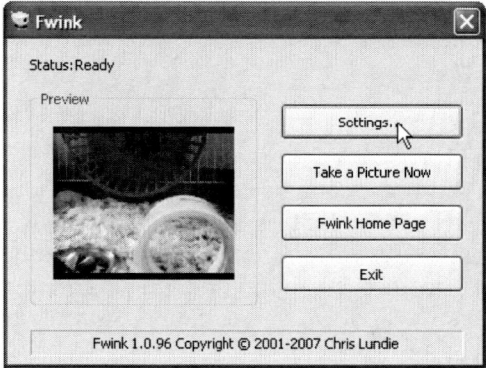

Figure 20.3
Fwink Window

The Fwink Settings window (Figure 20.4) is where you select the time between captures and the name of the file to store the image in. I store the image of the inside of the Mini's cage in a file in the C drive root directory called webcampix.jpg. This is also where LabVIEW picks it up for display. I take a new image only every 10 seconds to limit the impact on the computer while the cage monitor is running.

Figure 20.4
Fwink Settings Window

When you are done configuring Fwink, you should Close it only as shown in Figure 20.5. Do *not* select Exit, as that will completely terminate the program. When Fwink is working, you will see only its icon in the tool tray, as shown in Figure 20.6, but it is running in the background updating the picture every 10 seconds. This is also what the program will do when you launch it from now on. Just click on the icon to bring up the Figure 20.3 window if you need to make changes.

Figure 20.5
Closing Fwink

Figure 20.6
Fwink Icon

Automatic Error Handling

LabVIEW and Fwink are running independently at the same time, and that may lead to a small problem. Fwink might be writing a new version of the image just when LabVIEW tries to read the image to display it. LabVIEW will automatically display a warning that there was a problem reading the file and it stops until you tell it what to do about it. However, it really isn't that big of a deal if the picture isn't updated for just a second.

You get around the automatic warning by changing an Execution Property of the VI. Go to the File menu in the Toolbar and select VI Properties, as shown in Figure 20.7. Select Execution in the Category box and then uncheck Enable automatic error handling (see Figure 20.8). From now on, LabVIEW will assume that any errors will be taken care of by you. In this case, we aren't doing anything with the error. It will occur and the picture will go blank for a second till it tries again. This happens so rarely that you may never actually see it happen.

Figure 20.7
Changing VI Properties

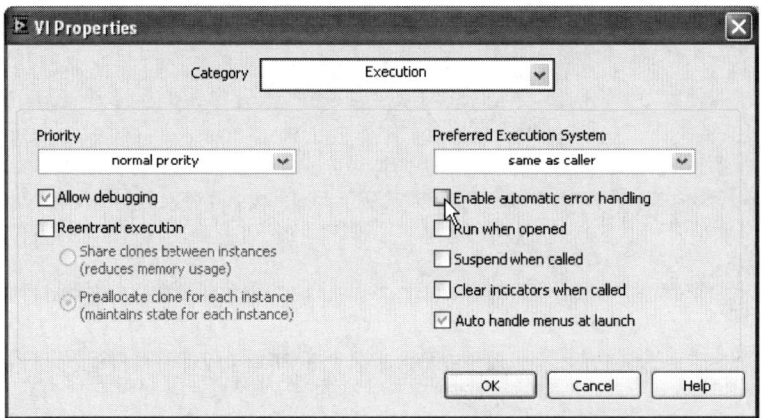

Figure 20.8
Disable Automatic Error Handling

Web Publishing Tool

With the minifigweb program running, go to the Tools pulldown menu and select Web
Publishing Tool. . . , as shown in Figure 20.9. A series of windows will take you through
setting up a new web page. Having the program running makes it a little easier.

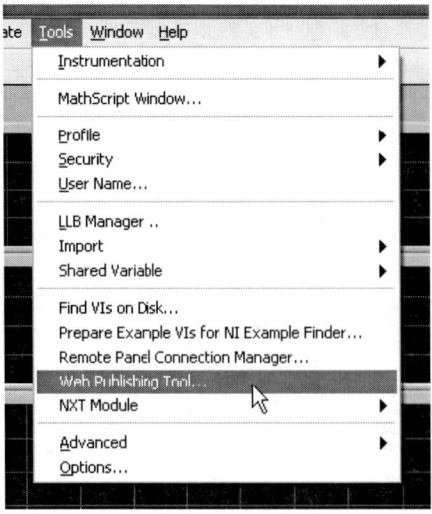

Figure 20.9
Launching Web Publishing Tool

Figure 20.10 shows the first window in the setup. In the VI name box you select the VI that is currently running. In the Viewing Mode select Snapshot. That mode merely converts the Front Panel into an image and sends it to any computer that asks for it. Monitor does the same thing, except that it sends some additional commands to the computer to reload the image periodically. Embedded allows the other computer to actually control the Front Panel but requires that some additional software be installed. I suggest you investigate the LabVIEW documentation if you really want people to be able to do that. The other thing you need to do from this window is Start the Web Server. After that click Next>.

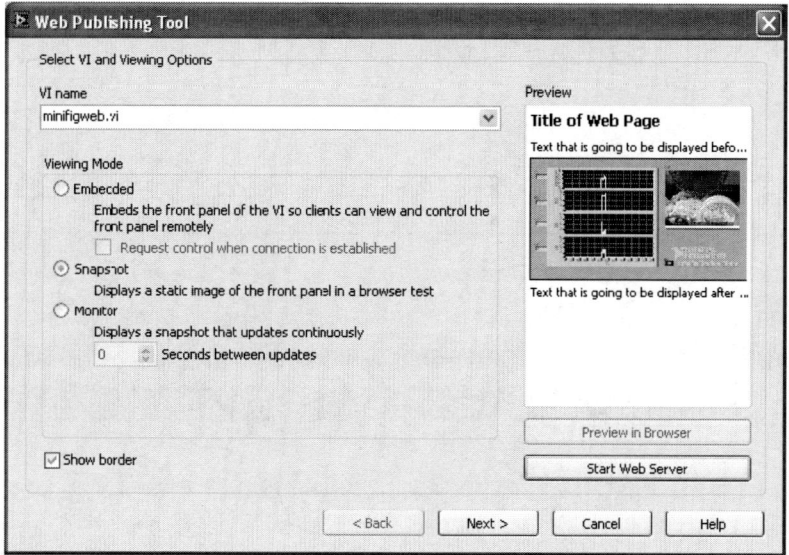

Figure 20.10
Web Publishing Tool First Window

In the window shown in Figure 20.11 you can enter a Document Title and some text that will go before and after the Front Page image. If you know Hypertext Markup Language (HTML), that can be inserted here to really spruce up the page. Then click Next>.

Figure 20.12 shows the last step, which is saving everything to disk. The URL is what you would type into a browser to see the web page. All web pages actually have a unique sequence of numbers like this, called the IP address, but they are usually disguised with a fancy domain name like www.ni.com to make it easier to remember. We will get to this later.

When you save the setup, another window will tell you the URL again and give you the option of launching your computer's web browser to see it. Just click OK, as

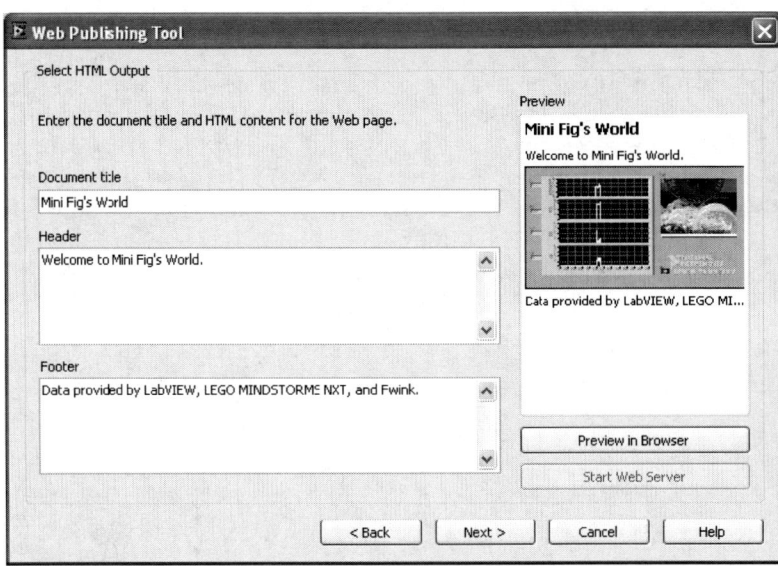

Figure 20.11
Web Publishing Tool Second Window

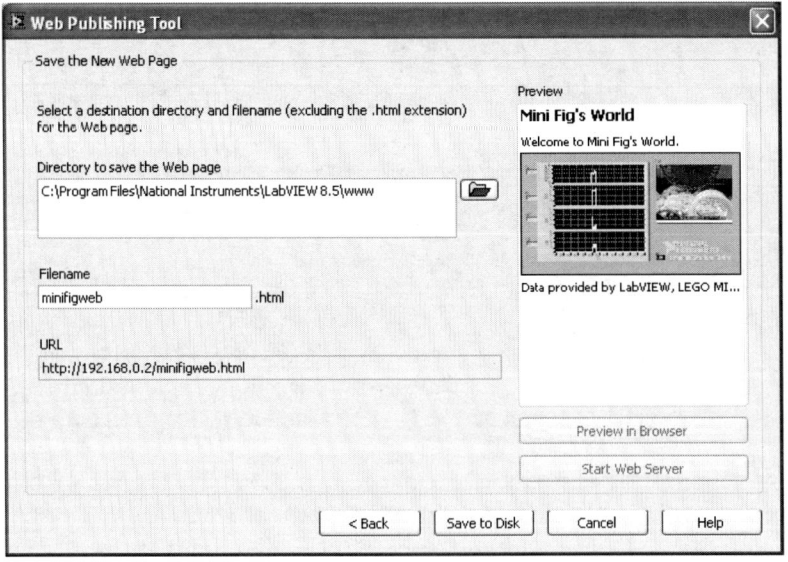

Figure 20.12
Web Publishing Tool Final Window

shown in Figure 20.13. With the Web Server and minifigweb running, you can now open your web browser and type in the URL to see the web page version of your Front Panel. Because we selected Snapshot, it will load the page once, and you will need to reload it to see any changes.

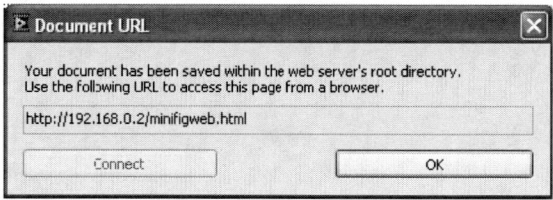

Figure 20.13
Document URL

While you are in your web browser, type www.myIPaddress.com, and a window like the one in Figure 20.14 will appear. If the URL number you listed is the same as the one in the LabVIEW setup, anyone in the world can enter the URL and see exactly the same thing you see from your computer. If not, read on.

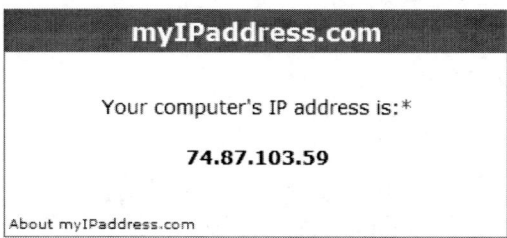

Figure 20.14
myIPaddress.com Page

Port Forwarding

You probably have Internet access with a modem that is followed with a device called a router. In most cases the URL that appears in the setup is actually good only for computers on the same side of that router. That could be all of the computers in your home or business, and that might be all you want. If you need wider access, you will have to log in to the router to control something called Port Forwarding. You will need the manual for the router to learn how to do that, but usually you end up at a menu that looks something like the one in Figure 20.15. There you tell the router to

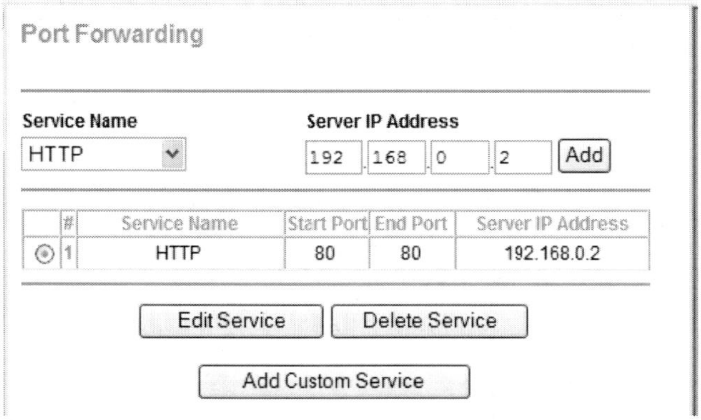

Port Forwarding
Service Name
Server IP Address
HTTP
192
168
0
2
Add
#
Service Name
Start Port
End Port
Server IP Address
1
HTTP
80
80
192.168.0.2
Edit Service
Delete Service
Add Custom Service

Figure 20.15
Typical Router Port Forwarding Window

forward anything that is trying to get HTTP to your specific computer. The Server IP address is the same one LabVIEW gave you.

Now your web page is available at the URL made up of the numbers given by myIPaddress.com and the file name given by the LabVIEW setup. In this case it is HTTP://74.87.103.59/minifigweb.html. Figure 20.16 shows the finished web page

Mini Fig's World
Welcome to Mini Fig's World.
Temp
71.4
Wheel
75
Sound
3
Light
62
Time
Picture
Saturday, April 26, 2008 @ 11:03:26 AM
stop
STOP
NATIONAL INSTRUMENTS
LabVIEW Student Edition
Data provided by LabVIEW, LEGO MINDSTORMS NXT, and Fwink.

Figure 20.16
Minifigweb Web Page

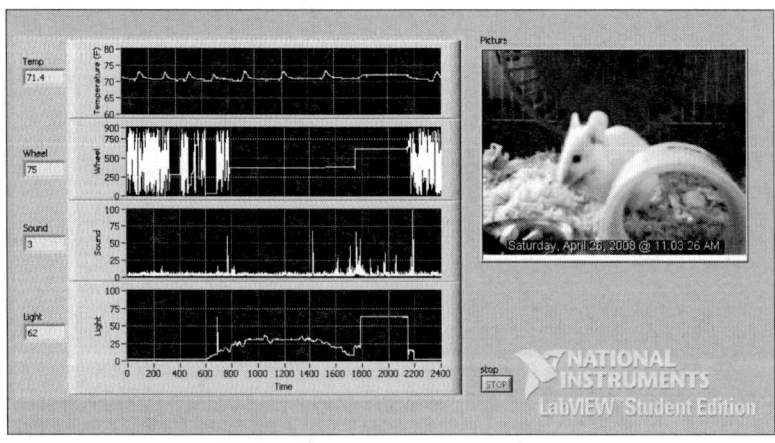

with a day's worth of activity plotted and Mini eating a seed. Depending on your Internet provider, this address may change every time you connect to the network.

Reflections

That is as far as I will take you in this book. You should know all the NXT and Direct Commands blocks, along with a few a few primitive ones. We have only scratched the surface of LabVIEW's features, but we have still created some pretty complex programs. There is a tutorial on building NXT-G blocks in Appendix C and two Appendixes remaining that describe each block in more technical detail.

Final Reflections

21

Study without reflection is a waste of time; reflection without study is dangerous.
—*Confucius*

There is much more to learn about both MINDSTORMS and LabVIEW than what I've presented here. In this chapter I'm going to provide a few of my favorite information sources for you. Naturally the list grows all the time, so make sure you do a little digging on your own.

More MINDSTORMS

There is a wide variety of what I call "project" books available for the NXT that have an assortment of interesting construction projects with step-by-step instructions. They come in handy when you are stuck for an idea or need some inspiration. I suggest you look into few of them to find one that matches up with your interests, but there are two books that I'd specifically recommend. because they go far beyond construction projects.

Extreme NXT: Extending the LEGO MINDSTORMS NXT to the Next Level, by Michael Gasperi and Philippe and Isabelle Hurbain deals with hardware and not just software for the NXT. The projects in the book show you how to build your own sensors and actuators and how to broaden the NXT beyond the limits of what came inside the box. I think it widens your MINDSTORMS experience to include at least a few of the skills you need to build more complex and elaborate robots.

LEGO MINDSTORMS NXT Power Programming: Robotics in C, by John C. Hansen is similar to the present book, but it is written only for the C language. Even if you don't intend to program in C, Hansen's book has information about the low-level interfaces and operations of the NXT. You will recognize many of the system calls and IOMap manipulations that you learned from this book. I even referred to Hansen's book often during the writing of this book to make sure I had all of the details right.

It is probably obvious to mention, but the official LEGO MINDSTORMS website is the first place to look for more information about MINDSTORMS. The base URL is www.mindstorms.com. Most importantly, the site provides news and documentation about both the hardware and the software. In particular, the extreme topics page at mindstorms.lego.com/Overview/NXTreme.aspx is well worth visiting. The site also has a comprehensive list of books available for the NXT.

Since the NXT first became available, a web community blog and forum called NXTasy has provided a central meeting ground for individuals using the NXT. The URL is www.nxtasy.org. The site is run by Guy Ziv, who also was the technical reviewer for this book. Among the many invaluable services offered at the NXTasy site is a repository of Custom NXT-G blocks. Another blog devoted to MINDSTORMS is The NXT Step. Its URL is www.thenxtstep.blogspot.com, and it provides NXT-related information as well as more general news of a robot-oriented nature. Dating back to well before the arrival of MINDSTORMS is the general LEGO News Group called Lugnet. In particular, the robotics subgroup at www.lugnet.com/robotics is still a major clearinghouse for news about the MINDSTORMS product. There are even more specific MINDSTORMS-related subgroups hosted there.

The web is also full of sites hosted by fanatics and educators who spend a great deal of personal time and effort sharing what they know about MINDSTORMS. By far the best of these is hosted by my colleague Philo Hurbain at www.philohome.com. His site is a goldmine of information. A massive site, run by a school in Luxembourg, is called Boulette's Robotics page at www.convict.lu/Jeunes/RoboticsIntro.htm. Another site run by an educational organization is the Tufts University Center for Engineering Educational Outreach which is dedicated to providing educators with resources for teaching engineering using LEGO at www.legoengineering.com. My own site, www.extremenxt.com, tries to provide information about a wide variety of MINDSTORMS topics. Many other people, including Matthias Paul Scholz at mynxt.matthiaspaulscholz.eu, Anders Søborg at www.norgesgade14.dk, Dave Astolfo at www.astolfo.com, Sivan Toledo at www.tau.ac.il/~stoledo/lego/, and Steve Hassenplug at www.teamhassenplug.org, provide great informational sites too. I've probably left out many important sites, but you can find them through links on the sites already mentioned or by searching further.

The Legacy Sensors and other MINDSTORMS-related merchandise can be purchased from LEGO's Education site at www.legoeducation.com. That site also has general information and offers a support community. There are three other sources of aftermarket sensors that are compatible with the NXT; HiTechnic Products at www.hitechnic.com, Mindsensors at www.mindsensors.com, and Vernier at www.vernier.com/nxt.

Finally, for those of you that are a little more aggressive, First LEGO League at www.firstlegoleague.org has information about a far-reaching competition that uses the LEGO MINDSTORMS NXT for children from 9 to 14. There is also a junior version that is designed for children from 6 to 9 years old.

More LabVIEW

National Instruments produces LabVIEW and a wide variety of both hardware and software products. Their main URL is http://www.ni.com. The LabVIEW language is popular well beyond MINDSTORMS, and there is an academic side of the company devoted to education. The answer to the question "How can I learn LabVIEW?" can be found at http://www.ni.com/academic/lv_training/how_learn_lv.htm. The academic side also dedicates a portion of its site specifically to MINDSTORMS at http://www.ni.com/academic/mindstorms, and there is a user forum at http://forums.ni.com/ni/board?board.id=beta18 for discussion and feedback.

For those of you who like printed materials, *LabVIEW for Everyone: Graphical Programming Made Easy and Fun*, by Jeffrey Travis and Jim Kring is a great book for learning LabVIEW. It is available from online booksellers and retail stores. You can also get a LabVIEW Student Version with an introductory textbook that covers the basics of the language.

NXT Block Reference

Common Information about All NXT Blocks

Sequence Flow

Sequence Flow input and output connections are provided in most NXT blocks to force execution sequence when needed. Blocks are wired so that the Sequence Flow Output of the first block is fed to the Sequence Flow Input of the next, and so on. The type is Boolean, but its value is not important.

Figure A.1
Sequence Flow

Defaults

Most inputs have default values, and they are usually listed within parentheses ().

Input Blocks

If you are using blocks for the same input in more than one place on the block diagram, you should tie the Input Port input of the later blocks to the Input Port Duplicator of the first block. That way if you change the port, it will automatically be changed for all the other blocks.

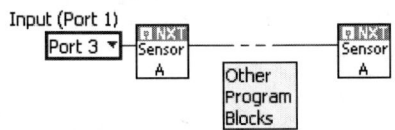

Figure A.2
Input Port Duplication

The NXT reads sensor values either with an analog-to-digital converter or through an I^2C or Low Speed LS communication bus. The analog-to-digital converter has a range from 0 to 1023, and this is available on some blocks as the Raw Value.

Distance Sensor

Figure A.3
Ultrasonic Distance Sensor

The Ultrasonic Distance Sensor measures the distance to the nearest object in front of it. It does this by sending out a pulse of ultrasonic sound and then timing how long it takes for the echo to return. The Distance is measured in centimeters, but can be converted to inches by setting the Convert input to True. The range is about 0 to 2.5 meters or 100 inches. Some problems occur when there are multiple Ultrasonic Sensors in the same room, because they can't tell the difference between another sensor's pulse and their own echo. It uses I^2C to communicate with the NXT, so it doesn't have a Raw Value.

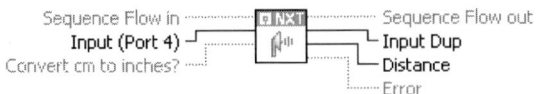

Figure A.4
Distance Sensor Block

`U8`	**Input Port** (Port 4)
	1–4
`TF`	**Convert cm to inches? (F)**
	True = inches
	False = cm
`TF`	**Error**
	True if there was an I^2C communication fault.
`U8`	**Distance**
	0–255 cm
	0–100 in
`U8`	**Input Port dup**
	Same as Input

Legacy Light Sensor

Figure A.5
Legacy Light Sensor

The Legacy Light sensor works like the NXT Light Sensor except that it doesn't have the option of turning off the built-in LED. Also, like the NXT Light Sensor, it uses a silicon-based phototransistor that is mostly sensitive to near-infrared light. It uses the LEGO Electric Plate–type connector, so it requires an adapter to connect to the NXT. It is read with the analog-to-digital converter, and the Raw Value is available.

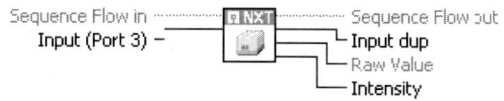

Figure A.6
Legacy Light Block

U8	**Input (Port 3)**
	1–4
U16	**Intensity**
	0–100
U16	**Raw Value**
	0–1023
U8	**Input dup**
	Same as Input

Legacy Rotation Sensor

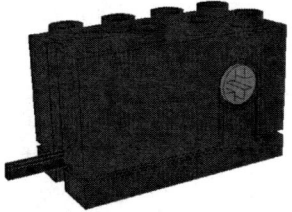

Figure A.7
Legacy Rotation Sensor

The Legacy Rotation Sensor looks like a large brick with an axle hole toward one end. Unlike the NXT Rotation sensor with one-degree accuracy, the Legacy produces only 16 ticks per revolution. Don't confuse these ticks with the time-related ticks; they are basically 22.5-degree increments. Clockwise is Fwd. when viewed as shown. The NXT will keep track of the ticks over time, and you can zero the count by setting the Reset input to True. As with other Legacy Sensors, it uses the LEGO Electric Plate connector. Although it is read with the analog-to-digital converter, the Raw Value is not available.

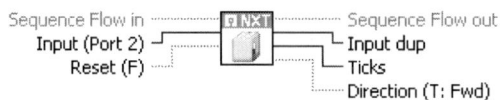

Figure A.8
Legacy Rotation Block

`TF`	**Reset (F)**	True = Set ticks to 0
`U8`	**Input (Port 2)**	1–4
`I32`	**Ticks**	0–2,147,483,647
`TF`	**Direction**	True = Fwd False = Rev
`U8`	**Input dup**	Same as Input

Legacy Temperature Sensor

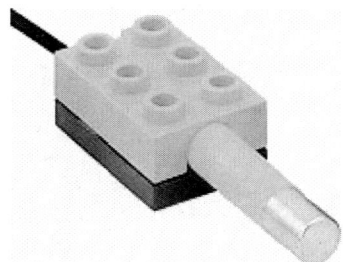

Figure A.9
Legacy Temperature Sensor

The Legacy Temperature sensor looks like a LEGO brick with a metal rod sticking out of its side. The output is in Fahrenheit by default but can be set to Celsius by setting Units to True. The Temperature output is 10 times the actual temperature. For example 68.3°F is read as a Temperature equal to 683, and that way you get 1/10 degree resolution with only an Integer value. The output range is from –20 to 70°C or –4 to 158°F. It uses the older LEGO Electric Plate–type connector. It is read with the analog-to-digital converter, and the Raw Value is available.

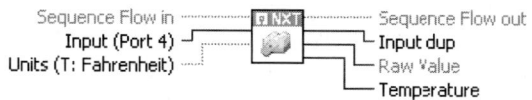

Figure A.10
Legacy Temperature Block

`TF`	**Units (T: Fahrenheit)** True = °F False = °C
`U8`	**Input (Port 4)** 1–4
`U16`	**Temperature x10** −200–700°C −40–1580°F
`U16`	**Raw Value** 0–1023
`U8`	**Input dup** Same as Input

Legacy Touch Sensor

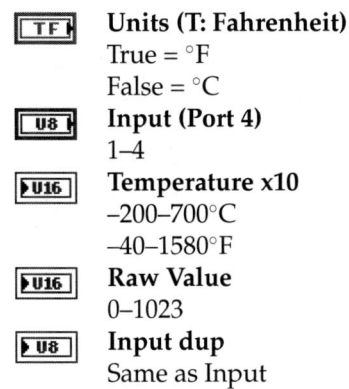

Figure A.11
Legacy Touch Sensor

Functionally, the Legacy Touch Sensor is the same as the NXT Touch Sensor. However, physically they are very different. The Legacy Touch Sensor has a softer switch mechanism that doesn't require as much travel to activate as the one on the NXT. Like the other Legacy blocks, it uses the older Electric Plate–type connector. It is read with the analog-to-digital converter, and the Raw Value is available.

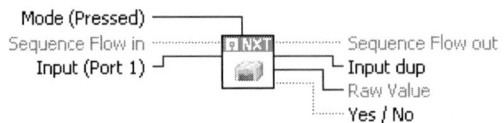

Figure A.12
Legacy Touch Block

`U8`	**Input (Port 1)**
	1–4
`U16`	**Mode (Pressed)**
	0 = Pressed
	1 = Released
	2 = Bumped
`U16`	**Raw Value**
	0–1023
`TF`	**Yes/No**
	True/False
`U8`	**Input dup**
	Same as Input

Light Sensor

Figure A.13
Light Sensor

The NXT Light Sensor block has an input for Port Number and the option to turn on the built-in LED with the Generate Light input. The default Input Port Number is 3, and you don't need to supply an input to this connection as long as you have the sensor plugged into port 3. The default condition of the Generate Light is True. The measured light level is the Intensity output connection that will have Integer values from 0 to 100. Because the sensor is read with the analog-to-digital converter, the Raw Value is available.

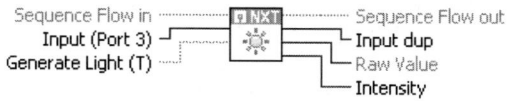

Figure A.14
Light Sensor Block

TF	**Floodlight (T)**
	True = Yes
	False = No
U8	**Input (Port 3)**
	1–4
U16	**Intensity**
	0–100
U16	**Raw Value**
	0–1023
U8	**Input dup**
	Same as Input

NXT Buttons

Figure A.15
NXT Buttons

Three of the buttons can be read with the NXT Buttons block. The Yes/No output reflects the physical condition of the button and the Mode input. When in Bumped mode, the output will be true if the NXT Button has been bumped (pressed then released) since the last button was read.

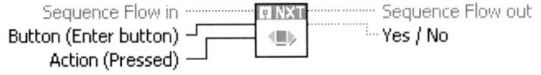

Figure A.16
NXT Buttons Block

`U16` **Button (Enter button)**
1 = Right
2 = Left
3 = Enter

`U16` **Mode**
0 = Pressed
1 = Released
2 = Bumped

`TF` **Yes/No**
True/False

Rotation Sensor

Figure A.17
Rotation Sensor

Rotation Sensors keep track of the rotation of the NXT motors. Usually they are used to regulate the speed and synchronization of motors. However, they can also be used just as sensors. The Degrees output is the total amount of rotation since the last time the sensor was reset with the Reset input. The Direction output tells you whether the Direction of rotation was forward or reverse. Because the Rotation Sensor is really part of a motor, it is connected to an Output Port.

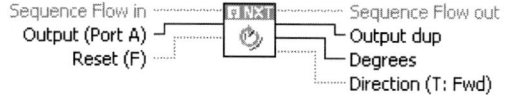

Figure A.18
Rotation Sensor Block

Reset (F)
True = set ticks to 0

Output (Port A)
0 = A
1 = B
2 = C

Degrees out
0–2,147,483,647

Output dup
Same as Input

Direction (T: Fwd)
True = Fwd
False = Rev

Sound Sensor

Figure A.19
Sound Sensor

The sensor reports the average Volume of the sound in the environment. That means it responds relatively slowly to sound level and does not rapidly pick up sound waves as does a microphone. There is an input to select a frequency sensitivity to favor the range of hearing for humans called dBA. The sensor is read with the analog-to-digital converter, and the Raw Value is available.

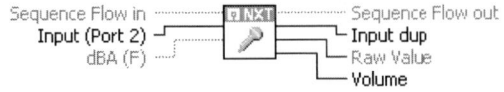

Figure A.20
Sound Sensor Block

`TF`	**DBA**	True = Yes False = No
`U8`	**Input (Port 2)**	1–4
`I32`	**Volume**	0–100
`U16`	**Raw Value**	0–1023
`U8`	**Input dup**	Same as Input

Touch Sensor

Figure A.21
Touch Sensor

The NXT Touch Sensor can be programmed with the Mode input to set the Yes/No output to a True when the switch is Pressed or when the switch is in the Released state. Bumped means the sensor has been touched and released since the last time it was examined. Because the sensor is read with the analog-to-digital converter, it has a Raw Value output.

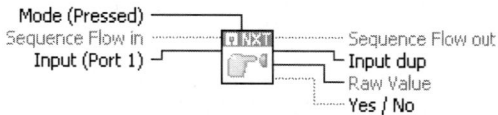

Figure A.22
Touch Sensor Block

`U8`	**Input (Port 1)**
	1–4
`U16`	**Mode (Pressed)**
	0 = Pressed
	1 = Released
	2 = Bumped
`U16`	**Raw Value**
	0–1023
`TF`	**Yes/No**
	True/False
`U8`	**Input dup**
	Same as Input

Output Blocks

If you are using blocks for the same output in more than one place on the block diagram, you can tie the Output Port input of the later blocks to the Output Port Duplicator of the first block. That way if you change the port, it will automatically be changed for all the blocks.

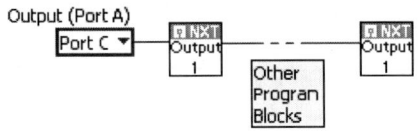

Figure A.23
Output Port Duplication

For most blocks you can choose whether the motor will brake or coast after finishing its action. Set the motor to brake if you want it to stop precisely at an exact position and (attempt to) hold that position. Braking requires additional battery power, because the motor does extra work to maintain the position. Coast is a good choice if this block is followed by another block controlling the same motor.

You can precisely control the acceleration of the motor by selecting "Ramp Up" or "Ramp Down." A motor set to "Ramp Up" will slowly increase its speed until it reaches specified power. A motor set to "Ramp Down" will slowly decrease its speed until it reaches zero power. A motor set to "Constant" will reach full power immediately and will stop quickly by either coasting or braking (depending on the setting).

Power control will attempt to compensate for any resistance or slippage that the motor encounters. It will increase power to a maximum of 100% to maintain the same rotation amount per second.

With "Wait for completion" selected, the motor will finish its action completely before allowing the program to move on. If you de-select "Wait for completion," other blocks in the program can proceed while your motor completes its action. For example, a Sound block placed after the Motor block could start playing a sound file while the motor continues its action.

Legacy Lamp

Figure A.24
Legacy Lamp

The Legacy Lamp block turns on a Legacy Lamp at the specified Intensity level or turns it off by setting Power to False.

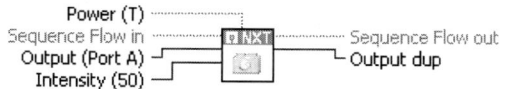

Power (T)
Sequence Flow in
Output (Port A)
Intensity (50)
Sequence Flow out
Output dup

Figure A.25
Legacy Lamp Block

I32 **Intensity (50)**
0—100

TF **Power (T)**
True = On
False = Off

U8 **Output (Port A)**
0 = A
1 = B
2 = C

U8 **Output dup**
Same as Input

Legacy Motor

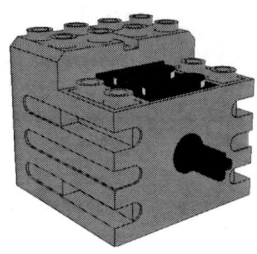

Figure A.26
Legacy Motor

The NXT has backward compatibility with the first-generation MINDSTORMS motors, but the Legacy Motor doesn't have the built-in Rotation Sensor. The block has the ability to Stop and apply a Brake, but it doesn't have the ability to Stop and Coast. You can use the Stop Motor block for that.

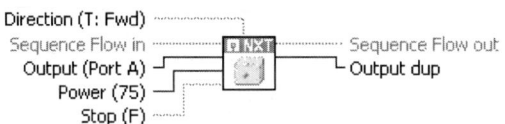

Figure A.27
Legacy Motor Block

I32 **Power (75)**
0—100

TF **Direction (T: Fwd)**
True = Fwd
False = Rev

TF **Stop (F)**
True = Stop
False = Go

U8 **Output (Port A)**
0 = A
1 = B
2 = C

U8 **Output dup**
Same as Input

Motor

Figure A.28
Motor

The Motor block is used to run a motor either for a specified distance or time, or for an unlimited duration.

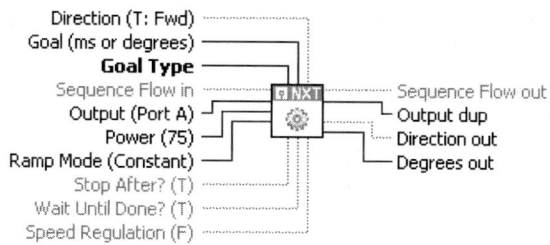

Figure A.29
Motor Block

`U8`	**Output (Port A)**
	0 = A
	1 – B
	2 = C
`U16`	**Goal Type**
	0 = Unlimited
	1 = Distance
	2 = Time
	3 = Stop
`U32`	**Goal (ms or degrees)**
	0—2,147,483,647 ms or degrees
`TF`	**Stop After? (T)**
	True/False

TF	**Wait Until Done? (T)**
	True/False
TF	**Speed Regulation (F)**
	True/False
I32	**Power (75)**
	0—100
U16	**Ramp Mode (Constant)**
	0 = Constant
	1 = Ramp Up
	2 = Ramp Down
TF	**Direction**
	True = Fwd
	False = Rev
I32	**Degrees out**
	0–2,147,483,647
TF	**Direction out**
	True = Fwd
	False = Rev
U8	**Output dup**
	Same as Input

Motor Distance

Figure A.30
Motor

Motor Distance takes care of turning a motor a specified Distance in Degrees, but there are various ways it can do that. Output port, Power level, Direction, Speed Regulation, and Sequence Flow are the same as Motor Unlimited. The Next Action input is the same as the Stop Motor, but there is an unexpected interaction with another of the block's inputs—Wait for completion. You can get the Brake Next Action only if you also choose to Wait for completion. If you don't Wait, you will always get Coast. Brake stops the motor very close to the target angle, but Coast can continue a full rotation before the motor finally comes to rest.

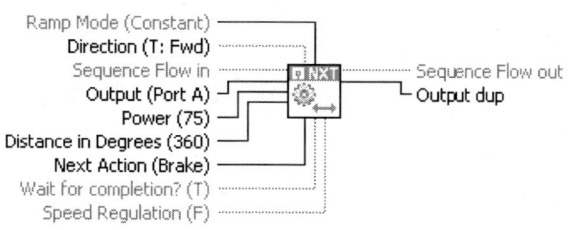

Figure A.31
Motor Distance Block

U8	**Output (Port A)**
	0 = A
	1 = B
	2 = C
TF	**Speed Regulation (F)**
	True/False
I32	**Power (75)**
	0–100
I32	**Distance in Degrees (360)**
	0–2,147,483,647 degrees
U16	**Ramp Mode (Constant)**
	0 = Constant
	1 = Ramp Up
	2 = Ramp Down
TF	**Wait for completion? (T)**
	True/False
U16	**Next Action (Brake)**
	0 = Brake
	1 = Coast
TF	**Direction (T: Fwd)**
	True = Fwd
	False = Rev
U8	**Output dup**
	Same as Input

Motor Time

Figure A.32
Motor

Motor Time runs a motor for Time on Output port, and at the specified Power and Direction with optional Speed Regulation and Next Action. The amount of Time is specified in milliseconds (ms), and the block always does a Wait for completion.

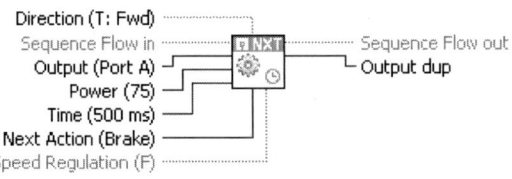

Figure A.33
Motor Time Block

`U8`	**Output (Port A)** 0 = A 1 = B 2 = C
`TF`	**Speed Regulation (F)** True/False
`I32`	**Power (75)** 0–100
`I32`	**Time (500 ms)** 0–2,147,483,647 ms
`U16`	**Next Action (Brake)** 0 = Brake 1 = Coast
`TF`	**Direction (T: Fwd)** True = Fwd False = Rev
`U8`	**Output dup** Same as Input

Motor Unlimited

Figure A.34
Motor

Motor Unlimited turns on a motor at the specified power and direction. It will remain on until a Stop Motor block turns it off. Speed Regulation controls whether the NXT will try to maintain a constant rotation speed regardless of the load.

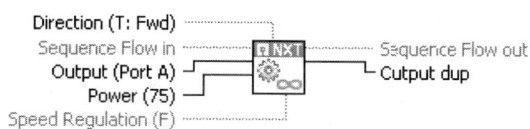

Figure A.35
Motor Unlimited Block

`U8`	**Output (Port A)** 0 = A 1 = B 2 = C
`I32`	**Power (75)** 0–100
`TF`	**Direction (T: Fwd)** True = Fwd False = Rev
`TF`	**Speed Regulation (F)** True/False
`U8`	**Output dup** Same as Input

Stop Motor

Figure A.36
Motor

Stop Motor Stops a motor from running by either braking or coasting.

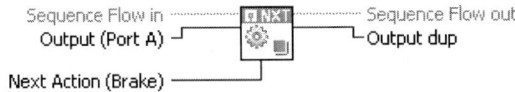

Figure A.37
Stop Motor

| U8 | **Output (Port A)**
0 = A
1 = B
2 = C

| U16 | **Next Action (Brake)**
0 = Brake
1 = Coast

| U8 | **Output dup**
Same as Input

Move

Figure A.38
Motors

Move can run up to three motors for a specified distance, time, or unlimited duration. The left and right motors will be synchronized. When two motors are synchronized, the firmware attempts to keep them turning at the same rate. The differential speed between the two motors can be controlled using the Steering input. Steering values are between –100 (left) and 100 (right).

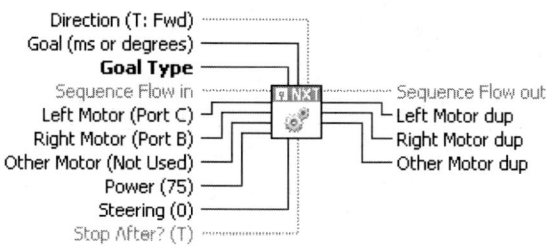

Figure A.39
Move Block

Goal (ms or degrees)
0–2,147,483,647 ms or degrees

Goal Type
0 = Unlimited
1 = Distance
2 = Time
3 = Stop

Power (75)
0–100

Steering (0)
-100–100

Stop After? (T)
True/False

Direction (T: Fwd)
True = Fwd
False = Rev

Left Motor (Port C)
0 = A
1 = B
2 = C

Right Motor (Port B)
0 = A
1 = B
2 = C

Other Motor (Not Used)
-1 = Not Used
0 = A
1 = B
2 = C

Right Motor dup
Same as Input

Other Motor dup
Same as Input

Left Motor dup
Same as Input

Sync Distance

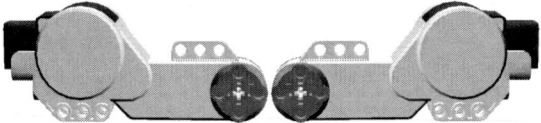

Figure A.40
Two Motors

Sync Distance is similar to Motor Distance with an added input for Steering from the
Sync Unlimited block. Steering, as you recall, varies from –100 to 100, with 0 used for
going straight. The block always does a Wait for completion.

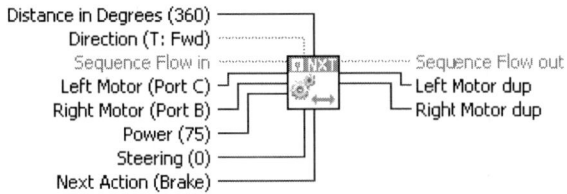

Figure A.41
Sync Distance Block

`U8` **Left Motor (Port C)**
0 = A
1 = B
2 = C

`U8` **Right Motor (Port B)**
0 = A
1 = B
2 = C

`I32` **Power (75)**
0–100

`I32` **Steering (0)**
-100–100

`I32` **Distance in Degrees (360)**
0–2,147,483,647 degrees

`U16` **Next Action (Brake)**
0 = Brake
1 = Coast

`TF` **Direction (T: Fwd)**
True = Fwd
False = Rev

`U8` **Left Motor dup**
Same as Input

`U8` **Right Motor dup**
Same as Input

Sync Stop

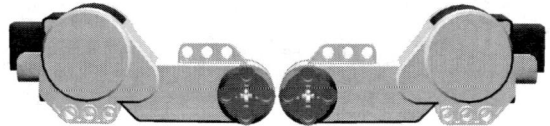

Figure A.42
Two Motors

Sync Stop stops two motors from running, by either braking or coasting.

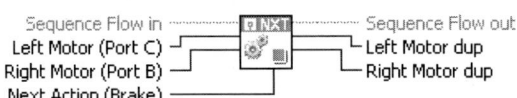

Figure A.43
Sync Stop Block

| **U8** | **Left Motor (Port C)**
| | 0 = A
| | 1 = B
| | 2 = C

| **U8** | **Right Motor (Port B)**
| | 0 = A
| | 1 = B
| | 2 = C

| **U16** | **Next Action (Brake)**
| | 0 = Brake
| | 1 = Coast

| **U8** | **Left Motor dup**
| | Same as Input

| **U8** | **Right Motor dup**
| | Same as Input

Sync Time

Figure A.44
Two Motors

Sync Time works much like Sync Distance, except that the move is defined by an amount of Time in milliseconds (ms). There are many factors such as battery level and friction that make movement based only on time unreliable. The preferred way to get from one point to another is by defining the distances to travel, but occasionally you might want a robot to dance or shake in a particular way that is better defined by time; in that case you would need the Sync Time block.

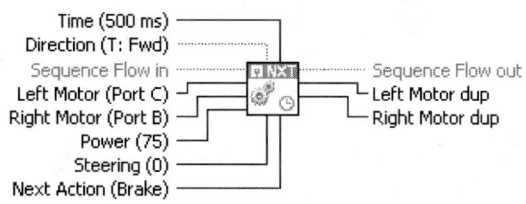

Figure A.45
Sync Time Block

U8	**Left Motor (Port C)**
	0 = A
	1 = B
	2 = C
U8	**Right Motor (Port B)**
	0 = A
	1 = B
	2 = C
I32	**Power (75)**
	0–100
I32	**Steering (0)**
	-100–100
I32	**Time (500 ms)**
	0–2,147,483,647ms
U16	**Next Action (Brake)**
	0 = Brake
	1 = Coast
TF	**Direction (T: Fwd)**
	True = Fwd
	False = Rev
U8	**Left Motor dup**
	Same as Input
U8	**Right Motor dup**
	Same as Input

Sync Unlimited

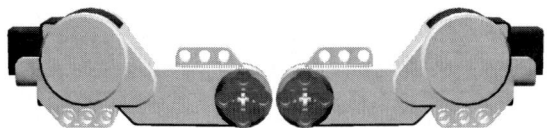

Figure A.46
Two Motors

Sync Unlimited turns on two motors and tries to synchronize their rotation. Steering should be between –100 (left) and 100 (right). The motors are turned off with the Sync Stop bock.

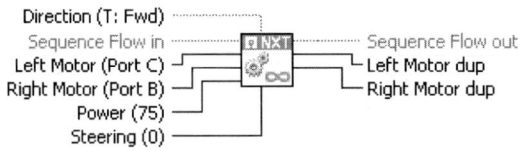

Figure A.47
Sync Unlimited Block

[U8] **Left Motor (Port C)**
0 = A
1 = B
2 = C

[U8] **Right Motor (Port B)**
0 = A
1 = B
2 = C

[I32] **Power (75)**
0–100

[I32] **Steering (0)**
-100–100

Direction (T: Fwd)
True = Fwd
False = Rev

Left Motor dup
Same as Input

Right Motor dup
Same as Input

Reset Motor

Figure A.48
Motors

Reset Motor resets up to three motors and clears their internal rotation counts.

Figure A.49
Reset Motor Block

Reset A
True/False

Reset B
True/False

Reset C
True/False

Display Blocks

The NXT display is 100 pixels wide and 64 pixels high, and the pixels can be only black or white. The Display blocks have the option of clearing the entire display before the operation with the Clear Display input. The origin (0, 0) is in the lower-left corner.

Display Circle

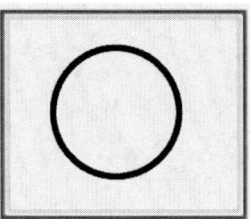

Figure A.50
Circle

Display Circle draws a one-pixel-thick circle at the Center Location with a specified Radius.

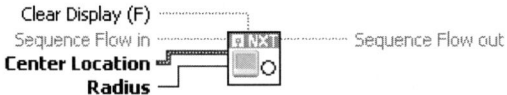

Figure A.51
Display Circle Block

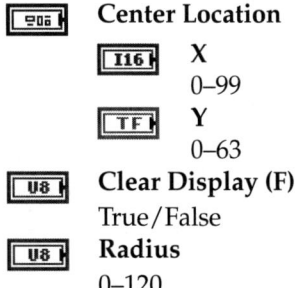

Center Location
    X
    0–99
    Y
    0–63
Clear Display (F)
True/False
Radius
0–120

Display Line

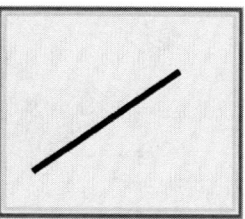

Figure A.52
Line

Display Line requires two Location inputs. One is called the Start and the other the End, but it doesn't really matter in which direction the line is drawn. It simply draws a line between the two coordinates, and it will look the same either way.

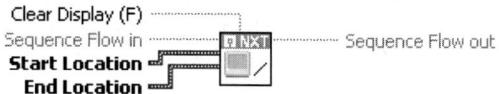

Figure A.53
Display Line Block

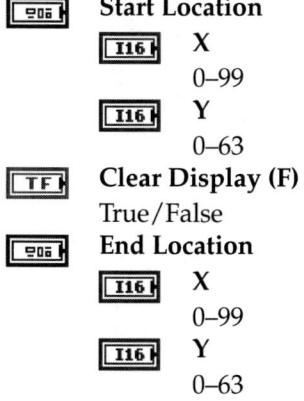

Start Location
    X
    0–99
    Y
    0–63
Clear Display (F)
    True/False
End Location
    X
    0–99
    Y
    0–63

Display Picture

Figure A.54
Picture

The name of the file to display is input as a String, and the convention is to use the .ric file extension for image files. The NXT image file format is rather involved. It has features that aren't implemented in the current version of the NXT software, and the Variables input is a hook for future expansion. The Location input defines the lower-right corner of the image.

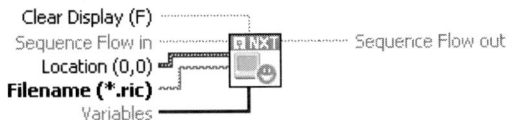

Figure A.55
Display Picture Block

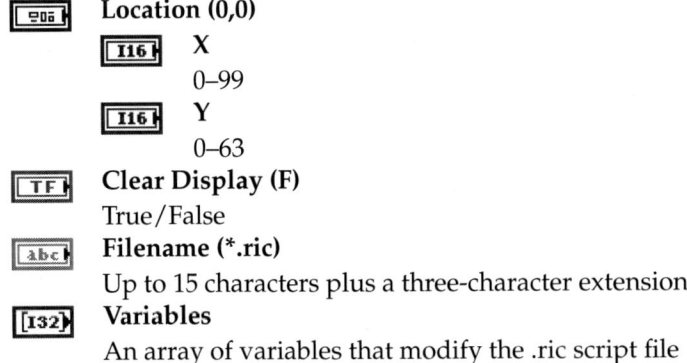

Location (0,0)
    X
    0–99
    Y
    0–63
Clear Display (F)
True/False
Filename (*.ric)
Up to 15 characters plus a three-character extension
Variables
An array of variables that modify the .ric script file

Display Point

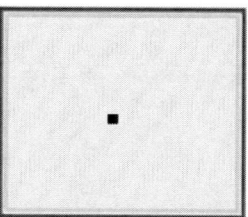

Figure A.56
Point

Display Point draws a single pixel point on the display at Location.

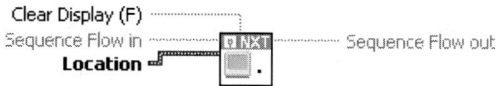

Figure A.57
Display Point Block

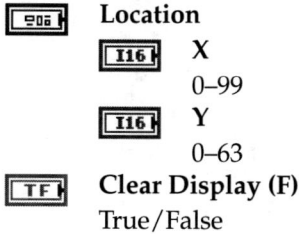

Location
   X
   0–99
   Y
   0–63
Clear Display (F)
True/False

Display Text

Figure A.58
Text

Display Text writes a Text String to the display at Location.

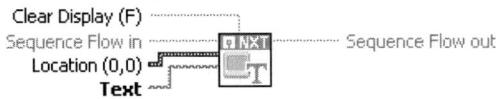

Figure A.59
Display Text Block

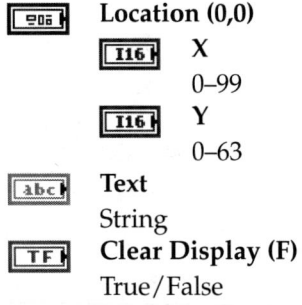

Location (0,0)

X
0–99

Y
0–63

Text
String

Clear Display (F)
True/False

Restore Default Display

Figure A.60
Default Screen

Restore Default Display puts the NXT display to its default state.

Figure A.61
Restore Default Display Block

Sound Blocks

Common information about Sound blocks includes the following:

- Waiting
- Repeat

Play Sound File

This block plays a Sound file on the NXT as defined by the Filename input. Volume control is available at four levels and mute. Options are to Wait for Completion and to Repeat the sound until it is stopped.

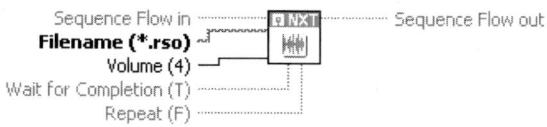

Figure A.62
Play Sound File Block

`abc`	**Filename (*.rso)**
	15 characters plus a three-character file extension
`U8`	**Volume (4)**
	0 = Mute
	1 = 25%
	2 = 50%
	3 = 75%
	4 = 100%
`TF`	**Wait for Completion (T)**
	True/False
`TF`	**Repeat (F)**
	True/False

Play Tone

This block plays a Tone of a specified Frequency on the NXT for a defined time Duration in milliseconds (ms). Volume control is available at four levels and mute. Options are to Wait for completion and to Repeat the sound until it is stopped.

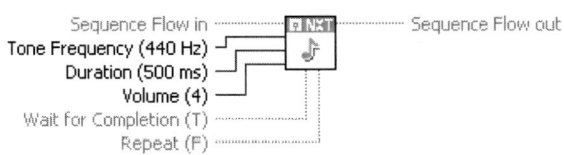

Figure A.63
Play Tone Block

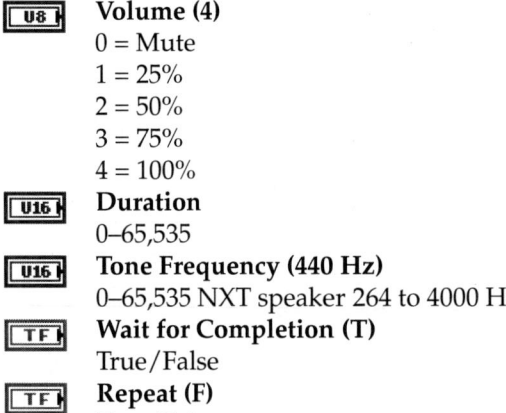

Volume (4)
0 = Mute
1 = 25%
2 = 50%
3 = 75%
4 = 100%

Duration
0–65,535

Tone Frequency (440 Hz)
0–65,535 NXT speaker 264 to 4000 Hz

Wait for Completion (T)
True/False

Repeat (F)
True/False

Stop Sound

The Stop Sound Block stops any sound generation on the NXT.

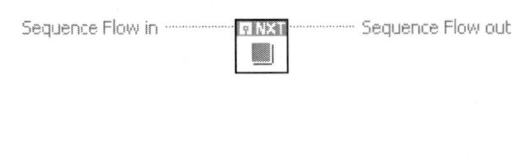

Figure A.64
Stop Sound Block

File Access Blocks

Easy file types use a text-style file format, and the size of the file is automatically adjusted as the file expands. The other file functions use a binary style file and must be either opened with enough room or manually expanded.

File error codes:

Error	Code
SUCCESS	0
NO_HANDLES	33024
NO_FILES	33536
PARTIAL_WRITE	33792
EOF	34048
FILE_NOT_FOUND	34560
FILE_CLOSED	34816
NO_LINEAR_SPACE	35072
GENERIC_ERROR	35328
FILE_BUSY	35584
NO_WRITE_BUFFERS	35840
ILLEGAL_APPEND	36096
FILE_FULL	36352
FILE_EXISTS	36608
ILLEGAL_FILE_NAME	37376
ILLEGAL_HANDLE	37632

Close File

This block closes the file specified by File Handle.

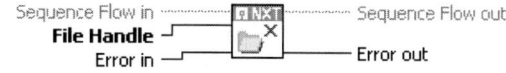

Figure A.65
Close File Block

`U16` **Error in**
Skips block if not 0

`U8` **File Handle**
Number from Open or Resolve

`U16` **Error out**
See table

Delete File

This block deletes the specified Filename.

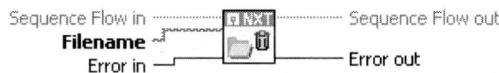

Figure A.66
Delete File Block

`abc►` **Filename**
15 characters plus a three-character file extension

`U16►` **Error in**
Skips block if not 0

`►U16` **Error out**
See table

Easy Close File

Easy Close closes the file Filename. You should make an effort to close files you have been writing. You can start reading at the beginning of a file again by closing it and reopening.

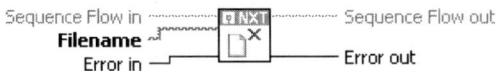

Figure A.67
Easy Close File Block

`abc►` **Filename**
15 characters plus a three-character file extension

`U16►` **Error in**
Skips block if not 0

`►U16` **Error out**
See table

Easy Read File

This block opens the specified file on the NXT for read, then reads a line and returns the text or number. File content is always ASCII text with CR and LF termination on each line.

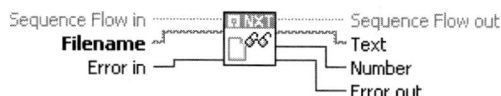

Figure A.68
Easy Read File Block

Filename
15 characters plus a three-character file extension

Error in
Skips block if not 0

Text
String

Number
–2,147,483,648–2,147,483,647

Error out
See table

Easy Write File

If the specified file already exists, Easy Write File opens the file for append; otherwise it creates a new file for write. It writes the provided number or text on a line in the file. If the file size is not sufficiently large, it resizes the file such that the data can be stored in the file. File size is used only when creating a new file, not when appending to an existing file. File content is always ASCII text with CR and LF termination on each line.

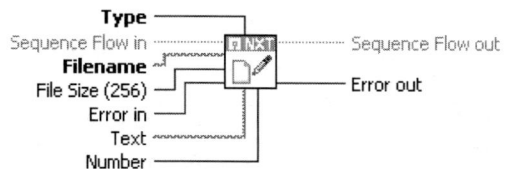

Figure A.69
Easy Write File Block

Text
String

Filename
15 characters plus a three-character file extension

Error in
Skips block if not 0

File Size (256)
0–32,767 Valid only when file is first created (i.e., "Write" and file doesn't currently exist). Determines file size. Can be used to avoid time penalty associated with auto-resizing a file.

Type
0 = Text
1 = Number

Number
-2,147,483,648–2,147,483,647

Error out
See table

Open File for Read

If a read handle already exists for the specified file on the NXT, the block returns that handle. If a write handle already exists, it returns an error. If the file currently has no handle, it tries to open the file for read.

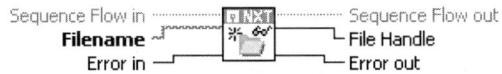

Figure A.70
Open File for Read Block

Filename
15 characters plus a three-character file extension

Error in
Skips block if not 0

File Handle
Created

Error out
See table

Open File for Write

If a write handle already exists for the specified Filename, this block returns that handle. If a read handle already exists, it returns an error. If the file already exists but currently has no handle, it opens the file for append; otherwise, it opens the file for write.

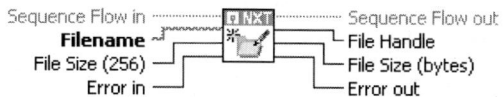

Figure A.71
Open File for Write Block

abc►	**Filename**
	15 characters plus a three-character file extension
U32►	**File Size (256)**
	0–32,767 Valid only when file is first created (i.e., "Write" and file doesn't currently exist). Determines file size. Can be used to avoid time penalty associated with auto-resizing a file.
U16►	**Error in**
	Skips block if not 0
►U8	**File Handle**
	Created
►U16	**Error out**
	See table
►U32	**File Size (bytes)**
	0–32,767

Read File

This block reads the number of bytes specified by Length from the source file referred to by the File Handle into a Buffer String. It also reports the actual number of bytes read.

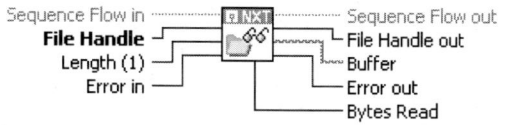

Figure A.72
Read File Block

⌈U8⌉   **File Handle**
Number from Open or Resolve

⌈U16⌉   **Error in**
Skips block if not 0

⌈U32⌉   **Length (1)**
Number of bytes to read

▶U16   **Error out**
See table

▶U8   **File Handle out**
Same as Input

▶abc   **Buffer**
String

▶U32   **Bytes Read**
Number of bytes read

Rename File

This block renames the file specified by Old Filename to the file specified by New Filename—useful as a step in extending the size of files.

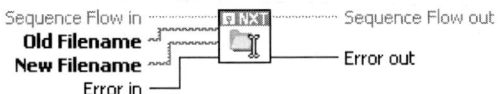

Figure A.73
Rename File Block

⌈abc⌉   **Old Filename**
15 characters plus a three-character file extension

⌈U16⌉   **Error in**
Skips block if not 0

⌈abc⌉   **New Filename**
15 characters plus a three-character file extension

▶U16   **Error out**
See table

Resolve File Handle

This block outputs the current File Handle for the specified Filename if it exists and also reports whether it was Open for Write or Read.

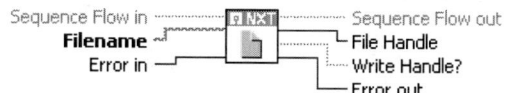

Figure A.74
Resolve File Handle Block

abc	**Filename**	15 characters plus a three-character file extension
U16	**Error in**	Skips block if not 0
U8	**File Handle**	Created
U16	**Error out**	See table
TF	**Write Handle?**	True/False

Write File

This block writes the Text String to the file specified by File Handle and reports the actual number of bytes written and any Errors that occurred.

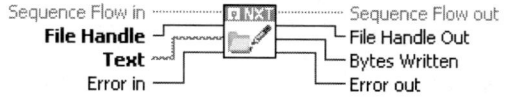

Figure A.75
Write File Block

U8	**File Handle**	Number from File Open
U16	**Error in**	Skips block if not 0
abc	**Text**	String
U16	**Error out**	See table
U32	**Bytes Written**	Number of bytes written to file
U8	**File Handle Out**	Same as Input

Bluetooth Message Blocks

See Chapter 11 for information about establishing Bluetooth connections. There are a variety of status codes generated by Bluetooth functions. Zero indicates no error, whereas negative values indicate unrecoverable errors.

Bluetooth Status Codes:

Error	Code
NO_ERR	0
STAT_EMPTY_MAILBOX	64
STAT_COMM_PENDING	32
ERR_INVALID_PORT	−16
ERR_INVALID_FIELD	−17
ERR_INVALID_QUEUE	−18
ERR_INVALID_SIZE	−19
ERR_NO_PROG	−20
ERR_COMM_CHAN_NOT_READY	−32
ERR_COMM_CHAN_INVALID	−33
ERR_COMM_BUFFER_FULL	−34
ERR_COMM_BUS_ERR	−35

Read Message

This block reads a Bluetooth message in the form of a Text String from the specified Mailbox. The Connection must be established with the NXT menu on the Master prior to usage. If there is a new message, Message Received will be True.

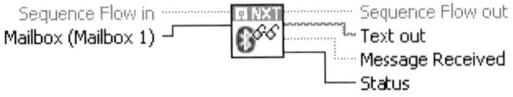

Figure A.76
Read Message Block

`U8` **Mailbox**
0–9 = Mailbox 1 to Mailbox 10

`abc` **Text out**
String limited to 58 characters

`TF` **Message Received**
True/False True for new message

`I8` **Status**
See Table

Write Message

This block writes a Bluetooth message in the form of a Text String to another NXT's Mailbox with the specified Connection number. The Connection must be established with the NXT Master menu prior to usage.

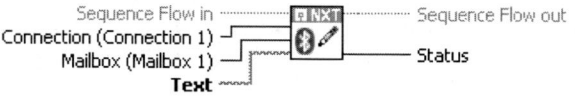

Figure A.77
Write Message Block

`U8` **Mailbox (Mailbox 1)**
0–9 = Mailbox 1 to Mailbox 10

`U8` **Message Connection**
0–3 = Connection 0 for Master and 1, 2, and 3
for Slaves

`abc` **Text**
String limited to 58 characters

`I8` **Status**
See Table

Record/Play

Play Action

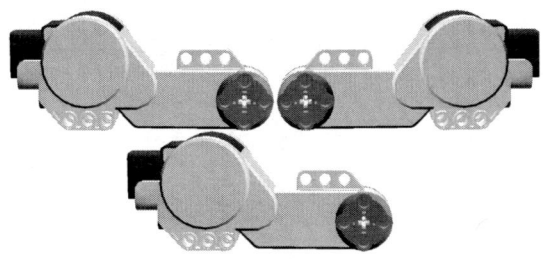

Figure A.78
Three Motors

Play Action plays back a recording made with the Record Action block of motor positions over time from a specified Filename.

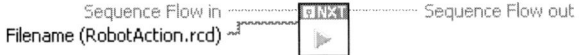

Figure A.79
Play Action Block

      Filename (RobotAction.rcd)
                 15 characters plus a three-character file extension

Record Action

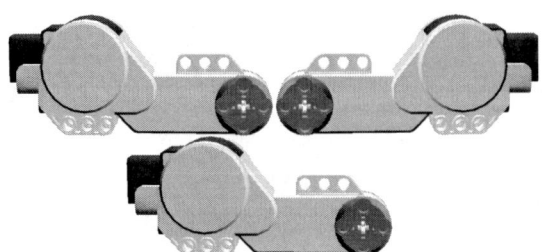

Figure A.80
Three Motors

Record Action records the position of the NXT motors at periodic intervals for a period of time and stores it in the specified Filename. The file is played back with the Play Action block.

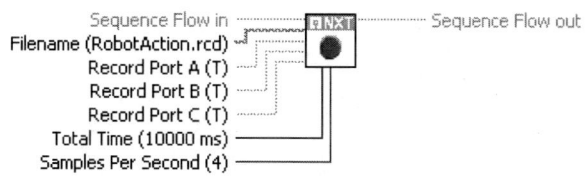

Figure A.81
Record Action Block

`abc` **Filename (RobotAction.rcd)**
15 characters plus a three-character file extension
`TF` **Record Port A (T)**
True/False
`TF` **Record Port B (T)**
True/False
`TF` **Record Port C (T)**
True/False
`I32` **Total Time (10000 ms)**
0–2,147,483,647ms
`U8` **Samples Per Second (4)**
0–255

Other

Calibration

Calibration updates the calibration values for the specified sensor. Sensor Name is a string that must be consistent for all uses of this VI for a given sensor. Use the text "Light Sensor," "Sound Sensor," and "Old Light Sensor" when calibrating these sensors. See NI Calibration program example for usage.

Figure A.82
Light, Sound, and Legacy Light Sensors

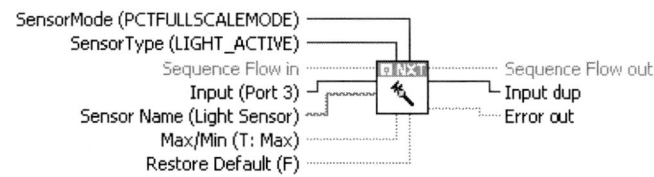

Figure A.83
Calibrate Block

`abc` **Sensor Name (Light Sensor)**
"Light Sensor"
"Sound Sensor"
"Old Light Sensor"

`TF` **Restore Default (F)**
True/False

`U8` **Input (Port 3)**
1–4

`U8` **SensorMode (PCTFULLSCALEMODE)**
Use PCTFULLSCALEMODE for all sensors

`U8` **SensorType (LIGHT_ACTIVE)**
LIGHT_ACTIVE = NXT Light Sensor
SOUND_DB = NXT Sound Sensor
REFLECTION = Legacy Light Sensor

`TF` **Max/Min (T: Max)**
True = Max
False = Min

`TF` **Error out**
True/False

`U8` **Input dup**
Same as Input

Keep Alive

This block resets the sleep timer and outputs the current setting for the automatic shut-off period in milliseconds (ms).

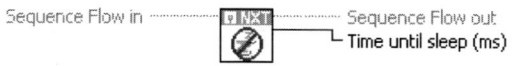

Figure A.84
Keep Alive Block

▶U32	**Time until sleep (ms)** 0–4,294,967,296 ms

Random Number

This block generates a random Number between and including Minimum and Maximum. All output Numbers have equal probability.

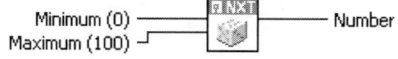

Figure A.85
Random Number Block

I16 ▶	**Minimum (0)** 0–32,767
I16 ▶	**Maximum (100)** 0–32,767
▶I32	**Number** 0–32,767

Timer

The NXT has four independent Timers. Timer Value is expressed in milliseconds (ms) from the last time it was Reset. All timers are reset when a program begins.

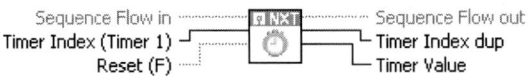

Figure A.86
Timer Block

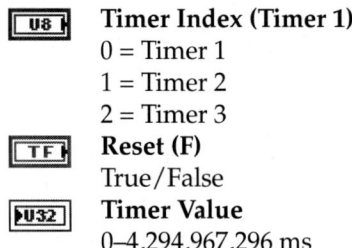

Timer Index (Timer 1)
0 = Timer 1
1 = Timer 2
2 = Timer 3
Reset (F)
True/False
Timer Value
0–4,294,967,296 ms
Timer Index dup
Same as Input

Wait

The Wait block waits the specified number of milliseconds and outputs the current
Tick value.

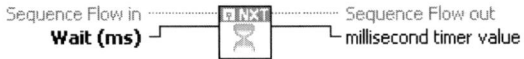

Figure A.87
Wait Block

Wait (ms)
0–4,294,967,296 ms
millisecond timer value
0–4,294,967,296 ms

Direct Commands Reference

B

Information Common to All Direct Commands

NXT Objects

Direct Commands employ a cluster of variables called the NXT Object, which includes all of the information used by the NXT operating system to define a particular connection. The values are for internal use only and 'are not described here in detail. The Direct Command blocks in a program are generally wired together with the NXT Object to transfer the connection properties as well as to control execution sequence.

Request Response and Read Buffer

Some Direct Command blocks have the option of Requesting Response to see the Read Buffer of the communications between the NXT and the PC from the command. This information is purely diagnostic and unimportant to the usage of the command. A complete description of the contents of the buffer is available in the LEGO documentation on Direct Commands.

Error In/Out

All Direct Command blocks pass an Error message of the following format:

error cluster is information wired from VI to VI. Use this information to decide whether any functionality should be bypassed in the event of errors from other VIs. The pop-up option **Explain Error** (or Explain Warning) gives more information about the error displayed.

> **status**
> True = Error
> False = No Error
>
> **code** The **code** identifies the error or warning.
>
> **source** The **source** string describes the origin of the error or warning.

Connection Blocks

Create NXT Object

Create NXT Object is usually the first block in a Direct Command program. It connects to an NXT and creates an NXTObject. If no VISA resource string is specified, it will connect to the first USB it finds. When connecting to an NXT via Bluetooth, it will attempt to pair to the NXT if not previously paired.

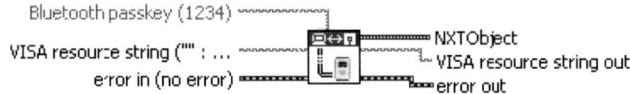

Figure B.1
Create NXT Object

> **VISA resource string ("" : find USB brick)**
> **Bluetooth passkey (1234)**
> **VISA resource string out**

Destroy NXT Object

Destroy NXT Object is usually the last block in a Direct Command program. It disconnects from an NXT and destroys the NXTObject. If connected using Bluetooth, this VI does not unpair when it disconnects.

Figure B.2
Destroy NXT Object

Find NXT

Find NXT scans for a particular NXT connected through USB or Bluetooth by specifying the NXT's name. The name must be specified, but the default name of NXTs is simply NXT.

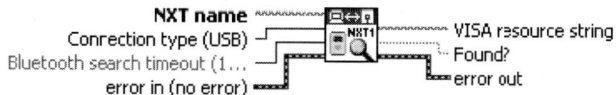

Figure B.3
Find NXT

NXT name
Usually NXT

Connection type (USB)
0 = Bluetooth
1 = USB

Bluetooth search timeout (10 sec)

VISA resource string

Found?
True/False

Info From Resource

Info From Resource determines the NXT name, connection type, and Bluetooth address associated with a given VISA resource.

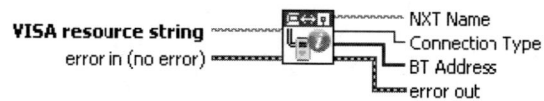

Figure B.4
Info From Resource

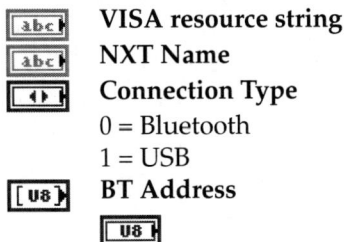

    VISA resource string
    NXT Name
    Connection Type
    0 = Bluetooth
    1 = USB
    BT Address

Is Paired

Is Paired determines whether an NXT has been paired with the PC using Bluetooth.

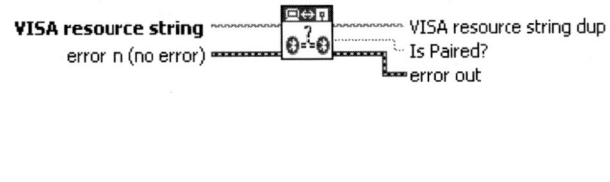

Figure B.5
Is Paired

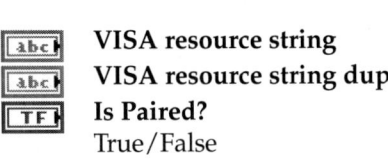

    VISA resource string
    VISA resource string dup
    Is Paired?
    True/False

Pair Bluetooth

Pair Bluetooth attempts to pair an NXT to the PC using Bluetooth. The passkey must be confirmed on the NXT to establish the pairing. After pairing, the NXT will have a different VISA resource string.

Figure B.6
Pair Bluetooth

    VISA resource string
    passkey (1234)
    VISA resource string out

Unpair Bluetooth

Unpair Bluetooth removes the pairing between the NXT and the PC. The NXT will require a passkey confirmation before it can be connected to again. An error occurs if the NXT was not paired in the first place.

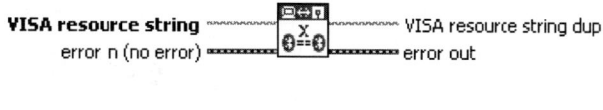

Figure B.7
Unpair Bluetooth

 **VISA resource string**
VISA resource string dup

Scan NXT

Scan NXT scans for NXTs connected through USB or available through Bluetooth and produces an array of VISA resource strings.

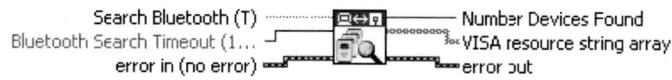

Figure B.8
Scan NXT

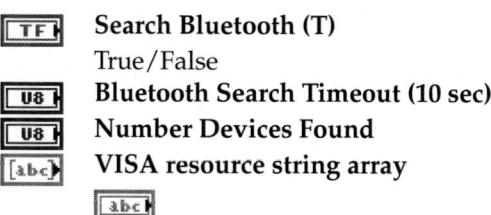 **Search Bluetooth (T)**
True/False
Bluetooth Search Timeout (10 sec)
Number Devices Found
VISA resource string array

Input Blocks

Clear Input Value

Clear Input Value sets the Scaled value for the specified Input Port to zero. It is used with count and angle type input modes to reset their retained values.

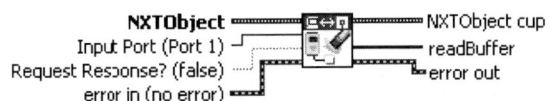

Figure B.9
Clear Input Value

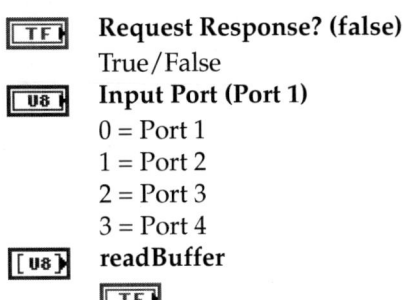

Request Response? (false)
True/False
Input Port (Port 1)
0 = Port 1
1 = Port 2
2 = Port 3
3 = Port 4
readBuffer

Get Input Values

Get Input Values returns the state of the specified Input Port. The values are in the Input Port Info Cluster and must be unbundled to derive specific information.

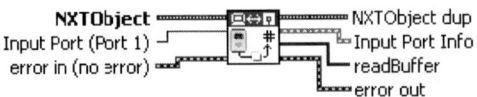

Figure B.10
Get Input Values

`[U8]` **Input Port (Port 1)**
0 = Port 1
1 = Port 2
2 = Port 3
3 = Port 4

`[[U8]]` **readBuffer**

`[⋯]`

`[TF]` **Input Port Info**

    `[TF]` **Valid?**
    True/False

    `[U8]` **Calibrated?**
    True/False

    `[U8]` **SensorType**
    0 = NO_SENSOR
    1 = SWITCH
    2 = TEMPERATURE
    3 = REFLECTION
    4 = ANGLE
    5 = LIGHT_ACTIVE
    6 = LIGHT_INACTIVE
    7 = SOUND_DB
    8 = SOUND_DBA
    9 = CUSTOM
    10 = LOWSPEED
    11 = LOWSPEED_9V
    12 = HIGHSPEED

    `[U16]` **Sensor Mode**
    0 = RAWMODE
    32 = BOOLEANMODE
    64 = TRANSITIONCNTMODE
    96 = PERIODCOUNTERMODE
    128 = PCTFULLSCALEMODE
    160 = CELSIUSMODE
    192 = FAHRENHEITMODE
    224 = ANGLESTEPMODE

    `[U16]` **Raw**
    0–1023 Ten-bit analog-to-digital converter value

    `[U16]` **Normalized**
    0–1023 Adjusted value to give full range

    `[I16]` **Scaled**
    0–100

    `[I16]` **Calibrated**

Read Ultrasonic

Read Ultrasonic reads the Ultrasonic Distance Sensor on the specified Input Port. This VI won't read if a program is running on the NXT; this is to prevent conflicts in low-speed communication commands. For specific information about the Ultrasonic Sensor, see the NXT block in Appendix A.

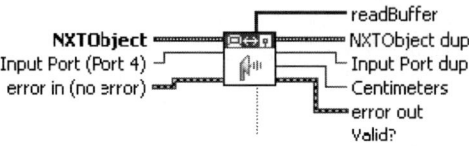

Figure B.11
Read Ultrasonic

Input Port (Port 4)
0 = Port 1
1 = Port 2
2 = Port 3
3 = Port 4

readBuffer

Centimeters

Valid?
True/False

Input Port dup
Same as Input Port

Get LS Status

Get LS Status returns the status of the low-speed digital communication for the specified Input Port. Can be used to determine when a low-speed Write operation has finished or when communication errors occur.

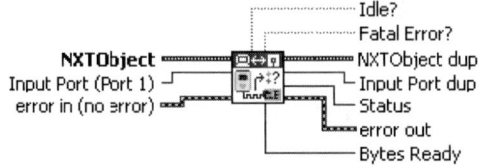

Figure B.12
Get LS Status

[U8] **Input Port (Port 1)**
0 = Port 1
1 = Port 2
2 = Port 3
3 = Port 4

[TF] **Idle?**
True/False

[TF] **Fatal Error?**
True/False

[I8] **Status**

[U8] **Bytes Ready**

[U8] **Input Port dup**
Same as Input Port

Lowspeed Read

Lowspeed Read performs a read using the low-speed digital protocol for the specified Input Port.

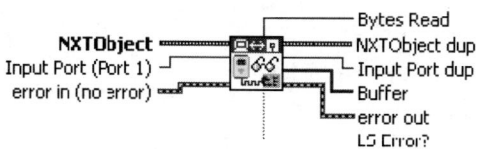

Figure B.13
Lowspeed Read

[U8] **Input Port (Port 1)**
0 = Port 1
1 = Port 2
2 = Port 3
3 = Port 4

[U8] **Buffer**
[U8]

[TF] **LS Error?**
True/False

[U8] **Input Port dup**
Same as Input Port

[U8] **Bytes Read**

Lowspeed Write

Lowspeed Write performs a write using the low-speed digital protocol to the specified Input Port.

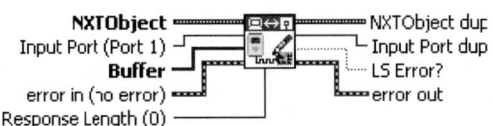

Figure B.14
Lowspeed Write

[U8] **Buffer**

[U8]

[U8] **Input Port (Port 1)**

0 = Port 1
1 = Port 2
2 = Port 3
3 = Port 4

[I32] **Response Length (0)**

[TF] **LS Error?**

True/False

[U8] **Input Port dup**

Same as Input Port

Read Light Sensor

Read Light Sensor reads the Light Sensor at the specified Input Port. The reading does not take into account any calibration that may exist on the NXT. For specific information about the Light Sensor, see the topic "NXT block" in Appendix A.

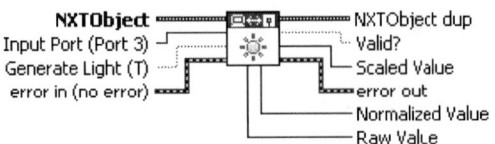

Figure B.15
Read Light Sensor

`U8` **Input Port (Port 3)**
0 = Port 1
1 = Port 2
2 = Port 3
3 = Port 4

`TF` **Generate Light (T)**
True/False

`TF` **Valid?**
True/False

`I16` **Scaled Value**
0–100

`U16` **Normalized Value**
0 1023 Adjusted value to give full range

`U16` **Raw Value**
0–1023 Ten-bit analog-to-digital converter value

Read Input Value

Read Input Value reads a generic analog sensor at the specified Input Port. The sensor Type and Mode must be set in the firmware before a valid reading can occur. This VI will set the Type and Mode as long as a program is not currently running on the NXT.

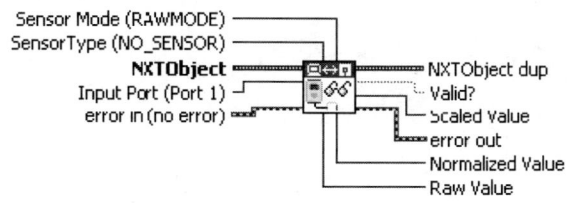

Figure B.16
Read Input Value

`U8` **Input Port (Port 1)**

0 = Port 1
1 = Port 2
2 = Port 3
3 = Port 4

`U8` **SensorType (NO_SENSOR)**

0 = NO_SENSOR
1 = SWITCH
2 = TEMPERATURE
3 = REFLECTION
4 = ANGLE
5 = LIGHT_ACTIVE
6 = LIGHT_INACTIVE
7 = SOUND_DB
8 = SOUND_DBA
9 = CUSTOM
10 = LOWSPEED
11 = LOWSPEED_9V
12 = HIGHSPEED

`U8` **Sensor Mode (RAWMODE)**

0 = RAWMODE
32 = BOOLEANMODE
64 = TRANSITIONCNTMODE
96 = PERIODCOUNTERMODE
128 = PCTFULLSCALEMODE
160 = CELSIUSMODE
192 = FAHRENHEITMODE
224 = ANGLESTEPMODE

`I16` **Scaled Value**

0–1023 Raw
0–1 Boolean mode
0–65535 Transition
0–65535 Period
0–100 Percent
–200–700 Celsius
-400–1580 Fahrenheit
0–65536 Angle

`TF` **Valid?**

True/False

`U16` **Normalized Value**

0 – 1023 Adjusted value to give full range

`U16` **Raw Value**

0 – 1023 Ten-bit analog-to-digital converter value

Sensor	Mode	Type
NXT Touch	BOOLEANMODE	SWITCH
NXT Sound	PCTFULLSCALEMODE	SOUND_DB or SOUND_DBA
NXT Light	PCTFULLSCALEMODE	LIGHT_ACTIVE or LIGHT_INACTIVE
Legacy Touch	BOOLEANMODE	SWITCH
Legacy Light	PCTFULLSCALEMODE	REFLECTION
Legacy Angle	ANGLESTEPMODE	ANGLE
Legacy Temperature	CELSIUSMODE or FAHRENHEITMODE	TEMPERATURE

Read Sound Sensor

Read Sound Sensor reads the Sound Sensor at the specified Input Port. The reading does not take into account any calibration that may exist on the NXT. For specific information about the Sound Sensor, see the topic "NXT block" in Appendix A.

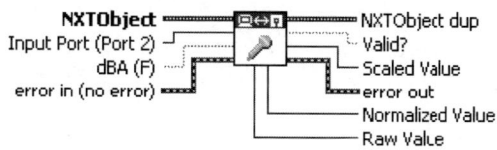

Figure B.17
Read Sound Sensor

[U8] **Input Port (Port 2)**
0 = Port 1
1 = Port 2
2 = Port 3
3 = Port 4

[TF] **dBA (F)**
True/False

[TF] **Valid?**
True/False

[I16] **Scaled Value**
0–100

[U16] **Normalized Value**
0–1023 Adjusted value to give full range

[U16] **Raw Value**
0–1023 Ten-bit analog-to-digital converter value

Read Touch Sensor

Read Touch Sensor reads the Touch Sensor at the specified input port. For specific information about the Touch Sensor, see the topic "NXT block" in Appendix A.

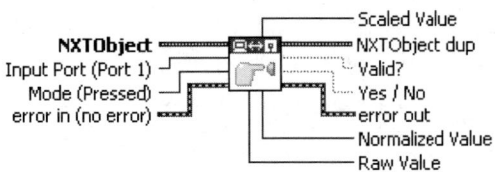

Figure B.18
Read Touch Sensor

| U8 | | **Input Port (Port 1)**
0 = Port 1
1 = Port 2
2 = Port 3
3 = Port 4

| U16 | | **Mode (Pressed)**
0 = Pressed
1 = Released
2 = Bumped

| TF | | **Valid?**
True/False

| I16 | | **Scaled Value**
0–1

| U16 | | **Normalized Value**
0–1023 Adjusted value to give full range

| U16 | | **Raw Value**
0–1023 Ten-bit analog-to-digital converter value

| TF | | **Yes/No**
True/False

Set Input Mode

Set Input Mode sets the sensor type and mode for the specified input port. It can also be used to configure the port for low-speed communications.

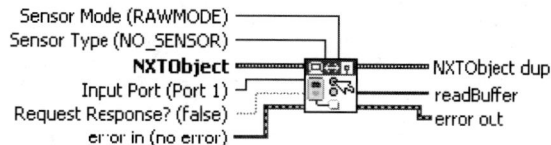

Figure B.19
Set Input Mode

TF **Request Response? (false)**
True/False
U8 **Sensor Type (NO_SENSOR)**
0 = NO_SENSOR
1 = SWITCH
2 = TEMPERATURE
3 = REFLECTION
4 = ANGLE
5 = LIGHT_ACTIVE
6 = LIGHT_INACTIVE
7 = SOUND_DB
8 = SOUND_DBA
9 = CUSTOM
10 = LOWSPEED
11 = LOWSPEED_9V
12 = HIGHSPEED
U8 **Sensor Mode (RAWMODE)**
0 = RAWMODE
32 = BOOLEANMODE
64 = TRANSITIONCNTMODE
96 = PERIODCOUNTERMODE
128 = PCTFULLSCALEMODE
160 = CELSIUSMODE
192 = FAHRENHEITMODE
224 = ANGLESTEPMODE
U8 **Input Port (Port 1)**
0 = Port 1
1 = Port 2
2 = Port 3
3 = Port 4
U8 **readBuffer**
[**U8**]

Output Blocks

Get Output Values

Get Output Values returns the state of the specified Output Port in a bundle of variables called Output Port Info. The block is particularly useful for reading the Rotation Sensor, whose value is found in RotationCount.

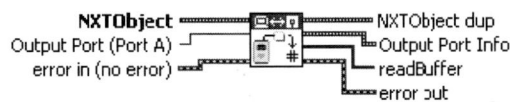

Figure B.20
Get Output Values

Output Port (Port A)
0 = A
1 = B
2 = C

readBuffer

Output Port Info

    Power
    −100–100

    Mode
    0 = COAST
    1 = MOTOR_ON
    2 = BRAKE
    3 = MOTOR_ON | BRAKE
    4 = REGULATED
    7 = MOTOR_ON | BRAKE | REGULATED

    RegMode
    0 = REG_IDLE
    1 = REG_SPEED
    2 = REG_SYNC

    TurnRatio
    −100–100

U8	**RunState**

    0 = RUN_STATE_IDLE
    16 = RUN_STATE_RAMPUP
    32 = RUN_STATE_RUNNING
    64 = RUN_STATE_RAMPDOWN

I32	**TachoLimit**
I32	**TachoCount**
I32	**BlockTachoCount**
I32	**RotationCount**

Motor Stop

Motor Stop stops a motor on Output Port from running, by either Braking or Coasting.

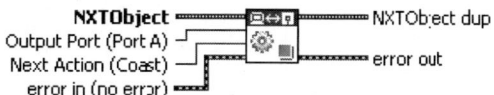

Figure B.21
Motor Stop

U8	**Output Port (Port A)**

    0 = A
    1 = B
    2 = C

U16	**Next Action (Coast)**

    0 = Brake
    1 = Coast

Motor Unlimited

Motor Unlimited turns a motor on at the specified power and direction.

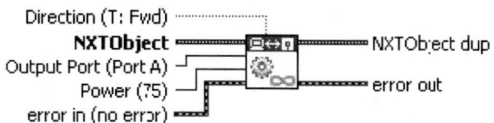

Figure B.22
Motor Unlimited

U8	**Output Port (Port A)**
	0 = A
	1 = B
	2 = C
I8	**Power (75)**
	–100–100
TF	**Direction (T: Fwd)**
	True/False

Reset Motor Position

Reset Motor Position resets the RotationCount of the specified Output Port. If Relative Position is True, it resets the BlockTachoCount.

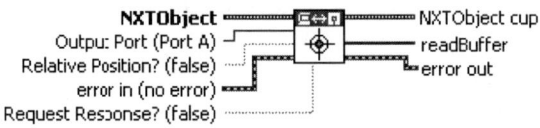

Figure B.23
Reset Motor Position

TF	**Request Response? (false)**
	True/False
U8	**Output Port (Port A)**
	0 = A
	1 = B
	2 = C
TF	**Relative Position? (false)**
	True/False
[U8]	**readBuffer**
	[U8]

Set Output State

Set Output State sets the state of the specified Output Port using a large bundle called Output Port Info.

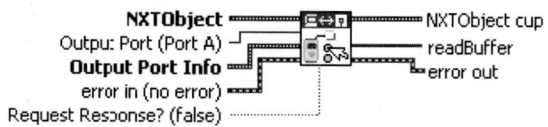

Figure B.24
Set Output State

	Request Response? (false)
`TF`	True/False
`U8`	**Output Port (Port A)**
	0 = A
	1 = B
	2 = C
`U8`	**Output Port Info**
`I8`	**Power**
	−100–100
`U8`	**Mode**
	0 = COAST
	1 = MOTOR_ON
	2 = BRAKE
	3 = MOTOR_ON | BRAKE
	4 = REGULATED
	7 = MOTOR_ON | BRAKE | REGULATED
`U8`	**RegMode**
	0 = REG_IDLE
	1 = REG_SPEED
	2 = REG_SYNC
`I8`	**TurnRatio**
	−100–100
`U8`	**RunState**
	0 = RUN_STATE_IDLE
	16 = RUN_STATE_RAMPUP
	32 = RUN_STATE_RUNNING
	64 = RUN_STATE_RAMPDOWN
`U32`	**TachoLimit**
`U8`	**readBuffer**
`U8`	

File Blocks

Defrag Files

Defrag Files defragments the file system on the NXT. Files can be potentially lost during this operation if communication to the NXT is disrupted.

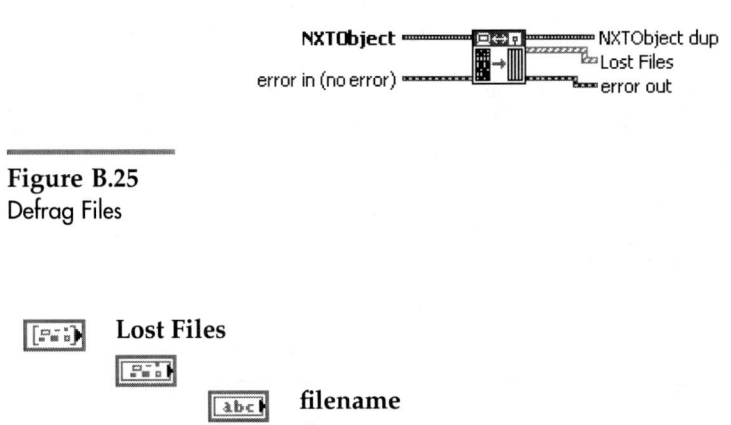

Figure B.25
Defrag Files

Lost Files

filename
data

Delete File

Delete File removes a file on the NXT. Filename can accept the "*" wildcard. For example, a filename of "*.*" will delete all files on the NXT.

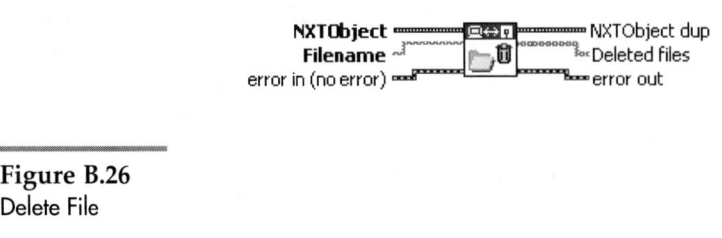

Figure B.26
Delete File

Filename
Deleted files
  filename

Download File

Downloads a file from the PC to the NXT. Filenames will be truncated to 15 characters, not including the three-character file extension.

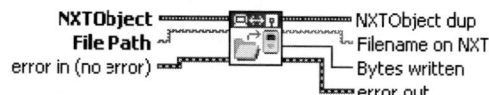

Figure B.27
Download File

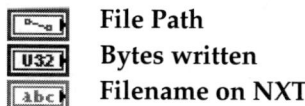

File Path
Bytes written
Filename on NXT

List Files

List Files lists files on the NXT that match the specified pattern. The pattern can accept the "*" wildcard in the following ways:

- List all files–*.*
- List all files with a given file extension–*.[file extension]
- List all types of files for a give filename–[Filename].*

Figure B.28
List Files

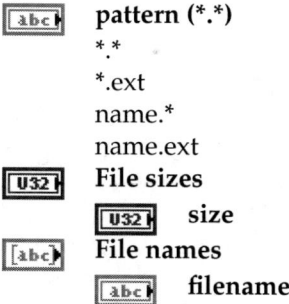

pattern (*.*)
* *
*.ext
name.*
name.ext
File sizes
   size
File names
   filename

Upload File

Upload File uploads a file from the NXT to the PC.

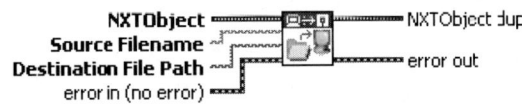

Figure B.29
Upload File

 Source Filename
Destination File Path

Bluetooth Blocks

Message Read

Message Read reads a text message from the specified Bluetooth message inbox on the NXT and optionally removes it from the message queue. Messages are limited to 58 characters.

When Read Master's inbox is true, this VI will read messages that the NXT has sent to Connection 0 (the Master connection slot). When it is false, it will read messages from the NXT's inbox. Note that Flatten to String and Unflatten from String behave differently on the NXT than on the PC. They cannot be used to send other data types as text messages in conjunction with this VI.

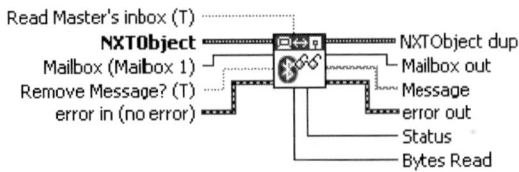

Figure B.30
Message Read

[U8] **Mailbox (Mailbox 1)**
0–9 for Mailbox 1 to 10
[TF] **Remove Message? (T)**
True/False
[TF] **Read Master's inbox (T)**
True/False
[U8] **Mailbox out**
Same as Mailbox
[U8] **Bytes Read**
[abc] **Message**
[U8] **Status**

Message Write

Message Write sends a text message to the specified Bluetooth message inbox on the NXT. Messages are limited to 58 characters. Note that Flatten to String and Unflatten from String behave differently on the NXT than on the PC. They cannot be used to send other data types as text messages in conjunction with this VI.

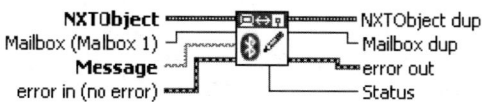

Figure B.31
Message Write

[U8] **Mailbox (Mailbox 1)**
0–9 for Mailbox 1 to 10
[abc] **Message**
[U8] **Mailbox dup**
Same as Mailbox
[U8] **Status**

Sound Blocks

Play Sound File

Play Sound File plays the sound file Filename on the NXT. Sound files usually have the .rso file extension.

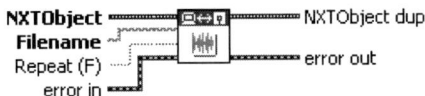

Figure B.32
Play Sound File

Filename
Repeat (F)
True/False

Play Tone

Play Tone plays a tone at the specified Tone frequency and length Duration on the NXT.

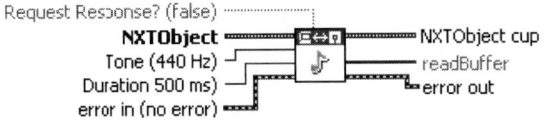

Figure B.33
Play Tone

Request Response? (false)
True/False
Tone (440 Hz)
Duration 500 ms)
readBuffer

Stop Sound

Stop Sound stops whatever sound file or tone that is currently playing on the NXT.

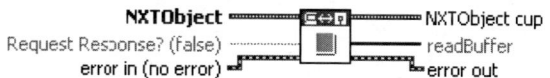

Figure B.34
Stop Sound

| TF | **Request Response? (false)**
True/False
| U8 | **readBuffer**
| U8 |

Program Blocks

Get Current Program Name

Get Current Program Name returns the name of the program currently running on the NXT.

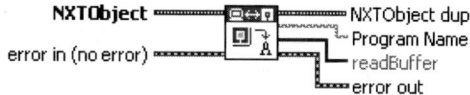

Figure B.35
Get Current Program Name

| TF | **readBuffer**
| U8 |
| abc | Program Name

Start Program

Start Program runs the program Filename on the NXT. The program must already be downloaded to the NXT. If a program is already running, it must finish executing before this one will start.

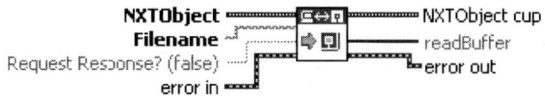

Figure B.36
Start Program

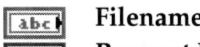

Filename
Request Response? (false)
True/False
readBuffer

Stop Program

Stop Program aborts the current program running on the NXT.

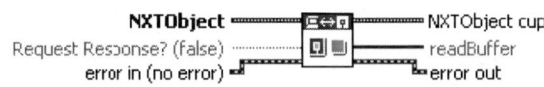

Figure B.37
Stop Program

Request Response? (false)
True/False
readBuffer

Utility Blocks

Get Battery Level

Get Battery Level returns the battery level of the NXT in millivolts.

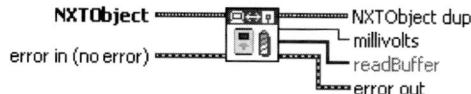

Figure B.38
Get Battery Level

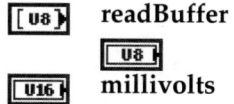

[U8] **readBuffer**

[U8]

[U16] **millivolts**

Get Firmware Version

Get Firmware Version returns the version of the firmware and communications protocol.

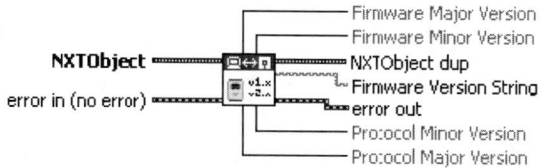

Figure B.39
Get Firmware Version

[abc] **Firmware Version String**
[U8] **Firmware Major Version**
[U8] **Firmware Minor Version**
[U8] **Protocol Minor Version**
[U8] **Protocol Major Version**

Get Resource String

Get Resource String returns the VISA resource string associated with an NXTObject.

Figure B.40
Get Resource String

 **VISA resource string**

Get Device Info

Get Device Info returns information about the NXT, including name, available flash memory, and Bluetooth address.

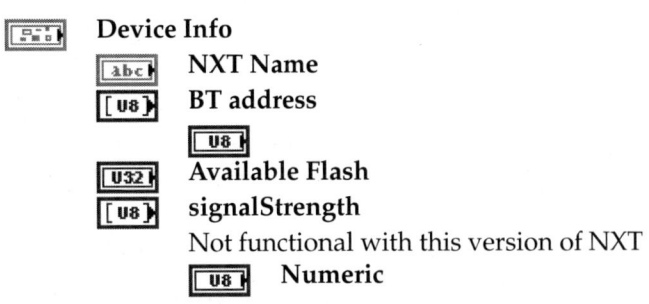

Figure B.41
Get Device Info

Device Info
   NXT Name
   BT address
      Available Flash
   signalStrength
   Not functional with this version of NXT
      Numeric

Keep Alive

Keep Alive resets the sleep timer on the NXT to prevent it from automatically turning off. It returns the number of milliseconds until the NXT goes to sleep.

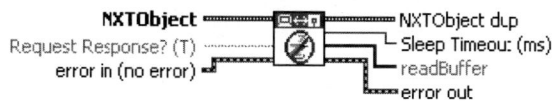

Figure B.42
Keep Alive

TF	**Request Response? (T)**
[U8]	**readBuffer**
U8	
U32	**Sleep Timeout (ms)**

Read IOMap

Read IOMap reads raw IOMap data for the specified firmware module.

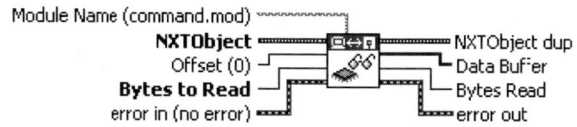

Figure B.43
Read IOMap

U16	**Offset (0)**
U16	**Bytes to Read**
abc	**Module Name (command.mod)**
[U8]	**Data Buffer**
U8	
U8	**Bytes Read**

Rename NXT

Rename NXT renames the NXT. The name is limited to 15 characters.

Figure B.44
Rename NXT

| abc | **New Name** |

Write IOMap

Write IOMap writes raw IOMap data for the specified firmware module. Use with extreme caution.

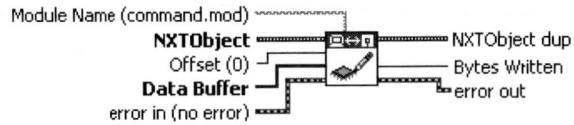

Figure B.45
Write IOMap

U16	**Offset (0)**
abc	**Module Name (command.mod)**
[U8]	**Data Buffer**
U8	
U8	**Bytes Written**

Creating Custom NXT-G Blocks

C

It may come as a surprise to you that the LEGO MINDSTORMS NXT-G programming environment was actually written in LabVIEW. Writing programs that control the NXT may seem complicated enough to you, but imagine producing an entire graphical user interface this way. The programming techniques are well beyond what you have learned from this book. Fortunately, you can bite off only as much as you want to chew simply by modifying some templates to add new blocks to the NXT-G environment. In addition to this Appendix, there is a short tutorial for writing custom blocks that comes with the NXT Toolkit. Also, people just like you have programmed their own blocks and shared them on the web at http://nxtasy.org/repository/nxt-g-blocks/. They serve as further examples of how to write custom blocks.

LabVIEW 7.1

The MINDSTORMS NXT-G environment was written with LabVIEW 7.1, and you must use this same version to add blocks to it. At the time of this writing, National Instruments offers a free copy of this version on its website. Actually LabVIEW 7.1 could be used for all the programming in this book, but once a VI has been saved in a higher version, such as 8.5, it can't be reopened by 7.1. If you were using a higher version, you will need to uninstall the NXT toolkit and reinstall it to 7.1.

Custom Angle Sensor

Typically, the need for new blocks results from the development of new sensors. For example, in the book *Extreme NXT*, a simple angle sensor was fashioned using a single electronic part called a potentiometer. I'm not going into the details of hardware in this book, but Figure C.1 shows the programming that is required to read and convert the raw analog-to-digital converter value from a potentiometer connected to Input Port 1 into an angle measurement in degrees. Admittedly, you could live with these four blocks and their constants and wiring in your program, or you could create a MyBlock that would hide some of these details. However, imagine how much cleaner and understandable it would be to see the block shown in Figure C.2 instead.

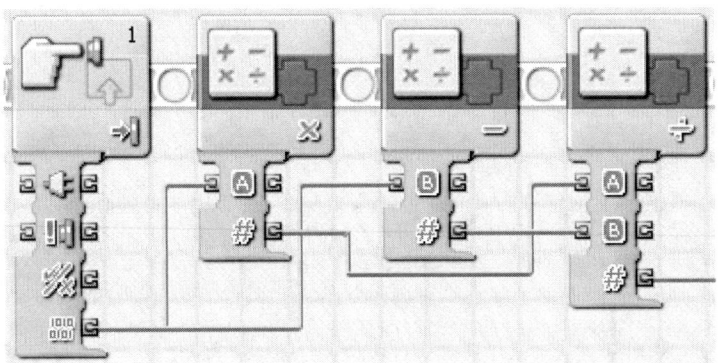

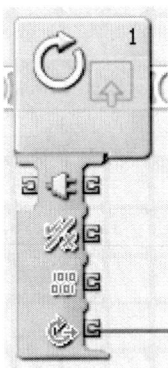

Figure C.1
NXT-G program to compute angle

Figure C.2
Custom NXT-G block

NXT Block Wizard

To build this block we start with the New NXT Block Wizard, which is found in the NXT Module, as shown in Figure C.3. There are four types of templates in the menu that appears (see Figure C.4), and the Simple Sensor Block is a good starting point for a plain input device such as this. You enter the name—Angle in this case—in the box labeled New Block Name and click the Create button. The Template Complete Sensor Block contains a lot of other controls and display features. After you master the Simple Sensor Block, you should try doing the Angle Sensor with that template. I'll show you the plain Template Block in a while, and the Template Output Block is another full-feature block like the Complete Sensor.

Navigate to the folder where you want the Wizard to place the new Angle block's components. For example, I will be keeping all my NXT-G blocks in a cleverly named

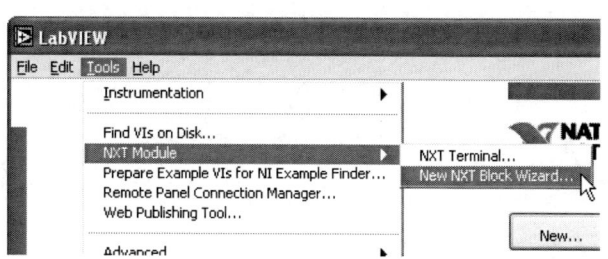

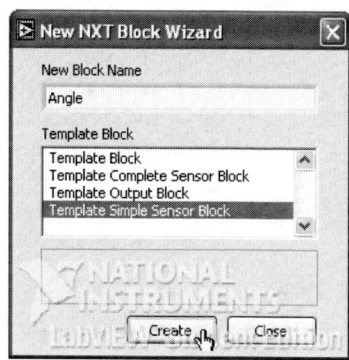

Figure C.3
Starting the New NXT Block Wizard

Figure C.4
Selecting Simple Sensor

folder called My NXTG Blocks. Then you need only to click on the Select Current Directory button, as shown in Figure C.5. All of the files will be put in a folder named Angle inside this folder. You don't enter a filename, because the Wizard takes care of that.

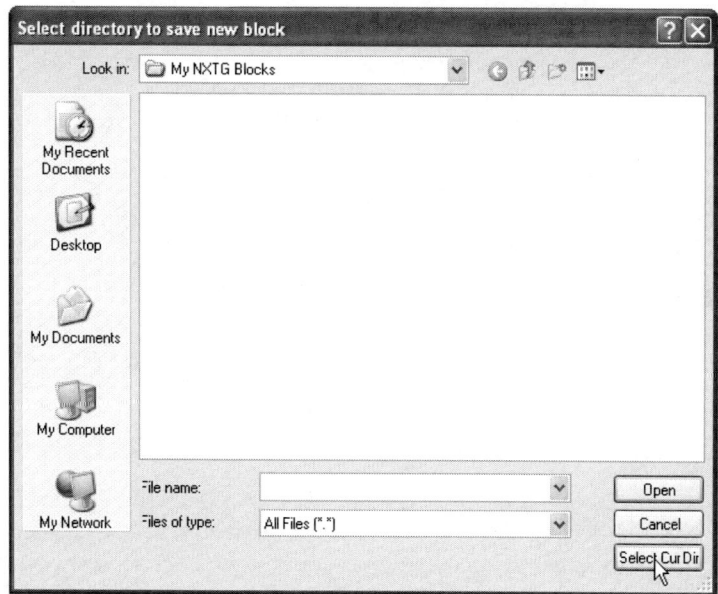

Figure C.5
Selecting Directory for Block Files

For the Simple Sensor there are 12 files created, and they are illustrated in Figure C.6. Config Angle.vi and Draw Angle.vi are used by the MINDSTORMS programming environment to configure and draw the block. Angle.vi and Angle Sub.vi are the parts of the block that actually execute inside the NXT. The rest of the files are used for graphics and support. Let's go deeper into each file.

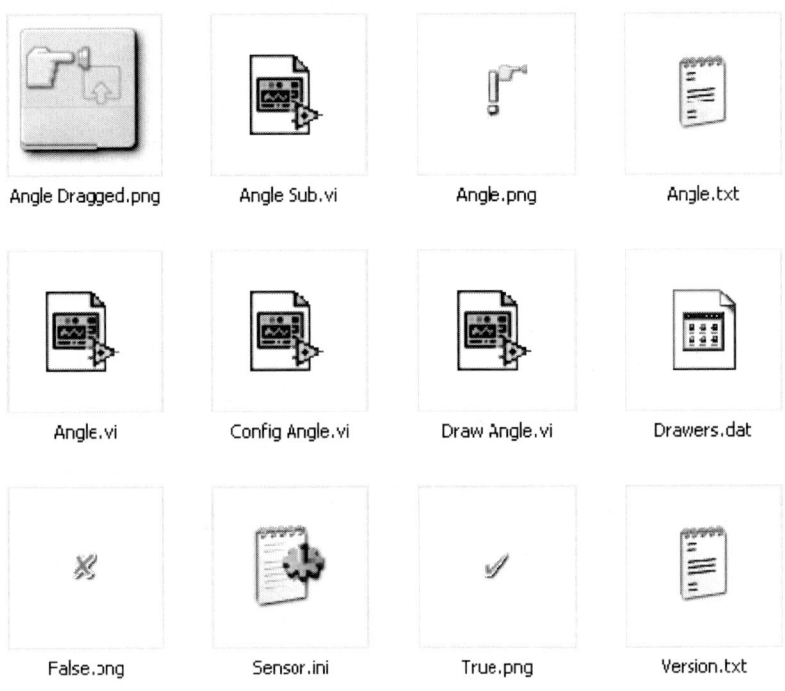

Figure C.6
Files used for Simple Sensor

Block Icon

Angle.png is the little icon that is used to select the block from the palette, and it is also superimposed on the block after it has been added to the program. The Wizard automatically creates the exclamation/touch icon shown in Figure C.6, but it is easy to obtain a more appropriate icon for our Angle sensor. There is a folder in which the MINDSTORMS programming environment stores all the icons intended for MyBlocks. You can copy and then modify these icons to make a special icon for your custom block. The folder is found at C:\ Program Files\LEGO Software\LEGO MINDSTORMS NXT\engine\Icons\MyBlock, and it contains the icons shown in Figure C.7.

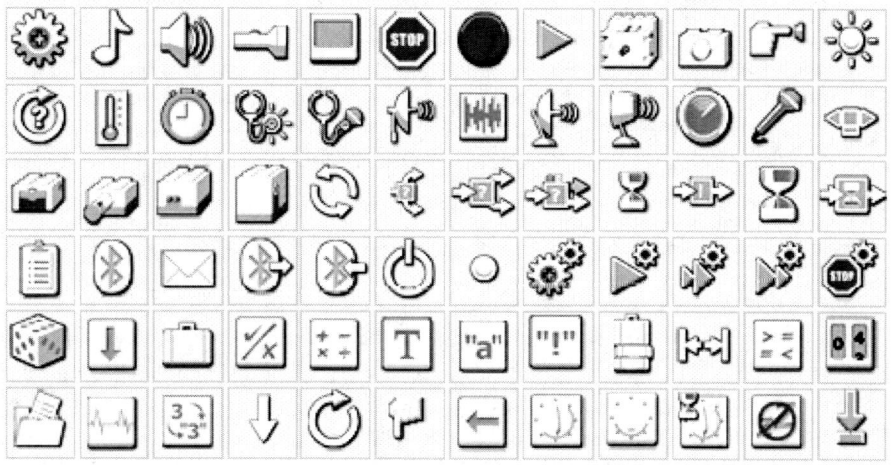

Figure C.7
Available Icons

When you look through the available icons, you will find one that can be used without modification. The Full circle.png icon, shown in Figure C.8, already has a definite angle characteristic. In fact the Rotation Sensor uses this with a question mark inside the circle. Delete the original file called Angle.png, make a copy of Full circle.png, put it into the Angle folder, and rename it Angle.png. Remember to copy the file; don't just move it to the Angle folder.

Full circle.png

Figure C.8
Full Circle Icon

Block Dragged

Angle Dragged.png is an image that is used when the block is first selected out of the palette before it has been placed into the NXT-G program. The image the Wizard automatically creates looks like the Touch Sensor block. I assume you have a graphics editing program that can modify images like this. Because there are so many differences in editing tools, I won't go into the details of how to erase the Touch Sensor icon from the existing image and paste the new Angle.png icon in its place. If you don't care whether the dragged image exactly matches your block, you can just leave it the way it is.

Block VI

Angle.vi is actually downloaded and executed inside the NXT. Its Front Panel, shown in Figure C.9, contains Radio Buttons for Input Port Number and Indicators for Yes/No, Raw Value, and Scaled. The Yes/No indicator is important for using the sensor with Switch or While Loops, and there is a separate file called Sensor.ini that takes care of that. Also notice the Sequence Flow input and output that are used to control execution flow. As long as you are looking at the Front Panel, change the label on the Scaled indicator to read "Degrees out." Make sure you spell it out and capitalize it exactly the way it is shown in Figure C.10.

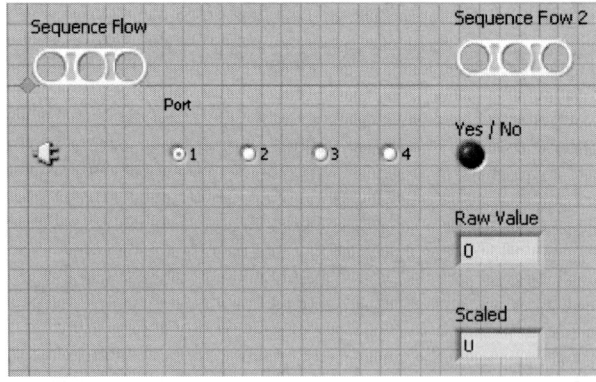

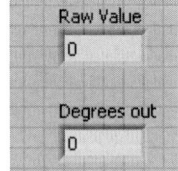

Figure C.9
Angle.vi Front Panel

Figure C.10
Changed Labels

This name will determine the little icon that appears on the drawer of the block when it is extended as shown in Figure C.2. If the variable name matches the filename of one of the icons in the directory Program Files\LEGO Software\LEGO

MINDSTORMS NXT\engine\EditorVIs\resources\BlockImages\DrawerImages, the
MINDSTORMS editor will show it. If not, it will use a generic icon based on the variable's type—Boolean, Integer, or String. In NXT-G those are Logic, Number, and Text.
Degrees out.png is just one of more than 50 icons to choose from, and Figure C.11
shows the three defaults along with some other common ones.

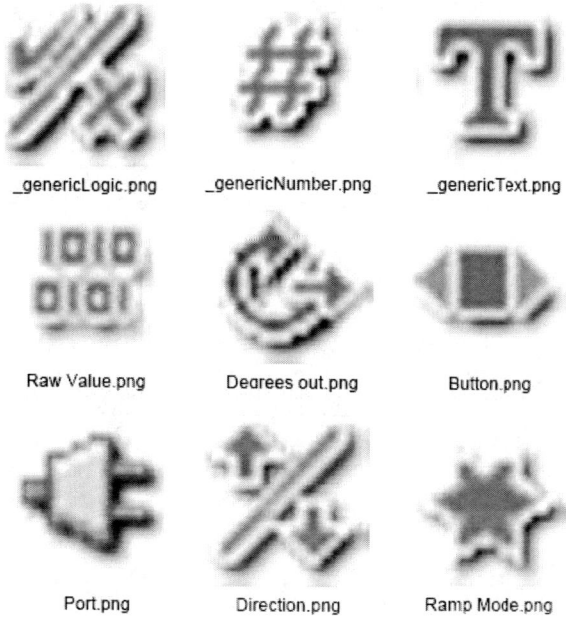

_genericLogic.png   _genericNumber.png   _genericText.png

Raw Value.png   Degrees out.png   Button.png

Port.png   Direction.png   Ramp Mode.png

Figure C.11
Some Available Drawer Icons

Now turn to the block's Block Diagram, shown in Figure C.12. It consists of only
another VI called Angle sub.vi. Yes, I know the text on the block says Simple Sensor
Sub, but that is only the block's icon, not its name. The reason for this seemingly
redundant construction is memory efficiency. No matter how many times you add
the Angle Block in a program, only the small amount of code at this level will be
duplicated. All the instances will share the same Angle sub.vi code.

Block Sub VI

Double-click on the block to open Angle sub.vi. Figure C.13 shows the Front Panel,
which has pretty much the same controls as its parent. It is alright that we don't change
the Scaled indicator to Degrees out as we did for Angle.vi, but if you change an input

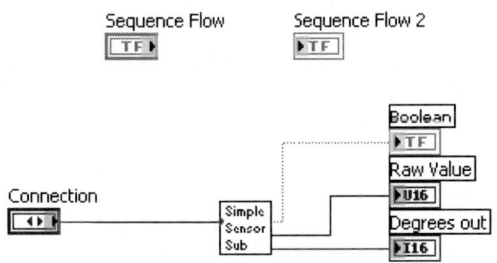

Figure C.12
Angle.vi Block Diagram

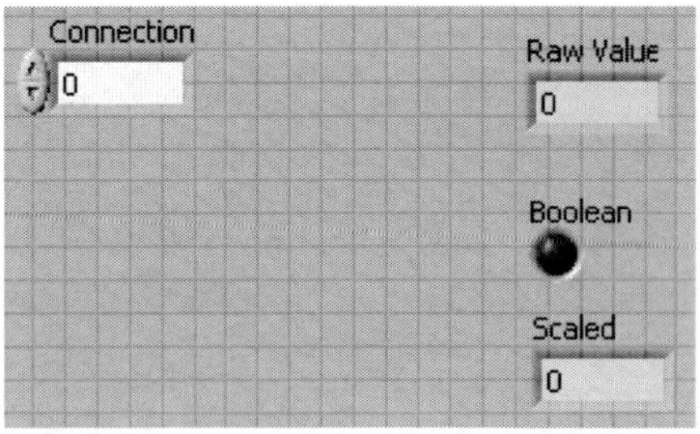

Figure C.13
Angle sub.vi Front Panel

Control such as Connection, it needs be changed everywhere. We'll see more about that later.

Figure C.14 is the block diagram as originally created by the Wizard. You should recognize the Property Node block that we learned about in Chapter 19. The other block is just an undocumented NXT Toolkit block (see Figure C.15) that is used to change a sensor's type and mode. It combines a Property Node to change the values as well as the logic to wait till the change has been recognized by the NXT operating system. The Angle sub.vi is outputting the Raw and Scaled values and comparing the Scaled to 50 to establish a Boolean output.

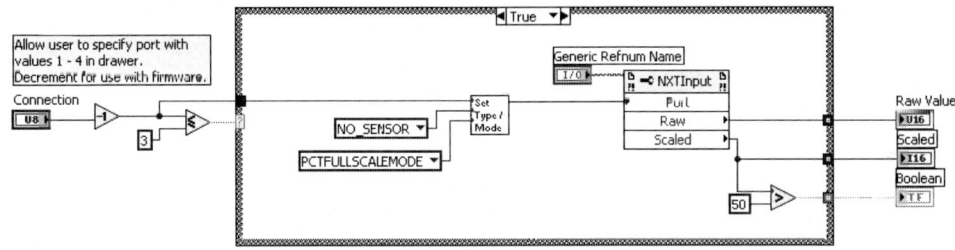

Figure C.14
Angle Sub.vi Block Diagram

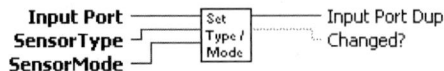

Figure C.15
Set Type/Mode

We edit the block in the lower-right corner of the True Case to change the Scaled output to be the angle of the sensor in degrees. That requires multiplying the Raw value by 54 and then dividing the result by 1023 minus the Raw value. The angle sensor has a range from 0 to 270 degrees, so the comparison is made at 134 or half range. In a more complex version of the block, you could input this comparison value so that it could be changed. We no longer make any use of the Scaled output of the Property Node.

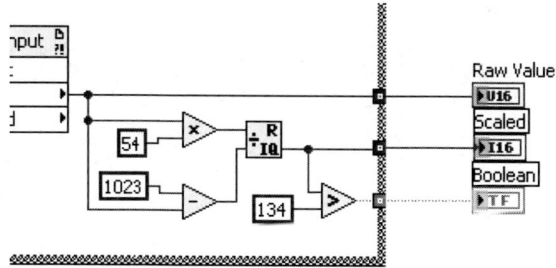

Figure C.16
Changes to Angle sub.vi

Configuration VI

In the MINDSTORMS editor there is a window in which block constants such as Port Number are entered, and Config Angle.vi creates that window for the Angle Sensor. The only things about the default Config Angle.vi that the Wizard created that should be fixed are the text label and the icon. If you move the mouse around the icon on the Front Panel, as shown in Figure C.17, you will find that it is just an image that was pasted there. Delete the exclamation/touch icon as shown in Figure C.18 and then add the Angle.png icon by selecting the file and dragging it onto the Front Panel, as illustrated in Figure C.19. Then change the Template Simple Sensor Block text to read Simple Angle Block(see Figure C.20) to finish the editing of this vi.

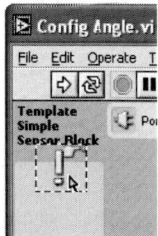

Figure C.17
Default Icon Image

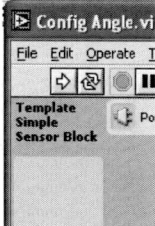

Figure C.18
Icon Deleted

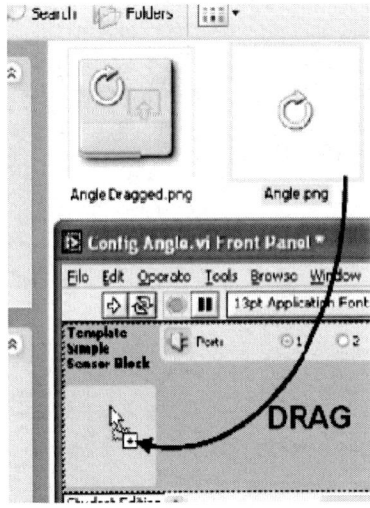

Figure C.19
Moving Icon to Front Panel

Figure C.20
Finished Icon Placement

Other Support Files

The Wizard creates the True and False.png files, because they are used by some sensor blocks to indicate the state of the sensor. We will not be using them, but leave them in the folder anyway. Angle.txt and Version.txt contain the name and version of the block, and the wizard automatically fills in the name Angle and makes it Version 1.0. Drawers.dat, shown in Figure C.21, is an optional file that controls the order of the icons in the drawer and that are visible when you first place the block. Figure C.22 shows the modified Drawers.dat file with changes for the Scaled output to Degrees out. By also adding Degrees out below OpenOnDrop it will show up when the block is first placed. Finally, Sensor.ini is necessary if you want the sensor to be used for Switch or While Loops in the NXT-G program. It just tells the MINDSTORMS editor that the block has a Yes/No Boolean output that will be used for this purpose.

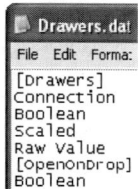

Figure C.21
Initial Drawers.dat

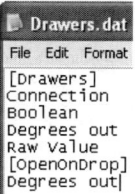

Figure C.22
Edited Drawers.dat

Import and Export Wizard

We are now ready to try out the block. This is done with the Block Import and Export Wizard, which is found in Tools dropdown menu, as shown in Figure C.23 Importing the Custom Block . This feature is built into version 1.1 of the MINDSTORMS environment and was available as an add-in for 1.0. I highly recommend that you upgrade to 1.1 if you intend to make custom blocks, because 1.1 doesn't require that you reload it after adding new blocks; it also has an easy way to delete blocks you don't want anymore.

Figure C.23
Importing the Custom Block

Click the Browse button in the Wizard and navigate to the directory in which the block's files are located. After a short time, the block name will appear in the Select Blocks to Import window. You must select the block by clicking on it so it becomes highlighted. Next, select the palette in which you want the block to appear—in this case the Sensor palette. Finally, select Import, as shown in Figure C.24 Selecting the Block.

When you open a new file and select the Sensor palette, the Angle Sensor block's icon should appear (see Figure C.25 Angle Block Icon). The program shown in Figure C.26 Test Program is a little test program that displays the current angle and produces a tone when the angle is greater than halfway. The Complete Sensor Template could be modified to create a block where this threshold angle is adjustable.

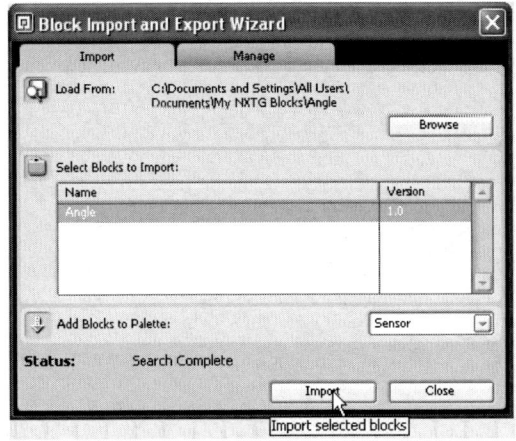

Figure C.24
Selecting the Block

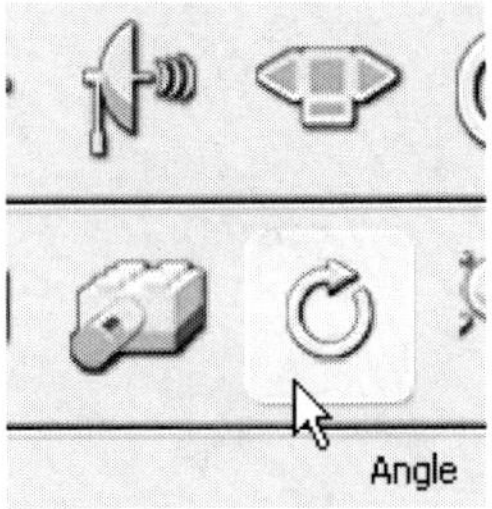

Figure C.25
Angle Block Icon

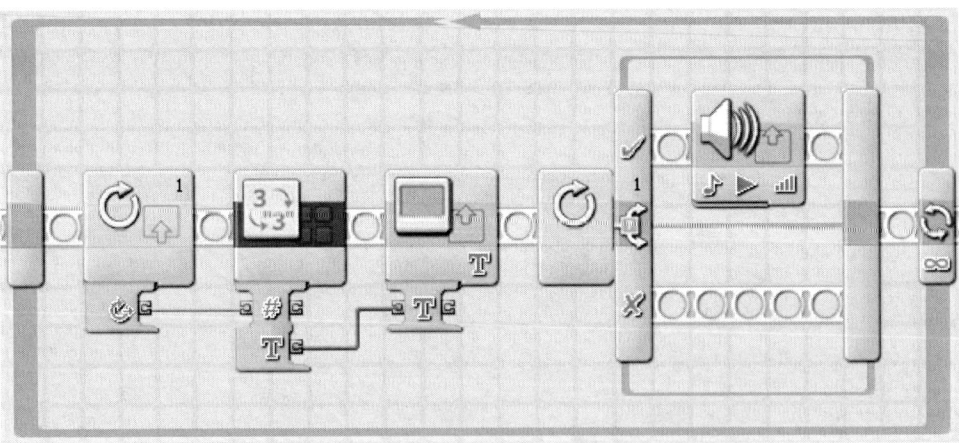

Figure C.26
Test Program

Custom LEDButtons Block

The Template Block is a little simpler than even the Simple Sensor. It was designed to allow for the creation of math functions not originally included in the MINDSTORMS environment. Most of the missing functions have already been created by other people and are available for download from the NXTasy site listed previously. Besides, the need for new blocks is generally the result of new hardware. In the *Extreme NXT* book, a four-LED display and a four-button input circuit was developed; it uses the low-speed communication bus. I'll illustrate a custom block to interface to this circuit that uses the Template Block.

The hardware uses a single 8-bit input and output port where the low four bits are the button inputs and the high four bits are the LED outputs. It is based on an integrated circuit called the PCF8574. To light an LED you actually put a zero in that LED's bit location. When a button is pressed, its bit will be zero. Decoding which button is pressed is a little complicated, since you could press more than one button at a time. For this example, I decided to decode just the lowest button, even if more than one is pressed. That way, no matter how many buttons you press, there is just a single Button number returned with zero, meaning no button. However, you might want to see all four buttons at once, so I will provide a Boolean to decide whether to decode or not.

Go to the New Block Wizard and create a block called LEDButton. The eight files shown in Figure C.27 Template Block Files will be created in the LEDButton folder. All of them should be familiar from the Simple Sensor block already described. I designed a custom icon for the LEDButton that combines a little light with a pointing finger. I also incorporated the icon into the LEDButton Dragged.png, as shown in Figure C.28 Edited Files. I actually started with the Calibration dragged.png, because it has the red color and checkerboard pattern of other blocks in the Advanced palette, which is where I want the LEDButton to be. You will find the file in C:\Program Files\LEGO Software\LEGO MINDSTORMS NXT\engine\vi.lib\LEGO\Blocks\Calibration.

Config LEDButton.vi   Draw LEDButton.vi   LEDButton Dragged.png   LEDButton Sub.vi

LEDButton.png   LEDButton.txt   LEDButton.vi   Version.txt

Figure C.27
Template Block Files

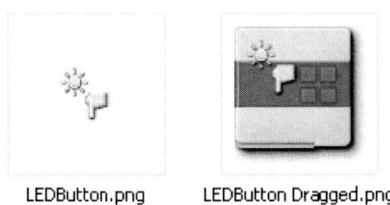

LEDButton.png   LEDButton Dragged.png

Figure C.28
Edited Files

Block VI

The LEDButton.vi Front Panel is shown in Figure C.29 LEDButton sub.vi Front Panel. We are going to change the names of all the variables into and out of the block, and this can be done from the Front Panel or from the Block Diagram, shown in Figure C.30 LEDButton sub.vi Block Diagram. It would be nice to have an appropriate value for the Port number, and the buttons are Decoded option True when you first place the block. Figure C.31 Setting Default Port Value shows how you enter the value you want for the default Port number and then right-click to Data Operations and Make Current Value Default. Do that to make the Decode True also. Change all the control labels to Port, Decode, Color, and Button, as shown Figure C.31 Setting Default Port Value. Then double-click on the Block Sub VI to edit the LEDButton sub.vi.

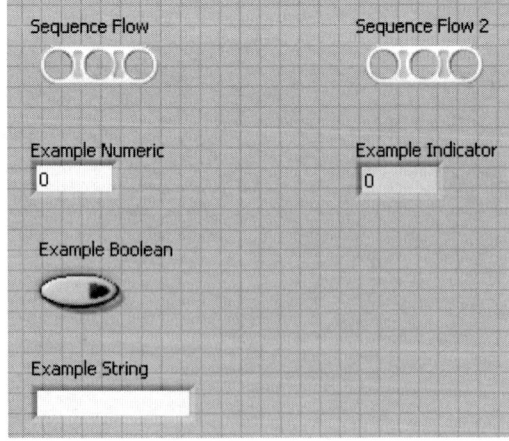

Figure C.29
LEDButton sub.vi Front Panel

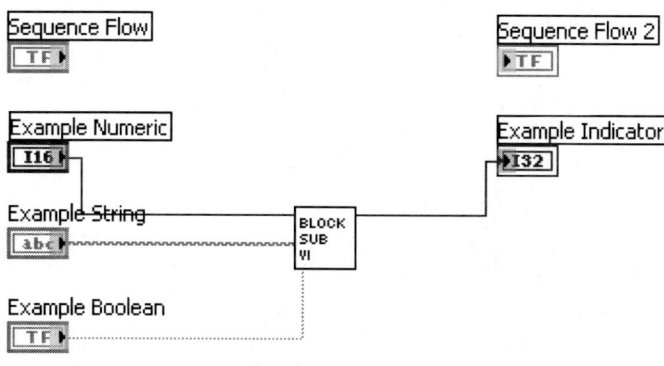

Figure C.30
LEDButton sub.vi Block Diagram

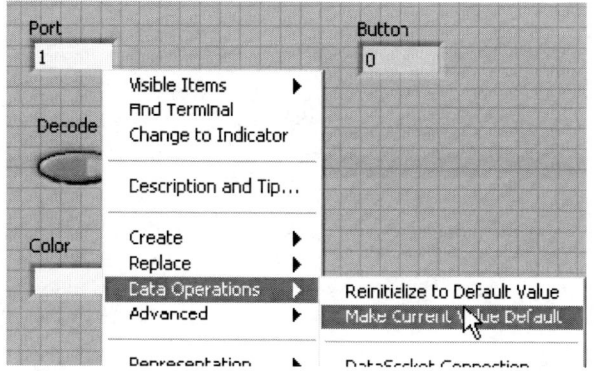

Figure C.31
Setting Default Port Value

Block Sub VI

The Wizard creates a block that is practically empty, but Figure C.32 LEDButton sub.vi shows the completed LEDButton sub.vi. It configures the Port for low-speed communications, writes two bytes to the port, reads a byte from the port, and decodes the buttons into a value. The particular LED you want to light is entered as a string with the values blue, green, yellow, and red. Entering nothing means to turn off all the LEDs. The block labeled LS Get Status is another undocumented

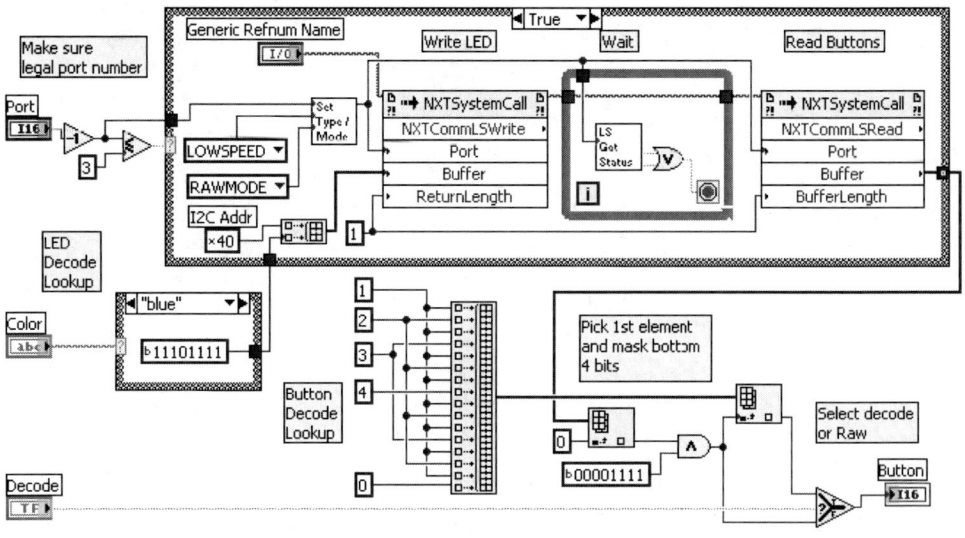

Figure C.32
LEDButton sub.vi

NXT block that watches the Invalid Data flag in the IOMap to determine that the NXT operating system has completed the LS Write or has experienced some failure. You can find the block at C:\Program Files\National Instruments\LabVIEW 8.2\vi.lib\addons\NXTToolkit\Library VIs\Block Support\LowSpeed.GetStatus.vi. The button decode is just a 16-element lookup table with all the possible combinations of four buttons decoding into a single Button number.

Configuration VI

There are a couple cosmetic changes to the Config LEDButton.vi, shown in Figure C.33 Config LEDButton.vi Front Panel. Change the Text to LED Button and the icon as you did for the Angle Sensor. By default, the color of the block in the lower left is orange for Data Operations. Since this is going to be an Advanced Block, we need to change it to red. In the All Controls palette select NXT Toolkit, then NXT Controls, then Config Decorations, then Advanced Decorations in the sequence covered by Figure C.34 NXT Controls through Figure C.37 Selecting Red Color Box. Replace the orange box with a red one from the palette. Finally change the captions to Decode, Port, and Color.

Now we need to edit the Block Diagram (see Figure C.38 Config LEDButton.vi Block Diagram) to change the names of the variables. This needs to be done in three different places. Figure C.39 Edited Variable Names shows the way the labels on the

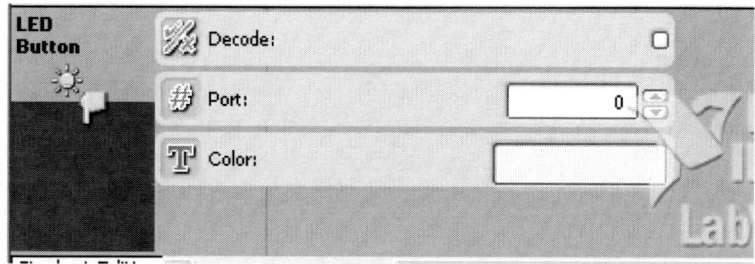

Figure C.33
Config LEDButton.vi Front Panel

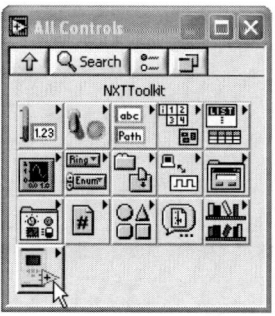

Figure C.34
NXT Controls

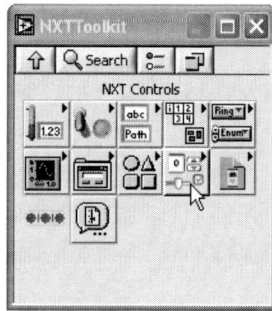

Figure C.35
Config Controls

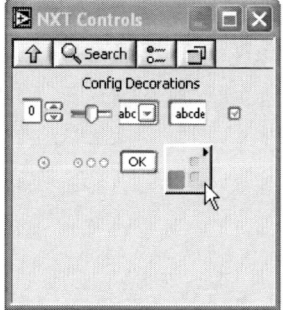

Figure C.36
Decorations

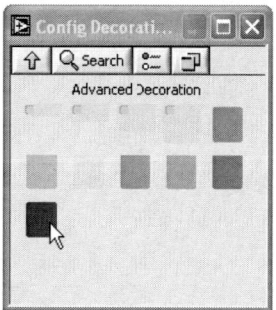

Figure C.37
Selecting Red Color Box

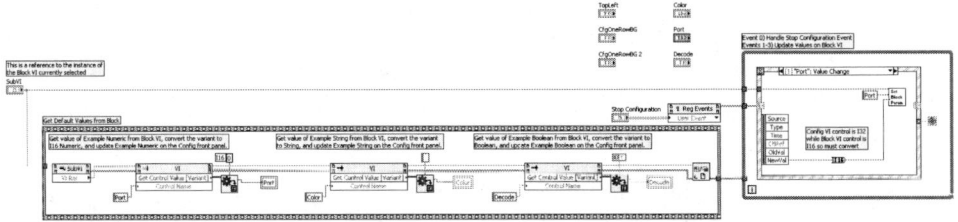

Figure C.38
Config LEDButton.vi Block Diagram

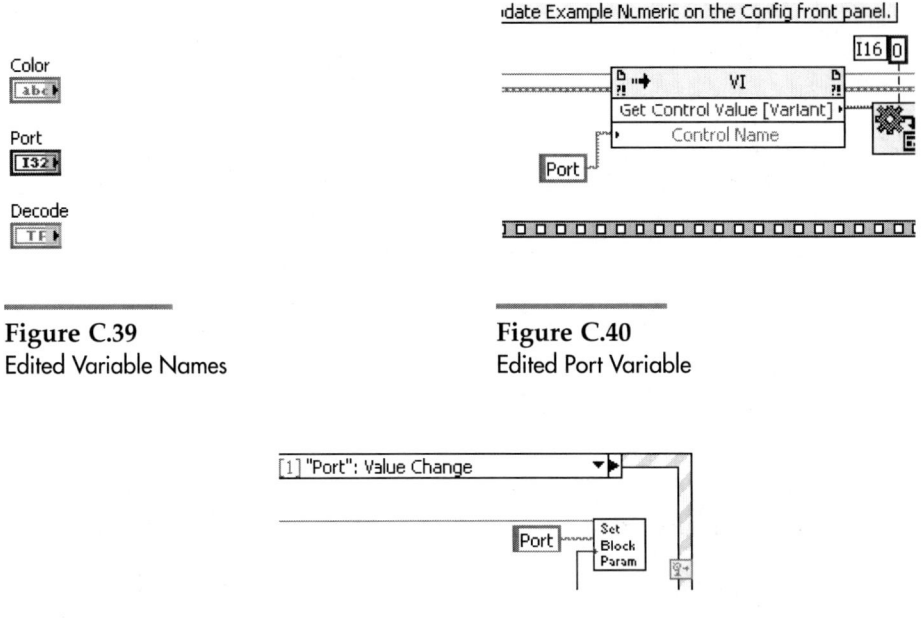

Figure C.39
Edited Variable Names

Figure C.40
Edited Port Variable

Figure C.41
Edited Port Value Change

controls should look. Figure C.40 Edited Port Variable shows the way the default values are brought up from the block's VI. All three values will need to be changed in the same way across the frame. Figure C.41 Edited Port Value Change shows the way the cases in the case structure need to be modified. All of the Value Change cases need to be changed this way.

Draw VI

We didn't look into the Draw VI for the Angle Sensor, but we need to modify it for the LEDButton because by default the block would go into the Data palette and it is really going to be in the Advanced palette. The Draw LEDButton.vi Front Panel is shown in Figure C.42 Draw LEDButton.vi Front Panel. We don't need to change anything here, but on the Block Diagram (see Figure C.43 Draw LEDButton.vi Block Diagram) we need to select a different Skin by right-clicking on the constant feeding into it and selecting Advanced, as shown in Figure C.44 Selecting Advanced Palette.

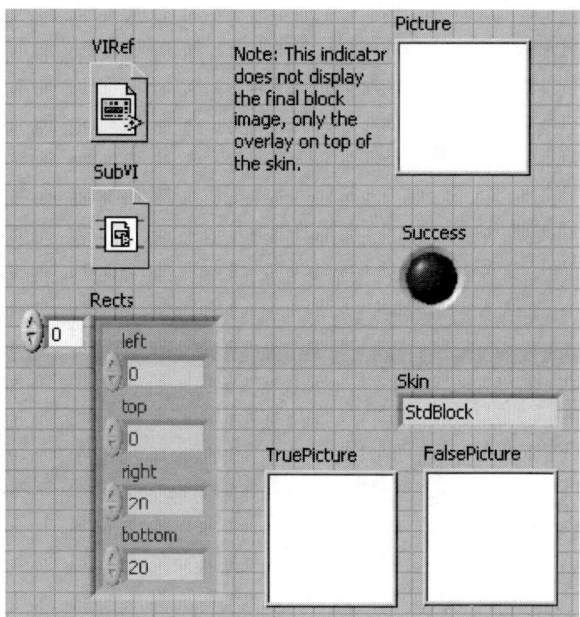

Figure C.42
Draw LEDButton.vi Front Panel

Import and Export Wizard

Import the LEDButton block just as you did for the Angle Sensor, only make sure you select the Advanced palette, as shown in Figure C.45 Importing LEDButton Custom Block. A little program that lights the LED across from the button that is being pressed is shown in Figure C.46 Testing LEDButton Block. Notice that the Plug and Button

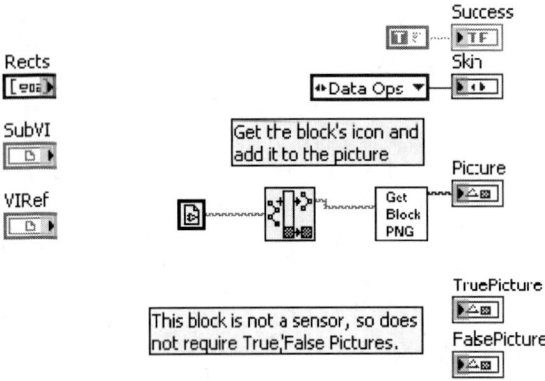

Figure C.43
Draw LEDButton.vi Block Diagram

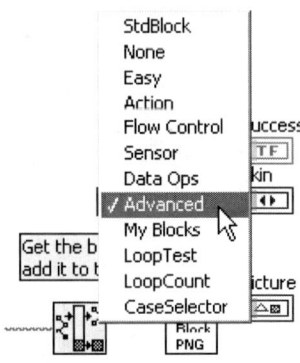

Figure C.44
Selecting Advanced Palette

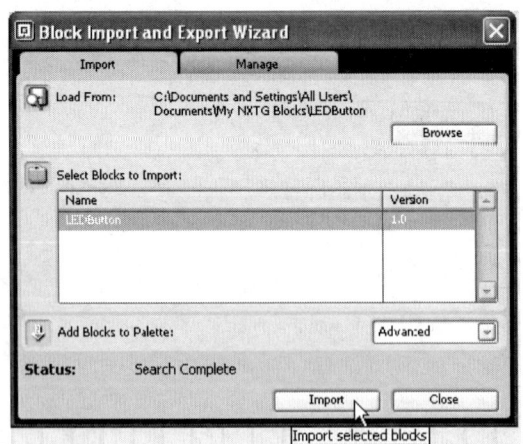

Figure C.45
Importing LEDButton Custom Block

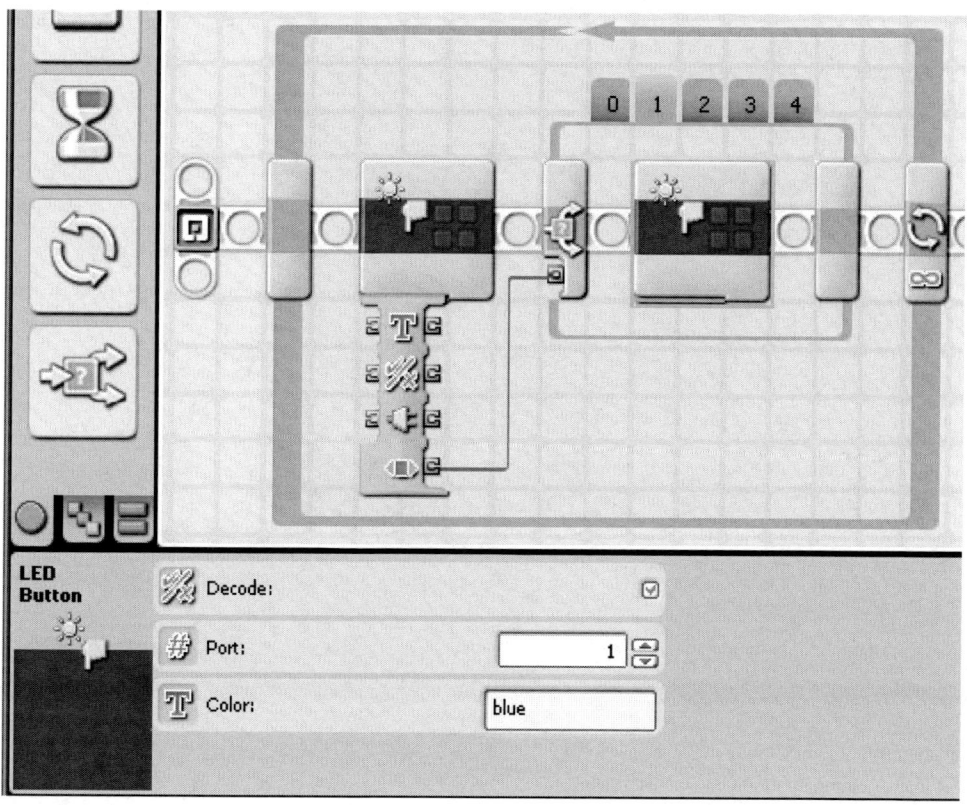

Figure C.46
Testing LEDButton Block

icons in the block's drawer match up with appropriate icons. Also notice that the default Port Number is 1 and the default is to Decode the buttons.

Reflections

The subject of writing custom NXT-G blocks could fill a book all by itself. Frankly, it can be challenging to get the configuration and draw blocks to work perfectly even for experienced LabVIEW programmers. I've tried to show you a few simple ways to build your own blocks. Bu using these, along with the National Instruments tutorial and online resources, you can likely build what you need.

Using Vernier Sensors with the NXT

D

In addition to the Lego Mindstorms sensors shipping with NXT kit, additional sensors can be attached to measure the world around your robot. The Vernier NXT Sensor Adaptor (order code BTA-NXT), makes it possible to connect more than 30 Vernier Analog (BTA) sensors to the LEGO NXT Robotic Invention Systems brick. The Vernier Sensor Adaptor allows the NXT to communicate with the sensor and take measurements in proper sensor units. Having the ability to connect Vernier sensors broadens the variety of scientific, engineering, and educational uses for the NXT system.

Vernier Software & Technology is an award winning company committed to education that has been creating sensors, software, and curriculum for science and engineering teachers for over 25 years. Over 50 different sensors ranging from force sensors to pH sensors to UV sensors are available.

As an example, the robot pictured below uses a Vernier Magnetic Field Sensor to locate a magnet hidden under one of the walnut shells in the classic shell game.

Photograph courtesy of Vernier Software & Technology.

Vernier Sensors Compatible with NXT

25-g Accelerometer

Low-g Accelerometer

Barometer

Charge Sensor

Colorimeter

Conductivity Probe

Current Probe

Differential Voltage Probe

Dissolved Oxygen Sensor

Dual-Range Force Sensor

Electrode Amplifier

Extra Long Temperature Probe

Flow Rate Sensor

Force Plate

Gas Pressure Sensor

Hand Dynamometer

Instrumentation Amplifier

Light Sensor

Magnetic Field Sensor

O_2 Gas Sensor

ORP Sensor

pH Sensor

Relative Humidity Sensor

Salinity Sensor

Soil Moisture Sensor

Sound Level Meter

Stainless Steel Temperature Probe

Surface Temperature Sensor

Thermocouple

Turbidity Sensor

UVA Sensor

UVB Sensor

Stainless Steel Temperature Probe   **Oxygen Gas Sensor**

Force Sensor

The sensors listed above can all be connected to the NXT system using the Vernier NXT Sensor Adaptor (BTA-NXT), shown below. The adaptor is certified by the LEGO company making it mechanically and electrically compatible with the NXT system and may be connected to any of the four sensor ports on the NXT.

Vernier NXT Sensor Adaptor

Using Vernier Sensors with Mindstorms NXT

To use Vernier sensors with NXT-G, download the Vernier Sensor block from http://www.vernier.com/nxt/downloads.html. This is a NXT-G block that handles the calibration of the various Vernier sensors. Vernier created the block in LabVIEW using the methods explained in Appendix C of this book.

Installing the Vernier Mindstorms NXT Block

Follow the instructions found on the downloads page to import the Vernier Sensor Block into MINDSTORMS NXT.

Programming Vernier Sensors in NXT

Once installed, the Vernier NXT-G block appears on the sensor menu and can be placed into a program in exactly the same way as any other sensor. Sensor type, port, threshold point and action can be set in the block's control panel. A simple NXT-G program to measure and display temperature is shown below.

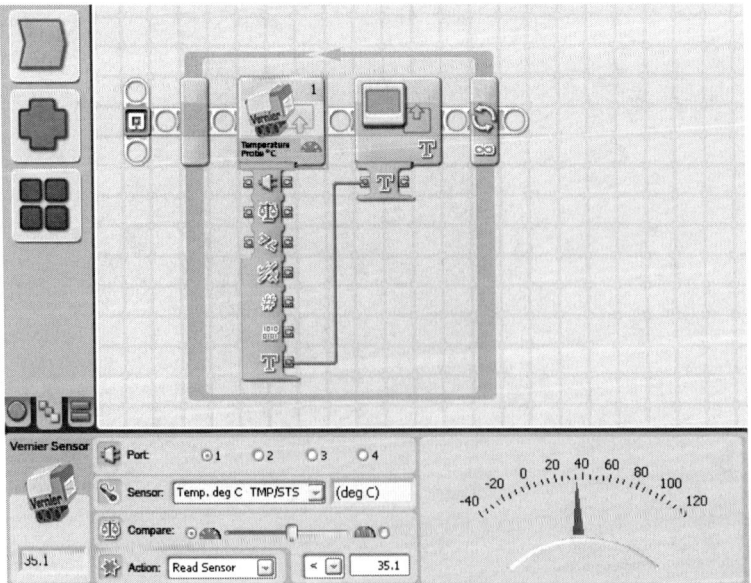

Using Vernier Sensors with LabVIEW

For those users who wish to program the NXT directly in the LabVIEW environment, Vernier Software and Technology has created a LabVIEW Toolkit and example VIs showing how to enable a Vernier sensor to function with the NXT system while exploiting the full programming potential of LabVIEW. The Vernier Sensor Toolkit and example LabVIEW programs may be downloaded from http://www.vernier.com/nxt/labview.html.

Installing the Vernier LabVIEW Toolkit and Examples

Locate the readme file on the download page for instructions on downloading and installing the Toolkit and LabVIEW examples.

Programming Vernier Sensors in LabVIEW

A single VI called Vernier Sensor NXT.vi can be configured to acquire data from each of the 30 BTA Vernier sensors listed above using the BTA-NXT Adapter. The subVI icon is shown below and is inputs and outputs are discussed in depth in the following sections.

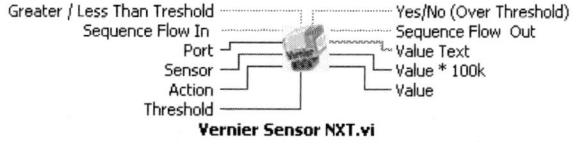

Vernier Sensor NXT.vi

The individual input and output connections are discussed in their own sections below. Below, an example LabVIEW program is shown using the Vernier Sensor NXT.vi subVI to acquire a temperature sensor and displaying the values on the NXT screen. A tone sounds if the temperature is below the set point.

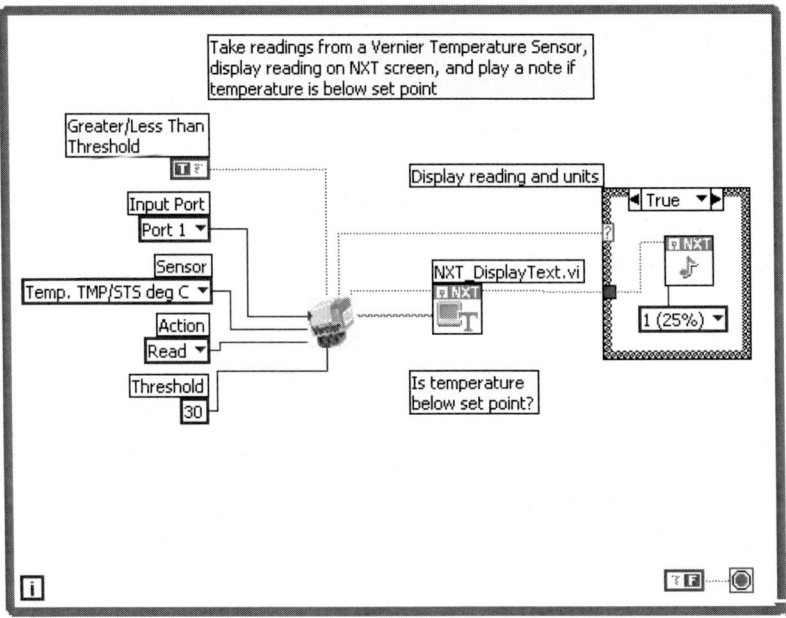

Once the Vernier Sensor NXT.vi is incorporated into your LabVIEW VI application, it may be downloaded to the NXT in the usual manner using the NXT terminal on the tools menu of LabVIEW.

SubVI Input Terminals

Sequence Flow In

This is the sequence flow input. The LabVIEW NXT Toolkit provides a special Boolean control called a Sequence Flow Boolean. The names of these controls must start with Sequence Flow. A sequence flow Boolean on one subVI is wired to one on another subVI to control the flow of the program. This is discussed in more detail in the body of this book.

Input Port

This control selects the NXT port connected to the Vernier NXT Sensor Adaptor (BTA-NXT). The range is 1 to 4, the default is port 1.

Sensor

The Sensor control lets the subVI know what type of Vernier Sensor is being used and automatically loads the correct calibration information and units for the sensor.

Action

The Action control determines whether the sensor should be read, zeroed, or reset at a given point in the program. See the section "Using the Zero/Calibrate and Reset Functions" below for information on these actions.

Threshold

Each sensor has the ability to be triggered above or below a set threshold. The trigger point is entered into this control as a numeric value in the correct units for the physical property under measure.

Greater/Less Than Threshold

This is a Boolean control that determines if the sensor should trigger (i.e. return a True value) if the reading is below or above the threshold. A value of True will make the sensor return True if the reading is below the Trigger Point setting.

SubVI Output Terminals

Sequence Flow Out

This is the sequence flow output. The LabVIEW NXT Toolkit provides a special Boolean control called a Sequence Flow Boolean. The names of these controls must start with Sequence Flow. When a sequence flow Boolean on one subVI is wired to one on another subVI the program treats this wire in exactly the same way as the sequence beam in LEGO's NXT-G programming environment.

Value Text

This output takes the reading for the sensor connected to the NXT, converts it to a text string and concatenates the appropriate units to the measurement. It is very useful for displaying the value measured on the NXT display and is more accurate than the Value output, which due to the lack of a floating-point processor in the NXT brick, rounds the reading to an integer value. Decimal readings can be displayed using this text output.

Value * 100,000

The NXT block uses a fixed point processor to perform its calculations. To maintain the precision of the Vernier Sensor used with the NXT the readings from the sensor are multiplied by 100,000 inside the subVI. This output gives access to that quantity at its full precision.

Value

The Reading output is the numerical value of the quantity under measure. It is expressed as the size of the physical quantity in the correct units. This is a simple output useful for beginning student's programs. However, note this output will always be a whole number; any fractional part of the measurement will be truncated.

Yes/No (Over Threshold)

This is a Boolean output that returns a value of True if the conditions set by the Threshold and Greater/Less Than inputs are met.

Using the Zero/Reset Functions

Zeroing Most Sensors

Using the Action control, you can set the Vernier Sensor NXT subVI to Zero/Calibrate. This provides a way to adjust the calibration of the particular sensor you are using.

As an example, if an accelerometer is not reading 0 m/s^2 when it is at rest, you can adjust it so it correctly reads zero. Build a program with the Vernier Sensor NXT subVI at the beginning. Choose Zero/Calibrate as the input into the Action terminal. When you download and run the NXT program, have the accelerometer oriented as you plan to use it and at rest. When this block of the program executes the reading will be adjusted so that the acceleration is defined as 0. This adjustment will be used in all other Vernier Sensor blocks in the program. This zero adjustment is saved in the Vernier Sensor.cal file on the NXT and will be used until you reset it to the default value. You can do this by choosing Reset as the input into the Action terminal of the Vernier Sensor NXT subVI, as described below.

Using the Action control, you can also set the Vernier Sensor NXT subVI to Reset. This provides a way for you to restore the calibration of the sensor to its default setting.

Build a program with Vernier Sensor NXT subVI at the beginning. Choose Reset as the input into the Action terminal. When you download and run the NXT program and the block executes, the calibration will be set to the default setting.

Note that zero/calibration action and reset actions work on all Vernier Sensors (except TMP and STS temperature probes) being used by the LabVIEW program. The way calibration is handled with the Vernier Sensor program on the NXT requires that all Vernier Sensor NXT subVIs use the same calibration file. This applies to sensors connected to different channels and even to different types of sensors. This means you should probably not use the Zero/Calibration action when you have two Vernier sensors of different types in one program. Even if you are using two of the same type of sensor, force for example, zeroing one force sensor will not properly zero the other one.

Zero/Calibration with a pH sensor

Since there is no such thing as 0 pH, an alternative way to adjust the calibration of the Vernier pH sensor is used. This calibration adjustment depends on the use of a pH 7 buffer. This is a solution available in most science classrooms that is made to have a pH of exactly 7.0. Build a program with Vernier Sensor NXT subVI with pH as the input for the Sensor input terminal. Choose Zero/Calibrate as the input into the Action terminal. When you download and run the NXT program, have the pH sensor in the pH 7 buffer. When the program executes the reading will be adjusted so that the pH reads exactly 7.0.

Additional Information

To learn more about the Vernier sensor adapter and how to take advantage of Vernier sensors on your NXT system, visit the Vernier website at http://www.vernier.com/nxt. There are a wide variety of examples on the site with programs in LabVIEW, NXT-G and NXT executables. Movies of many NXT LabVIEW projects may be found at the same site.

Index

A

Addons palette, 5-6,169-170
  NXT Direct Commands palette, 169-170
  NXT Toolkit palette, 5-6
Array Indicator, 109-111
Array palette, 67-68, 106
  Build Array block, 106
  Constant Array block, 67-68
  Index Array block, 67
ASCII codes, 111-113
Automatic error handling warning,
  247-248
Automatic Tool Selection, 39-40

B

Bang-Bang Control, 132-133
Battery Voltage program, 215-217
Binary files, 113-115
Block diagrams, 2-4, 59-60, 17-19, 166-167,
    171-172, 182, 187-188, 193-195,
    205-206, 223-224, 230, 235-236, 238
  block internal functions, 223-224, 230
  Charting program, 187-188, 193-15
  Connections Program, 171-172
  Control Datalog program, 182
  Controls using, 166-167
  Data Logging program, 59-60
  deleting elements, 17-19
  low-speed (LS) communication, 193-194
  Motor Control program, 205-206
  opening files, 17
  Period Count Sensor, 238
  Read Power, 235-236
  starting new programs, 1-3
Block internal functions, 223-241
  Block Support Controls, 238-239
  Class of functions, 225, 227
  Connector Pane Mapping, 231-232, 236
  Draw Circle program, 223-224
  Draw Rectangle program, 225-235
  Invoke Node block, 225-228
  LabVIEW warnings, 233
  Methods of functions, 225, 227
  NXTInputOutput functions, 225-226
  NXTSystemCall, 225-228
  Period Count Sensor, 237-240
  Read Power Block Diagram, 235-236
  Select a VI, 233-234
  Sequence Flow Controls, 226, 229-230
  SubVI creation, 226-234
  Test Read Power block, 235-237
Bluetooth communication, 155-160, 177-179,
    218-222
  Connection palette program, 177-179
  Direct command functions, 177-179,
    218-222
  Error with Timeout, 179
  Is Paired block, 177
  Master/Slave connections, 155-156
  Master/Slave programs, 157-158
  Message functions, 156-157, 218-222
  Message Read block, 220-221
  Message Remote block, 218-219
  Message Write block, 218
  NXT-to-NXT connections, 155-156
  NXT-to-PC connections, 158-160
  Pair Bluetooth block, 177-178
  Read Message block, 157
  Send Button, 221-222
  Unpair Bluetooth block, 177-178
  Write Message block, 156-157
Boolean palette functions, 36, 49-50, 51, 137,
    207-208
  changing variable representation, 49-50
  Controls palette, 164-166, 207-208
  converting to integers (numeric functions),
    51
  logic functions, 137
  Radio Buttons, 207-208
  variables (True/False), 36
Bouncy Ball program, 99-100
Bundle by Name block, 211
Buttons, 43-44

C

Cage Monitor program, 198-202
Calculate pi program, 141-142
Calibrate block, Legacy, 150-151
Case Structure, 43-45
Charting functions, 187-204
    Block Diagram, 187-188
    Clear Input Value block, 193
    Counting Modes block, 192-193
    exporting graphs, 203
    Front Panel, 187-188
    Get Input Values block, 192
    Keep Alive block, 200
    Legacy Sensor blocks, 189-192
    low-speed (LS) communication, 193-195
    Read NXT Sensor blocks, 189-191
    Read Sensor block, 190-191
    Reset Motor block, 197
    Rotation Sensor blocks, 195-198
    Set Input Mode block, 191
    Ultrasonic Distance Sensor, 193-195
Charts, 28-29, 89-100
    clearing screen displays, 91-92
    Debug button creation, 28-29
    Display Circle block, 99
    Display Line block, 94-96
    Display Picture block, 92-94
    improved, 89-91, 93-95
    NXT screen display for, 89-91
    Restore Default block, 98-100
    Save RIC Image window, 91-92
    Shift Registers, 94
    simple, 89-90
    SubIV, 96-98
Clap Control program, 135-136
Class of functions, 225, 227
Clear Input Value block, 193
Close file block, 103
Cluster palette, 77
Coercion dots, 87-88
Come-to-the-Light program, 36-42
Comments, 39-40
Comparison palette, 36-37, 48-50
    adding blocks using, 36-37
    changing variable representation, 49-50
    Select block, 48-50

Compile and Download button, 54
Concatenate String block, 120
Connect Wire Tool, 12, 22, 24-25, 35
Connections, 11-12, 20, 169-172, 231-232, 236
    Block Diagram of program, 171-172
    Block internal mechanisms, 231-232, 236
    Bluetooth Connection blocks, 177-179
    Connection palette, 169-179
    Connector Pane Mapping, 231-232, 236
    Connectors, 11-12
    Create NXT Object block, 173
    Destroy NXT Object block, 175
    Direct Command functions, 169-177
    Display Text, 12
    Find NXT block, 173
    Front Panel for, 175-176
    Get Battery Level block, 173-174
    Get Device Info block, 174
    Get Firmware Version block, 174
    Get NXT Info block, 172
    icons, 11-12
    Is Paired block, 177
    Light Sensor block, 20
    List Files block, 175
    output of program, 174-175
    Pair Bluetooth block, 177-178
    Pair Bluetooth program, 177
    Rename NXT block, 179
    Scan for NXT block, 172
    Unpair Bluetooth block, 177-178
Constant Array block, 67-68
Constant blocks, 10-11
Control characters, ASCII codes for,
        111-113
Controls, 24-25, 161-168, 238-239.
        See also Motor functions
    adding to programs, 24-25
    Block Diagrams for, 166-167
    Block Support, 238-239
    Boolean Controls Palette, 164-166
    changing into Constants, 238-240
    Connect Wire Tool, 24-25
    debugging, 161-168
    Front Panel for, 161-166
    Numeric Controls palette, 161-164
    NXT Controls palettes, 161-166
    pushbutton, 25

Converting numbers to strings, 21
Counting Modes block, 192-193
Create NXT Object block, 173
Critical Flow wiring, 104-105

D

Data Logging functions, 59-63, 181-186
  Block Diagrams, 59-60, 182
  Control Datalog program, 181-186
  Defrag Files block, 185-186
  Delete File block, 61, 185-186
  Download file block, 183
  Easy File Close block, 62
  Easy Write File block, 61
  Get Current Program Name block, 184
  Loop Iteration block, 62-63
  Read Text File Block, 185
  Start Program block, 183-184
  Stop program block, 185-186
  Upload File block, 184-185
  Wait block, 62
Data Manipulation blocks, 113-114
Debug Button, 27-29, 109-111
  Array Indicator created using, 109-111
  chart created by, 28-29
  NXT debugging, 27-28
Debugging, 23-28, 161-168
  Boolean Controls palette, 164-166
  Controls palettes, 161-168
  Controls, 24-25
  Debug button, 27-28
  Front Panel placement, 161-162
  Indicators, 25-28
  Numeric Controls palette, 161-164
  NXT programs, 23-28
Decrement block, 99,
Defrag Files block, 185-186
Delete File block, 61, 185-186
Deleting in LabVIEW, 17-18
Destroy NXT Object block, 175
Direct Commands palette functions, 169-221
  Bluetooth Connection blocks, 177-179
  Bluetooth message functions, 218-221
  Charting functions, 187-204
  Connection palette functions, 169-179
  Data Logging functions, 181-186
  IOMap functions, 215-217

Motor program functions, 205-212
  Sound output functions, 205-214
Display Circle block, 99
Display Format, 105
Display Line block, 94-96
Display Picture block, 92-94
Display Point block, 76-77
Display text, 11-13
Display Variable block, 82, 84-85, 87
Distance Sensor block, 140
Document URL window, 251
Download file block, 183
Draw Circle program, 223-224
Draw Rectangle program, 225-235
Drawing programs, 75-88
  Cluster palette, 77
  Coercion dots, 87-88
  Display Point block, 76-77
  Display Variable block, 82, 84-85, 87
  Quotient and Remainder block, 8-87
  Rotation Sensors, 75-76
  SubVIs, 78-86

E

Easy File Close block, 62
Easy Read File block, 66-67
Easy Write File block, 61
Edit Text tool, 39-40
Elmer program, 31-57, 130-131
Exporting graphs, 203

F

File Access palette, 59-60
File functions, 59-73, 101-116, 181-186
  Array palette, 67-68, 106
  ASCII codes, 111-113
  Binary, 113-115
  Close file block, 103
  Critical Flow wiring, 104-105
  Data Logging program, 59-63, 181-186
  Display Format, 105
  easy, 59-73
  Easy Read File block, 66-67
  File Access palette, 59-60
  Get File Handle block, 108-109
  not easy, 101-116

note representation and storage, 68-69
NXT Terminal storage, 64-65, 69-70
Open for Read block, 101, 104
Open for Write block, 101-102, 104
PC storage and viewing, 64-65
Play Action block, 71
Play Sound File block, 71-73
Read file block, 102
Record Action block, 70-71
Rename File block, 108
RIC Images, 91-92, 106-108
sending, 64, 69-70
Sound palette, 71-73
String palette, 109-111
viewing in Notepad and Excel, 64-65
Write file block, 103
Find NXT block, 173
Flat Sequence Structure block, 210-211
Floating Point warning, 87-88
Flow, *see* Sequence Flow
Forward One Second program, 210
Front Panels, 2-3, 161-166, 175-176,
        187-188
    Boolean Controls, 164-166
    changing scale range, 163-164
    charting, 187-188
    Connections program, 175-176
    Controls placement, 161-166
    Numeric Controls, 161-164
    window in LabVIEW, 2-3
Function blocks, 3, 11-13
Functions palette, 5-6, 169
Fwink program, 243-246

G

Get Battery Level block, 173-174
Get Current Program Name block, 184
Get Device Info block, 174
Get File Handle block, 108-109
Get Firmware Version block, 174
Get Input Values block, 192
Get NXT Info block, 172

H

Hello, World program, 1-16, 17-19
Hour Clock program, 18-120

I

Icon Edit tool, 81-82
Idle status, 14
Index Array block, 67
Indicators, 25-28, 122-123
Input, *see* Data Logging functions;
        Sequence Flow
Integers, *see* Numeric Cases
Invoke Node block, 225-228
IOMap functions, 215-217
IP address, 249, 251
Is Paired block, 177

K

Keep Alive block, 117-118, 200

L

Labels, 37-38
LabVIEW, 1-16, 17-30, 87-88, 233,
        247-248, 257
    Block Diagram, 2-4
    charts, 28-29
    connecting wires manually, 22-23
    controls, 24-25
    converting numbers to strings, 21
    creating constants, 10-11
    debugging, 23-24, 27
    deleting, 17-19
    display text, 11-13
    Function blocks, 3, 11-13
    Function palette, 5-6
    Indicators, 25-28
    launching, 1
    Light Sensors, 19-21
    NXT Terminal tool, 1416
    opening files, 17
    resources, 257
    saving files, 13-14
    starting new programs, 1-3
    tools, 9-10, 12, 14-16, 22
    Virtual Instruments (VIs), 2-3,
        13-14
    warnings, 87-88, 233, 247-248
    While loops, 6-9

Lamp block, Legacy, 146
Legacy functions, 145-154, 182-192
   Calibrate block, 150-151
   calibration, 149-153
   Charting functions, 189-192
   Get Input block, 192
   Lamp block, 146
   Legacy block, 147-148
   Light Sensor block, 147-148
   Motor block, 145-146
   Read Sensor block, 190-191
   Rotation Sensor block, 148-149
   Set Input Mode block, 191
   Temperature block, 147
   Touch Sensor block, 148
Light Meter program, 149-153
Light sensors, 19-21, 36-37, 131-134, 147-153
   Bang-Bang Control, 132-133
   block connections, 19-21
   Comparison palette for intensity of, 36-37
   Motor blocks and, 131-134
   Proportional Control, 133-134
List Files block, 175
Local Variable block, 123-124
logic functions for, 137
Look File program, 109-115
Loops, 6-9, 34-35, 39-40, 41-42, 62-63
   comments added to, 39-40
   infinite, 41-42
   Loop Condition box, 9
   Loop Iteration block, 62-63
   Run-until-Touched, 35
   Wait-until-Touched, 34
   While, 6-9, 35, 41
Low-speed (LS) communication, 193-195.
     See also Ultrasonic Distance Sensor
   charting functions, 193-195
   LS Get Started block, 195
   LS Read block, 195
   LS Write block, 194

M

Mailbox program, 218-222
Make Icon program, 103-105
Message Read block, 220-221
Message Remote block, 218-219
Message Write block, 218

Methods of functions, 225, 227
MINDSTORMS project resources, 255-256
Mini Fig Mouse programs, 198-202, 243-253
Motor functions, 129-144, 145-146, 205-212
   Bang-Bang Control, 132-133
   Bundle by Name block, 211
   Direct Command, 205-212
   Flat Sequence Structure block, 210-211
   Legacy, 145-146
   Light Sensor block, 131-134
   logic functions for, 137
   Motor block, 138-139
   Motor control Block Diagrams, 205-206
   Motor Distance block, 134-135
   Motor Time block, 137-138
   Motor Unlimited block, 129-130,
     205-206, 209
   NXT-G configuration, 138-139
   Proportional Control, 133-134
   Radio Buttons, 207-208
   Reset Motors block, 142-143
   Rewire blocks, 211-212
   Set Output State block, 208-209
   Sound Controls, 135-136
   Sound Sensor block, 136-137
   Stop Motor block, 130, 206
   Structures palette, 210-211
   Sync distance block, 139-140
   Sync Time block, 143
   Ultrasonic Distance Sensor, 140-142
Music Box program, 65-66, 68-73

N

Negate block, 99-100
Numeric Cases, 50-54, 86-88, 105, 111-112
   adding multiple Cases, 52-54
   ASCII codes, 111-112
   blocks, 51-52
   Case Selector labels, 51-25
   Coercion dots, 87-88
   conversion from Boolean variables, 51-52
   Default Case, 51
   Display Format for files, 105
   Division block, 86-88
   Floating Point warning, 87-88
   Numeric palette, 51-52, 105
   Quotient and Remainder block, 8-87

Numeric Controls palette, 161-164
NXT-G Motor configuration, 138-139
NXT Library, 20, 150-151
    Input palette, 20
    Calibration, 150-151
NXT Terminal, 14-16, 19-20, 23-24, 27-28,
        64-65, 69-70, 84-86, 89-92, 106-108,
        155-156, 158-160
    Bluetooth communication, 155-156,
        158-160
    chart display, 89-91
    clearing screen displays, 91-92
    debugging, 23-28
    downloading and running files using,
        69-70
    downloading and running LabVIEW
        using, 14-16
    file storage, 64-65, 69-70
    Light Sensor, 19-20, 149-153
    RIC images, 91-92, 106-108
    stop button, 16, 28
    test screen display, 84-86
NXT Toolkit, 5-6
NXTInputOutput functions, 225-226
NXTSystemCall, 225-228

O

Open for Read block, 101, 104
Open for Write block, 101-102, 104
Opening files, 17
Operate Value tool, 9
Output, *see* Sequence Flow
Output palette, 32-33, 195

P

Pair Bluetooth block, 177-178
PC storage and viewing, 64-65
Period Count Sensor, 237-240
Play Action block, 71
Play Sound File block, 71-73, 213-214
Play Tone block, 46-47, 212-213
Port Forwarding, 251-253
Print command, 54-55
Programming TriBot robots, 31-42, 43-57
    Boolean (True/False) variables, 36,
        49-50, 51

buttons, 43-44
Case Structure, 43-45
comments, 39-40
Comparison palette, 36-37, 48-50
Compile and Download button, 54
decisions, 43-57
fixing broken wires, 40-41
Labels, 37-38
loops within loops, 41-42
Numeric Cases, 50-54
Print command, 54-56
Robo center, 31-32
Select block, 48-50
Sequence Flow, 35
Sound palette, 45-48
Sync Unlimited, 32-34
Tools palette, 38-40
Touch Sensor, 34-36
Proportional Control, 133-134
Pushbutton control, 25

Q

Quotient and Remainder block, 8-87

R

Radio Buttons, 207-208
Random Number block, 125
Reaction Timer block, 124-125
Read file block, 102
Read Message block, 157
Read Sensor block, 190-191
Read Text File Block, 185
Record Action block, 70-71
Rename File block, 108
Rename NXT block, 179
Reset Motors block, 142-143
Restore Default block, 98-100
Rewire blocks, 211-212
RIC Images, 91-92, 106-108
    MyIcon.ric, 108
    Save RIC Image window, 91-92, 107
    Square.ric Picture file, 106-108
Robo center, 31-32
Rotation Sensors, 75-76, 148-149, 195-198
    Charting program functions, 195-198
    Get Output Values block, 198

Legacy functions, 148-149
NXT functions, 75-76
Read Rotation block, 195-196
Reset Motor block, 197
Unbundle RotationCount block, 197
Run-until-Touched loops, 35

S

Save RIC Image window, 91-92
Saving files, 13-14
Scan for NXT block, 172
Select block, 48-50
Selection tool, 9
Send Button, 221-222
Sensors, 19-21, 34-37, 75-76, 131-134,
        136-137, 140-142, 148-153, 189-198,
        237-240
    calibration of, 149-153
    Charting functions, 189-198
    Legacy, 148-153, 189-192
    Light, 19-21, 36-37, 131-134
    Period Count, 237-240
    Rotation, 75-76, 148-149, 195-198
    Sound, 136-137, 149-153
    Touch, 34-36, 148
    Ultrasonic Distance, 140-142, 193-195
Sequence Flow input/output, 35, 104-105,
        226, 229-230
    adding to blocks, 35
    Block internal functions, 226, 229-230
    changing in blocks, 226, 230
    Critical Flow wiring, 104-105
    Sequence Flow Controls, 226, 229-230
Set Input Mode block, 191
Set Output State block, 208-209
Shift Registers, 94
Sketch program, 75-88
Sound program functions, 45-48, 71-73,
        135-137, 149-153, 212-214
    calibration of Sound Sensor, 149-153
    Direct Command, 212-214
    Motor programs using, 135-136
    output programs, 212-214
    Play Sound File block, 71-73, 213-214
    Play Tone block, 46-47, 212-213
    Sound Controls, 135-136
    Sound palette, 45-48, 71-73

Sound Sensor block, 136-137
Stop Sound block, 46, 213
Splash screen, 1-2
Start Program block, 183-184
Starting new programs, 1-3
Stop block, 126-127
Stop button, 16, 28
Stop Motor block, 130, 206
Stop program block, 185-186
Stop Sound block, 46, 213
String Constant block, 12-13
String data, 12
String palette, 109-111, 120
    Array Indicator, 109-111
    Concatenate String block, 120
Structures palette, 210-211
SubVIs, 78-86, 96-98, 226-234
    Block Diagram, 82
    Block internal functions, 226-234
    Chart, 96-98
    creating, 78-83, 226-234
    Display Variable block, 82, 84-85
    Icon Edit tool, 81-82
    NXT test screen display, 84-86
    Select a VI, 233-234
    using, 84-86
Synchronous operation, 31-35, 139-140
    Motor functions, 137-140, 143
    Motor Time block, 137-138
    Run-until-Touched Loop, 35
    Sequence Flow input/output, 35
    Sync distance block, 139-140
    Sync Stop block, 33-34
    Sync Time block, 143
    Sync Unlimited block, 32-35
    Touch Sensor functions, 34-36
    Wait-until-Touched Loop, 34

T

Temperature block, Legacy, 147
Test Read Power block, 235-237
Three Ways program, 189-192
Tick Count block, 118
Time functions, 62, 117-127, 137-138
    Concatenate String block, 120
    event time logging, 122-126
    Indicators, 122-123

Keep Alive block, 117-118
Local Variable block, 123-124
Motor Time block, 137-138
Random Number block, 125
Reaction Timer block, 124-125
Stop block, 126-127
Tick Count block, 118
Timer blocks, 126
Wait block, 62, 121-123
Wait for Completion block, 126
Time Logging program, 122-127
Timer blocks, 126
Tools palette, 38-40
Touch Sensor, 34-36, 148
Tunnels, 35

U

Ultrasonic Distance Sensor, 140-142, 193-195
    Charting functions, 193-195
    Distance Sensor block, 140
    pi measurement using, 141-142
Unpair Bluetooth block, 177-178
Upload File block, 184-185
URL designation, 249-251

V

Variables, *see* Boolean palette
Virtual Instruments (VIs), 2-3, 13-14, 233-234,
        237. *See also* SubVIs
    Blank VI creation, 2-3
    changing VI Properties, 247

file, 13-14
Select a VI function, 233-234

W

Wait block, 62, 121-123
Wait for Completion block, 126
Wait-until-Touched loops, 34
Web Publishing Tool, 248-250
Web Server program, 243-253
    automatic error handling warning,
        247-248
    changing VI Properties, 247
    Document URL window, 251
    Fwink, 243-246
    IP address for, 249, 251
    Port Forwarding, 251-253
    URL designation for, 249-251
    Web Publishing Tool, 248-250
While loops, 6-9, 35, 41, 94
    infinite, 41
    LabVIEW use of, 6-9
    Sequence Flow input for, 35
    Shift Registers added to, 94
Wires, 12, 22-23, 24-25, 35, 40-41, 104-105,
        211-212
    Connect Wire Tool, 12, 22, 24-25, 35
    connecting manually, 22-23
    Critical Flow for files, 104-105
    fixing broken, 40-41
    Rewire blocks, 211-212
Write file block, 103
Write Message block, 156-157